Fetch a Cloth. It's

THE OTTER'S POCKET

A Moist Box of Delights Dripping with Seedy Pearls
Snatched from Issues 222~231

Turfers' Knees
Graham Dury and Simon Thorp

Mermaids' Flannels
Mark Bates, Julian Boffin, Alex Collier, Terry Corrigan, Jeff Dugdale, Simon Ecob, Tom Ellen, Chad Elliott, Andy Fanton, Barney Farmer, David Glasper, Dave Greene, Graeme Harper, Jason Hazeley, Lee Healey, Andy Hepworth, Carl Hollingsworth, Alan Hunter, Davey Jones, Martin Meeks, Joel Morris, Graham Murdoch, Paul Palmer, Tom Paterson, Cat Sullivan, Kent Tayler, Jonathan Thomas.

Cods' Wetsuits
Russell Blackman and Stephen Catherall

Published by Dennis Publishing Ltd
30 Cleveland Street, London W1T 4JD

ISBN 9 781781 064856
First Printing Autumn 2015

THE ADVENTURES OF
8
ACE

CUM ALONG, EIGHT... WE'RE GUNNEH BE LATE FOH ME SCHOOL REUNION IF YOO KEEP FUCKIN' DAWDLIN'...

... AN' STOP SCUFFIN' YER FUCKIN' SHOES. A WANT YER TER MEK A GOOD IMPRESSION. A DUN'T WANT ME OWLD CLASSMATES FINDIN' AHT A'M MARRIED TEH A USELESS DRUNKEN FUCKIN' BASTOD.

EVEREHONE ELSE'S 'USBANDS IS MEN O' FUCKIN' STANDIN', EIGHT... DOCTEHS... LAWYEHS... ENTREHPREFUCKINEURS... & THEH PROFESSIONAL PEOPLE WOT FOWK LOOK UP TER...

I'M TH'AWNLEH ONE WOT'S ENDED UP 'ITCHED TER A FUCKIN' 'OPELESS CUNT WOT SHITS 'IS SHELLBOTTOMS AN' LIVES IN A FUCKIN' SHED.

SO KEEP YER FUCKIN' MOUTH SHUT, REYT..? A'LL DO ALL T'TALKIN' AT FUCKIN' DO...

... AN' IF YER DUN'T LET US DAHN AN' SHOW US UP, A'LL GIVE YER ONE FORTEH-NINE TER SPEND ON EIGHT CAN OF ACE AT END OF TH'EVENIN'.
SCHOOL REUNION

JUST KEEP SMILIN' AN' TRY TER LOOK A BIT FUCKIN' PROSPEROUS.

SEE 'IM OVEH THEER? 'E'S A SELF-MED MAN... SIX FUCKIN' CARPET WARE'OUSES 'E'S GOT, APPARENTLEH...
...AND A ROLLS FUCKIN' ROYCE.

DID YOO 'EAR THAT, EIGHT? SIX FUCKIN' CARPET WARE-'OUSES, 'E'S GOT... AN' A ROLLS ROYCE. YOO'D'VE 'AD SIX CARPET FUCKIN' WARE'OUSES IF YER 'ADN'T SPENT EVEREH PENNEH YER EVEH OWNED ON ACE.

...'ER THEER.. THEH SAY 'ER 'USBAND'S A FUCKIN' 'IGH COURT JUDGE, EIGHT... A FUCKIN' 'IGH COURT JUDGE..!

'E'S MED SUMMAT OF 'IS FUCKIN' SELF, EIGHT. 'E'S GOT SUMWHEER. 'IS MISSUS IS FUCKIN' PROUD OF 'IM, EIGHT... 'E'S TEN TIME TH'FUCKIN' MAN WOT YOO'LL EVEH BE.

LOOK AT ALL THIS LOT... SHE'S MARRIED TER A EMINENT BRAIN SURGEON... 'ER 'USBAND'S A FUCKIN' OLYMPIC DRESSAGE CHAMPNION... 'IM ON TH'END... 'E'S TH'CONDUCTEH OF TH' LONDON FUCKIN' SYMPHONEH ORCHESTREH.

AN' WOT 'AVE I GOT? A USELESS FUCKIN' CUNT WOT CAN'T GET THROO A DAY WI'OWT GETTIN' PISSED UP ON CHEAP BOOZE.

I'M MARRIED TER SUMONE 'OO A'VE GOT TER BRIBE WI' ACE 'COS A DARESN'T EVEN LERRIM SPEAK IN FUCKIN' PUBLIC FER FEAR OF 'IM SHOWIN' US UP.

'ERE YER ARE... 'ERE'S YER ONE FORTEH-NINE. GO ON... FUCK OFF. A'M SICK OF TH'FUCKIN' SIGHT OF YER.

SHORTLY...
PATEL
24 HOUR MANO MART
GET CHEAP BOOZE HERE!
OPEN

POLISH COOKING SHERRY
JAGUAR

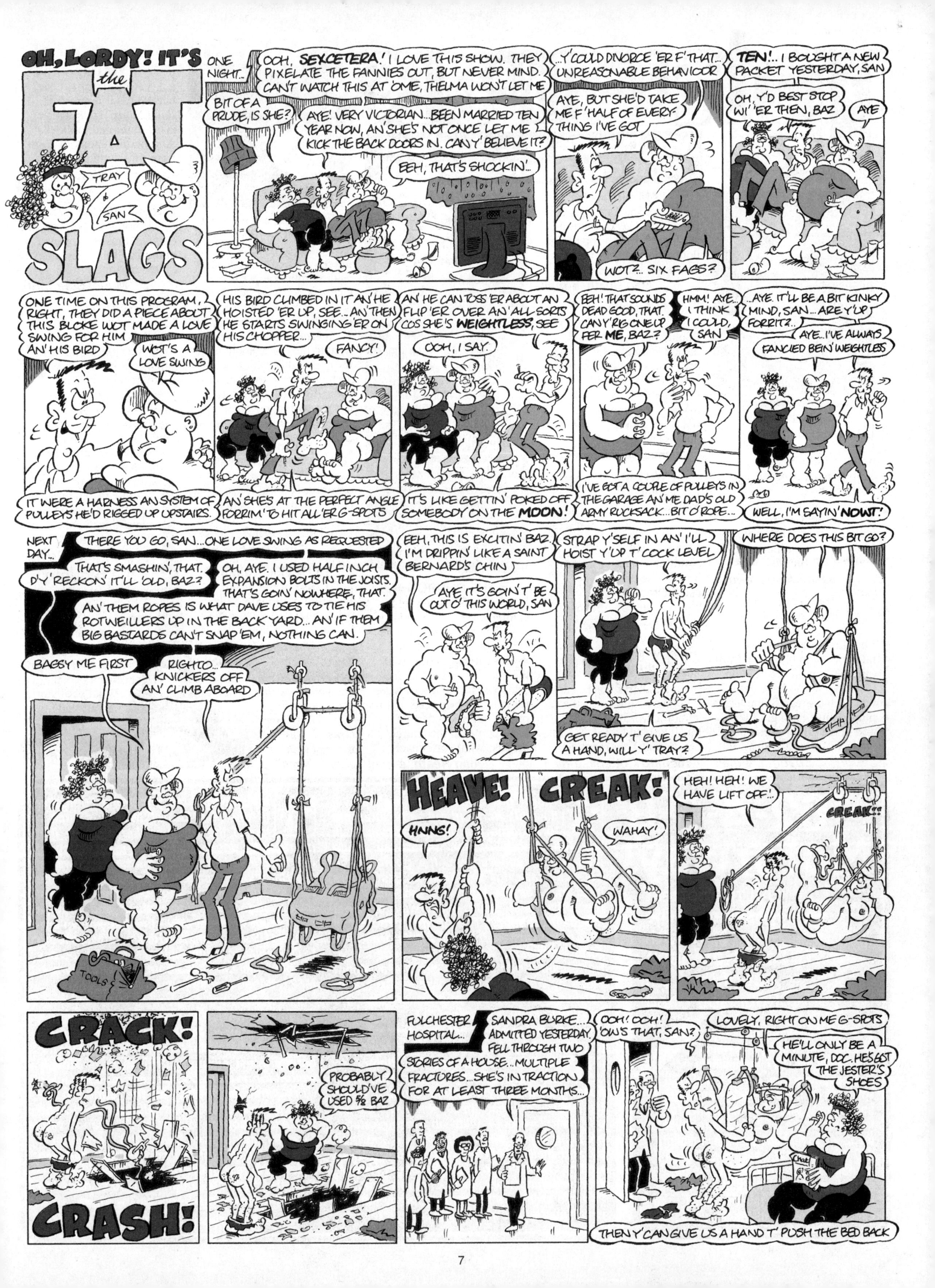
OH, LORDY! IT'S the FAT SLAGS
TRAY & SAN
ONE NIGHT...
OOH, SEXCETERA! I LOVE THIS SHOW. THEY PIXELATE THE FANNIES OUT, BUT NEVER MIND. CAN'T WATCH THIS AT 'OME, THELMA WON'T LET ME
BIT OF A PRUDE, IS SHE?
AYE! VERY VICTORIAN...BEEN MARRIED TEN YEAR NOW, AN' SHE'S NOT ONCE LET ME KICK THE BACK DOORS IN. CAN Y' BELIEVE IT?
EEH, THAT'S SHOCKIN'...
...Y' COULD DIVORCE 'ER F' THAT... UNREASONABLE BEHAVIOUR
AYE, BUT SHE'D TAKE ME F' HALF OF EVERY-THING I'VE GOT
WOT?... SIX FAGS?
TEN!... I BOUGHT A NEW PACKET YESTERDAY, SAN
OH, Y'D BEST STOP WI' 'ER THEN, BAZ
AYE
ONE TIME ON THIS PROGRAM, RIGHT, THEY DID A PIECE ABOUT THIS BLOKE WOT MADE A LOVE SWING FOR HIM AN' HIS BIRD
WOT'S A LOVE SWING
IT WERE A HARNESS AN SYSTEM OF PULLEYS HE'D RIGGED UP UPSTAIRS.
HIS BIRD CLIMBED IN IT AN' HE HOISTED 'ER UP, SEE... AN' THEN HE STARTS SWINGING 'ER ON HIS CHOPPER...
FANCY!
AN' SHE'S AT THE PERFECT ANGLE FORRIM' TO HIT ALL 'ER G-SPOTS
AN' HE CAN TOSS 'ER ABOUT AN FLIP 'ER OVER AN' ALL SORTS COS SHE'S WEIGHTLESS, SEE
OOH, I SAY.
IT'S LIKE GETTIN' POKED OFF SOMEBODY ON THE MOON!
EEH! THAT SOUNDS DEAD GOOD, THAT. CAN Y' RIG ONE UP FER ME, BAZ?
HMM! AYE... I THINK I COULD, SAN
I'VE GOT A COUPLE OF PULLEYS IN THE GARAGE AN' ME DAD'S OLD ARMY RUCKSACK...BIT O' ROPE...
...AYE. IT'LL BE A BIT KINKY MIND, SAN... ARE Y' UP FORRIT?
AYE... I'VE ALWAYS FANCIED BEIN' WEIGHTLESS
WELL, I'M SAYIN' NOWT!
NEXT DAY...
THERE YOU GO, SAN... ONE LOVE SWING AS REQUESTED
THAT'S SMASHIN', THAT. D'Y' RECKON' IT'LL 'OLD, BAZ?
OH, AYE. I USED HALF INCH EXPANSION BOLTS IN THE JOISTS. THAT'S GOIN' NOWHERE, THAT.
AN' THEM ROPES IS WHAT DAVE USES TO TIE HIS ROTWEILLERS UP IN THE BACK YARD... AN' IF THEM BIG BASTARDS CAN'T SNAP 'EM, NOTHING CAN.
BAGSY ME FIRST
RIGHTO... KNICKERS OFF AN' CLIMB ABOARD
TOOLS
EEH, THIS IS EXCITIN' BAZ. I'M DRIPPIN' LIKE A SAINT BERNARD'S CHIN
AYE IT'S GOIN' T' BE OUT O' THIS WORLD, SAN
STRAP Y'SELF IN AN' I'LL HOIST Y' UP T' COCK LEVEL
GET READY T' GIVE US A HAND, WILL Y' TRAY?
WHERE DOES THIS BIT GO?
HEAVE!
CREAK!
HNNG!
WAHAY!
HEH! HEH! HEH! WE HAVE LIFT OFF!..
CREAK!!
CRACK!
CRASH!
PROBABLY SHOULD'VE USED 5/8 BAZ
FULCHESTER HOSPITAL...
SANDRA BURKE... ADMITTED YESTERDAY. FELL THROUGH TWO STORIES OF A HOUSE... MULTIPLE FRACTURES... SHE'S IN TRACTION FOR AT LEAST THREE MONTHS...
OOH! OOH! 'OW'S THAT, SAN?
LOVELY, RIGHT ON ME G-SPOTS
HE'LL ONLY BE A MINUTE, DOC. HE'S GOT THE JESTER'S SHOES
THEN Y' CAN GIVE US A HAND T' PUSH THE BED BACK

Letterbocks

Viz Comic P.O. Box 841
Whitley Bay NE26 9EQ

letters@viz.co.uk

☐ **USAIN** Bolt gets loads of praise for running the 100m in under 10 seconds. Yet despite perfecting the art of shagging the missus in a similar time, all I get is abuse. Once again it's one rule for Olympic Gold-winning athletes and another for the rest of us.

Jason Ayres, e-mail

☐ **I IMAGINE** that the first two blood types discovered were A and B. I bet Ladbrokes stopped taking bets on C when a third one was announced. £20 on O at 18/1 would have netted you £360 less tax. Some lucky punter must have got the nod off the International Society of Blood Transfusion.

Spenner, e-mail

☐ **I AM** not sure that medical tourism is a good idea. I certainly would not fancy having an operation done whilst lying on the beach covered in sun tan lotion.

Alan Heath, e-mail

☐ **I'VE ONLY** ever met two women from Sri Lanka, but both of them have had an absolutely back-breaking set of knockers. Is this is a consistent trend amongst Sri Lankan women? Or is two not really a statistically reliable number?

Charles Harrisson, e-mail

☐ **WHY** would somebody want a touchscreen television, for heaven's sake? I for one will continue to sit on my arse and use the remote control the way nature intended.

Ross Kennett, e-mail

☐ **I DOUBT** Ben E. King would have sung the immortal words 'Stand By Me' if he could smell the farts I'm dropping this morning.

Richard Cotterill, e-mail

STAR LETTER

☐ **LAST NIGHT** I dreamt that I was a poet and I wrote a poem called *On the tidy stairs*. It was just a one line poem which went: *'On the tidy stairs, lives my constitution.'* I don't know anything about poetry so perhaps one of your readers could tell me if this is a real poem or just a stupid sentence. I don't really know what the last word means.

Wallace Wainhouse, e-mail

☐ **THE CHURCH** in Italy is organising a campaign to keep Sunday a day of rest. I was therefore very surprised to see on my recent trip to Italy that the churches were full on Sundays, and that they were fully staffed by priests. Don't priests deserve a day off? I say, come on the church, practise what you preach.

Alan Heath, e-mail

☐ **IN 1982** when I was 9, I wrote to Jimmy Savile asking him to fix it for me and my cub pack to take penalties against Spurs keeper Ray Clemence. I never heard back. Ten months later, another cub pack from Kent showed up on *Jim'll Fix It* doing just that. I went to the police about it but they just didn't want to know. Just another example of a code of silence that went right to the very top.

Pete Cashmore, Wolves

☐ **THAT** old adage 'See a penny, pick it up, all day long, you'll have good luck' is obviously bollocks. I just saw a penny on the floor, bent down to pick it up and hurt my back. I wouldn't call that very lucky.

Chris Bush, e-mail

☐ **I HAVE** a really bad case of the hiccups. I wonder could you write something very surprising for me? Much obliged.

Chandler Raymond, e-mail

* *Certainly, Chandler. Did you know that comedian Larry 'Shut That Door' Grayson was married with eight children?*

☐ **IF YOU** play *Merry Xmas (War Is Over)* backwards it is *(Revo Si Raw) Samx Yrrem* which is just complete bollocks! And people speak of John Lennon's 'genius'.

Richard Cotterill, Chesterfield

☐ **I FIND** dolls creepy, along with clowns and carnival masks. However, I quite like Toby jugs. They're quite charming.

Muriel Stoad, Hull

☐ **I HEARD** that Hurricane Sandy cost the USA $200 billion or something like that. These Americans have clearly got more money than sense. If I had that type of money I wouldn't spend it on hurricanes. Instead I would get myself a bigger camper van and maybe a posh sleeping bag to go with it and maybe one of those map things that talk. I would spend any remaining money on beer and Crunchie bars.

Alan Heath, e-mail

☐ **I THOUGHT** Paris was supposed to be one of the most romantic cities in the world? When I was there I saw an old tramp shag a bench. What's romantic about that?

Dr Andrew Turner, e-mail

M62-4-6-8 Motorway!

All the hottest goss about the M62 with Tom Robinson out of the Tom Robinson Band

"Hi! Tom Robinson here. As you might guess from the title of my 1977 Top 5 single *2-4-6-8-Motorway*, I have a real soft spot for the east-west transpennine link highway affectionately known to motorists as the M62. Well here's what I managed to find out about my favourite 107 miles of limited access multiple carriageway road not crossed on the same level by other traffic lanes for the exclusive use of certain restricted classes of motor vehicles this week!"

*Tough guy actor **Ross Kemp** will have his work cut out as he attempts to become the first person to walk the full length of the motorway while maintaining an erection. It's going to be no easy task for the former EastEnders hard man, as the M62 was recently voted the UK's least erotic motorway by Heat magazine readers! The previous record of 68.7 miles was set by BBC sports presenter John Inverdale, who lost tumescence at Hartshead Moor services despite a valiant effort by well-wishers who lined the crash-barriers holding up photos of tits and fannies to keep him going!*

*Talking of records, BBC's **Matthew Amroliwala** is set to attempt to drive the full length of the M62 while busting for a piss. According to offical rules, the News 24 heart-throb will have to set off from Liverpool with an uncomfortable pressing sensation on his bladder and then try and make it all the way to Hull without wetting himself. To make matters worse, road widening works at Rochdale's Junction 20 have created a temporary bumpy surface which may lead to involuntary bladder release!*

*My spies tell me that World Footballer of the Year **Lionel Messi** is such a fan of the transpennine highway that he recently decided to get a giant tattoo of the M62 inked in across his back! However, the Barcelona number 10's body art scheme hit a snag when the bungling tattooist misunderstood his instructions and drew a completely different M62 - the little-known arc-shaped US state trunk road linking Edwardsburg to Dowagiac in southwestern Michigan - across his back instead! Talk about having the wrong M62 tattooed across your back!*

*Get-this! Big-lipped Rolling Stones frontman **Mick Jagger** reportedly halted production of new tracks for the band's latest album GRRR! as he anxiously waited for news to come in about resurfacing work affecting traffic at the Junction 22 eastbound turnoff for Huddersfield and Halifax. A source close to the band, who recently celebrated their 50th anniversary, told us: "Mick couldn't concentrate and had to take the rest of the day off. He was worried that the roadworks might lead to congestion as far back as Birch Services."*

More M62 news next week! *Tom*

PRIZE HEADLINE COMPETITION

EACH ISSUE we ask you to write a tabloid headline to accompany a fictitious news article...

Last week we asked you to imagine that *Are You Being Served?* actor ***John Inman*** had been released from police custody following an arrest the night before. The winning headlines were:

"Are You Being Served? Star Bailed"
(Nick Tagnuts, Woking)

"John Inman's Police Cell Shame"
(Alan Otterspocket, Goole)

"Police Release TV's Mr Humphries"
(Barry Clockweights, Hull)

* Each winner receives a £1 cheese token and a year's supply of pornography

This issue, we want you to imagine that Rolf Harris asks a passing rugby team to apprehend and hogtie a large wallaby which has broken into his back garden. What is YOUR headline?

Send your headlines to:
Viz Headline Competition, PO Box 841, Whitley Bay, NE26 9EQ.

I JUST received a notification from Ticketmaster advising me: "Jools Holland tickets still available." Would anyone like to tell me something else fucking obvious?
Neil Shand, e-mail

WHO said birds are light? There is one running across my roof as I type and it sounds like that fat sod Giant Haystacks is tapdancing on my tiles. Or is the saying light as a feather? I can't remember. It doesn't matter.
Warren Clark, e-mail

ME AND my mates were trying to decide whether it's the number of fit birds in a town, the percentage of birds that are fit, or the ratio of fit birds to blokes that's most important. Can your readers help? Of course, it's all academic for us because we live in St Helens.
Spenner, St Helens

IF I WAS Moses, I would part the water in the bottom of the bog so I wouldn't get a splash of water shooting up my ringpiece every morning.
Ross Kennett, e-mail

LIKE me, I hope other readers are glad to see the contestants on *Dragons' Den* now don't have to go up those rickety old stairs anymore. Instead they climb downstairs into what is presumably a basement lair for the Dragons. I always said the old steps were a deathtrap. However, according to my mate Bazzer, his gran says more injuries are caused going downstairs than up. What do your readers think?
Jack Hough, Staines

** Well, readers, are more injuries caused going upstairs or downstairs? Tell us what you think, and exactly how you come to that conclusion. Please do not write to us if you simply 'feel' that one way is more dangerous than the other, in a faith-based manner. You must back up your belief with evidence. Write to the usual address, marking your envelope 'Stair danger facts.'*

I AM fed up with hearing about companies saying that they do so well because they "listen to their clients." I am a major pop singer and I expect my clients to listen to me.
David Bowie, California

IF that tosser Prince Charles ever becomes king, I would imagine he'll demand 3 fucking boiled eggs for breakfast instead of the normal 2. That's 21 eggs per week at 4 minutes per egg = 84 minutes. Times 52 weeks = 4368 minutes boiling time per year. What a fucking waste of resources.
Charlie Itchyarse, e-mail

TOP TIPS

MOTORISTS. Fool other motorists into thinking that you've got these expensive automatic windscreen wipers that switch themselves on when it starts raining by switching your windscreen wipers on when it starts raining.
Talbot Clark, Willingham

MEASURE your vocabulary by going through the *Oxford English Dictionary* and placing a tick next to each word you have used in the past. (Try to be honest about it). Then count the ticks to give you an exact figure. Then simply improve your vocabulary by going back through the dictionary and learning the words that don't have a tick against them, and then putting a tick against them.
Andrew McLeish, e-mail

CONVINCE people you are a tour guide by walking around London holding a furled umbrella in the air.
Matthew Richardson, e-mail

TYING a sparkler to your budgie's back and lighting it makes for a great spaceship if you're making a very low-budget version of *Blake's 7*.
M Litoris, e-mail

CELEBRITIES appearing on *Saturday Kitchen*. tell James Martin that your 'food hell' is something you really love, like cake. Just remember to pull a pissy face when he makes you taste it and no one will be any the wiser.
Kate Lynch, e-mail

BARBERS in Westerns. Save money and time by only soaping up half the face of your cowboy customers as they'll invariably be shot mid-way through the shave.
Fluff Freeman, e-mail

MOTORISTS. Avoid spending money on expensive motorway tolls in France, Italy and Spain by never leaving the motorway. Simply drive until you're close to where you want to be and then abandon your vehicle and get the bus.
Alan Heath, e-mail

HOBBYISTS. Buy hundreds of packets of pork scratchings to construct a shoddy 3D pig jigsaw.
Wilma Rubble, e-mail

MAKE yourself look more intelligent by drawing a pair of spectacles on your face.
Craig, Leeds

CONFUSE archaeologists years from now, by arranging to be buried with your car keys and some bronze arrowheads.
Craig Scott, e-mail

I OFTEN wonder if an old gypsy woman put a curse on my mother as a girl, saying that none of her children would reach six foot. If she did, the curse certainly worked, as I am 5' 11" and both of my brothers are 5' 10".
Hampton York, Devizes

I RECENTLY answered the door of my bungalow to a smartly-dressed, official-looking young chappie who informed me that I owed my electricity company £500. I gave him the cash, but unfortunately it later turned out to be a huge swindle. However, I must say how impressed I was with the young man's demeanour and overall standards of courtesy. Why can't all doorstep swindlers up their game like this fellow did?
Beryl Labia, e-mail

THEY say that all roads lead to Rome. Well, I recently took the Italian A1 motorway south from Bologna and ended up in Rome. So maybe it is correct. Looks like I was not conned this time.
Alan Heath, e-mail

IS IT me or were mainstream Hollywood film hookers in the 1970's a lot more jovial and upbeat than the modern portrayal? Every time you see working girls on screen now they are always so depressed and downbeat. They should take a leaf out of their predecessors' book and portray some bubbly enthusiasm for their chosen trade.
Richard Deakin, e-mail

WHICHEVER high-powered Italian fashion king decided that fit girls should wear nothing but leggings should be given a medal for services to arse-watching. Then he should have it taken off him because of the fat lasses who do it as well.
Dr Andrew Turner, e-mail

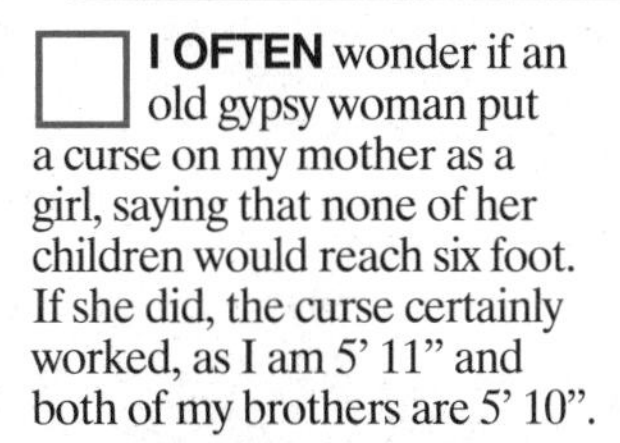

A Thrilling Tale of the Life and Death Struggle in the Blood-Soaked Arenas of Ancient Rome...

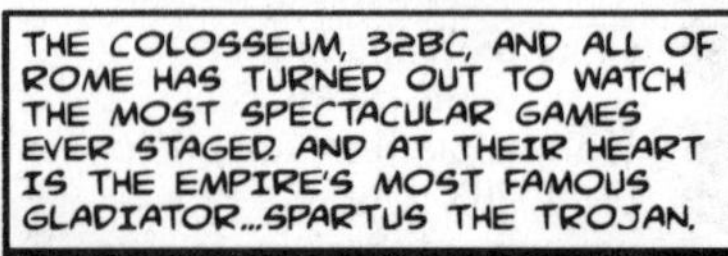

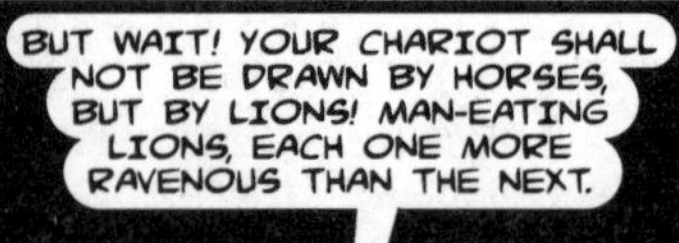

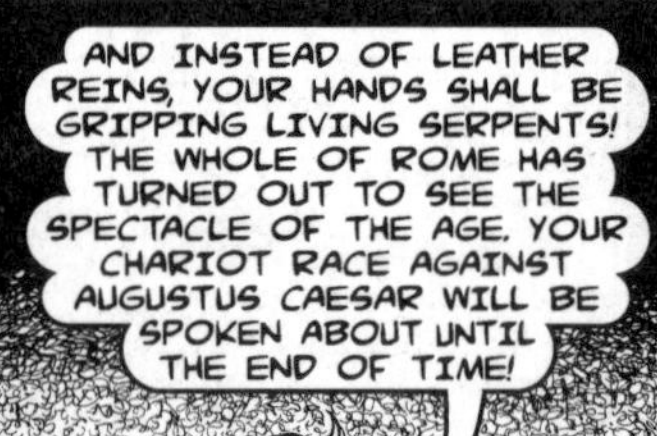

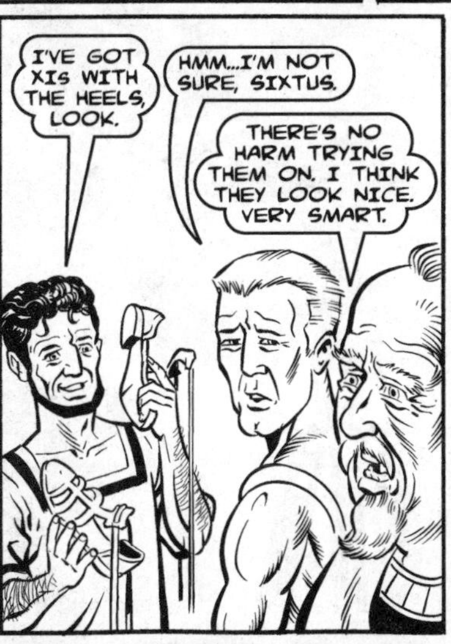

WILL SPARTUS CHOOSE THE TAN OR THE OXBLOOD SANDALS?...

WILL HE BUY AN AMPHORA OF THE RECOMMENDED SPRAY-ON SUEDE PROTECTOR?...

WILL HE PERISH IN HIS FORTHCOMING WILD ANIMAL BURNING CHARIOT RACE OF DEATH?

FIND OUT NEXT WEEK!

Take a Shit

WINNER MAGAZINE OF THE YEAR ~Take a Shit Magazine of the Year Awards

Up...In...Out... and Off Home

THEY'RE paid millions of dollars to act out our wildest sexual fantasies on screen - *blowjobs, DPs, gang bangs, anal facials* and *sticky belly flapcocks* are just another day at the office for them. They're PORNSTARS - and they have the best job in the world.

Bongo vid actress **Savannah Sugarwalls** talks to *Take-a-Shit* about her life off-screen

But what do they do when the filming is over and the director shouts "Cut!"? What are their lives like away from the camera? One woman who knows the unbelievable truth about the secret lives of the hardcore grumble movie XXX-listers is *SAVANNAH SUGARWALLS*. And now the 22-year-old veteran of over 6,000 explicit films and DVDs has decided to lift the lid and afford her legions of fans a privileged peek at her amazing private life.

"After so many years in the adult film industry, the public have seen every part of my body from every angle imaginable, in close-up pink. I've been filmed doing everything you can imagine," says Savannah. *"...And a few things you **couldn't** imagine doing in your **wildest dreams!"***

But according to the grumble star, the contrast between the steamy things she gets up to on screen and her everyday life away from the porn set could not be bigger. Now she's decided that it's high time her fans discovered the hidden side of Savannah Sugarwalls.

And in her new book **Up, In, Out and Off Home** *(Toast Publishing, £3.99)*, she reveals all about the extraordinary goings-on that only start once the day's shoot is over.

"In the porn industry no two two days' filming are ever the same. One day you could be having sex with a man dressed as a fireman, the next day you're having sex with two men dressed as firemen.

I remember one day, I'd spent the morning shooting *Big Cock Plumber 23.* In the movie, I was having trouble with a leaking tap and a plumber came round to fix it. Needless to say, before long things heated up, involving three-hole action and culminating in a red-hot oral cumshot scene. It was a tiring shoot and I got the bus home, calling in at the Spar to pick up a lasagne ready-meal on the way. The no-holes-barred sex I had had on set left me exhausted and spent, so I didn't really fancy cooking anything special for my lunch.

There was a long queue at the Spar because it was a new girl on the till and by the time I got home, I was gasping for a cuppa. But when I went to fill the kettle the tap wouldn't turn. I couldn't believe it. I'd spent all day engaged in hardcore porn action with a pretend plumber and now I was going to have to call in the real thing! I rang AAA1 Plumbers out of the Thomson's Local. I'd had them before when the toilet stopped flushing and they'd done a good job. Half an hour later the plumber arrived. I asked him into the kitchen and I looked him up and down.

> ***"There was a long queue at the Spar because it was a new girl on the till and by the time I got home, I was gasping for a cuppa"***

The plumber I'd been with at the porn studios had been a fit young man in his twenties, six feet tall with pecs, abs and broad shoulders. The paunchy, balding specimen standing before me peering through his thick glasses was five foot two at most, and looked like he was well overdue for retirement. But like his adult movie counterpart he was straight down to business, and it wasn't long before he was rummaging about in the cupboard under the sink, expertly finding the stopcock and turning off the main water supply. Within another five minutes he had taken the top off the cold tap and replaced the washer.

I offered to make him a cup of tea for his trouble, but he said he had another job to go to and left in his van. Whilst my morning with a movie plumber at the porn studios had left me breathless and drained yet sexually-fulfilled, my afternoon

***And CUT!:** Red-hot action cools down for Savannah when the cameras stop rolling.*

***Big Drip:** Broken tap was the only thing the plumber serviced.*

Sofa, so good: *Savannah's settee where she and her girlfriend got up to nothing much really.*

with his real-life counterpart had left my purse lighter to the tune of £48 plus £20 callout plus VAT on the whole lot. ”

Actresses with Savannah's sexy talents are thin on the ground so she's much in demand, often shooting three, four or even five porn movies in a day. As you can imagine, finding time for a normal social life in amongst such a hectic filming schedule can be as hard as one of her co-stars' manhoods. On one of her rare mornings off, Savannah arranged to call round at a girlfriend's house for a coffee and a chat. What happened next was completely mundane.

“I was on the sofa when my friend came in with a tray of coffee and a packet of biscuits and sat beside me. In my movies, when that happens the other woman is usually naked or at least has some sexy lingerie on, but on this occasion my friend had just had the dog out so she was wearing joggers and a thick jumper. She told me she was thinking of getting a new stair carpet, and that she'd recently increased her hours at work. As we got chatting, she confided that the people next door were thinking of moving and that she'd recently taken advantage of a Marks & Spencer meal deal, buying a main course, a side dish, dessert and bottle of wine, all for £10.

By this point in one of my lesbian porn videos, we would both have been kissing passionately, frantically fingering each other and pushing our breasts together whilst crying out in orgasmic ecstasy. However once again real life was nothing like its porn counterpart. As we drank our coffees, my friend remembered she had to take a library book back and asked me if I'd read the *da Vinci Code*. ”

If Savannah finds herself alone in an office with two men during working hours, there's usually only one way the scenario can end - a red hot spit roast across the desk with the men high-fiving each other whilst telling her to "suck it real good, bitch". So, when she went into the bank for a routine meeting with the manager, she was very surprised when events took a very different - and completely ordinary - turn.

“I was considering buying a Vauxhall Nova, but my savings account was £500 short so I was thinking of asking for a short term extension to my overdraft facility. I was shown into an office where there were two men - the bank manager and his assistant. They were both very friendly as I told them about the car I was hoping to purchase. The manager sat behind his desk and brought my records up on his computer screen.

'Well now, Miss Sugarwalls, if we sort this money out for you, what are you going to do for us in return?' I expected him to say, removing his glasses and leaning back in his chair to reveal an impressive bulge in the front of his trousers.

But to my amazement, that didn't happen. The manager explained that, as I had a reasonable credit history, he would be prepared to extend my overdraft facility subject to 12 monthly repayments at an APR of 4.2%. Then his assistant, instead of sidling over and sliding his hands down the front of my blouse to cup my breasts, handed me a series of forms on which he had put pencil crosses to show me where to sign. ”

“As we got chatting, she confided that she'd recently taken advantage of a Marks & Spencer meal deal, buying a main course, a side dish, desert and bottle of wine, all for £10.”

***NEXT WEEK:** Whilst visiting a department store to buy a new kettle, porn star Savannah gets stuck in a lift with the Dallas Cowboys American football team, and they chat awkwardly for ninety minutes whilst waiting to be rescued by the engineer.*

The new Archbishop of Canterbury Dr Justin Welby answers your ecumenical queries

Dear Dr Welby...

I UNDERSTAND that the threat of eternal damnation in Hell, coupled with the promise of eternal life at God's right hand, are what make religious people behave themselves nicely while they're alive. But what keeps them on the straight and narrow once they've passed on and joined the Angelic Host? Since they've already been promised everlasting life in Paradise, what sanction does the Lord have to stop them shoplifting, doing graffiti or downloading illegal pornography to their heart's content once they get up to Heaven?

Audrey Toothache, Harrogate

● *You're quite right to say that God would not break His sacred covenant by sending people to Hell once they had been admitted to His heavenly kingdom. That said, rules have to be enforced, and the Ten Commandments are no exception. I consider it quite likely that the Lord has built some sort of prisons up in Heaven to house those who transgress His laws. Of course, these jails will be nothing like the austere establishments we know on earth. They'll be made out of clouds for one thing, sentencing will be much less harsh and there probably won't be as much bumming in the showers.*

Dear Dr Welby...

MY HUSBAND died thirty years ago, and on his deathbed he confessed to having had a fling with a woman from the launderette. A couple of weeks ago I heard that she had also passed on following a short illness and now I am worried that he may have taken up with this floozie again in Heaven.

Irene Abcess, Cheltenham

● *I can put your mind at rest straight away, Mrs Abcess. Your husband is very unlikely to have re-kindled his romance with her from the launderette. If they have indeed met up on the other side I can assure you that their relationship will be quite platonic, as there is none of that sort of thing permitted in Heaven. And even if it was, which I am quite sure it isn't, she'll now be at least thirty years older than she was when he last had carnival knowledge of her, so there's very little chance that he would still fancy her.*

Dear Dr Welby...

I AM absolutely convinced that the doctrine of Papal Infallibility is true. But many people are not. Would it not, therefore, be a good idea to prove this matter once and for all by making the Pope sit a Further Maths A-Level paper, so that he could get 100% in it and show these doubting Thomases what's what?

Rita Pyorrhoea, Leamington

● *The Holy Father of Rome is a very wise man with whom I share many religious beliefs, such as God, Jesus and the Bible etc. However, the Pope is a Catholic and I am Church of England, and as such I am not required to accept the idea that he is incapable of making a mistake. I suspect that if he were to sit A-Level Further Maths, he would get about 95% - not perfect, but still enough for an A*.*

Dear Dr Welby...

I HAVE always lived an ethical and good life, obeying the Ten Commandments and religiously attending church every Sunday. As a result, I will be very disappointed to say the least if I don't get to Heaven when I die. However, as a keen naturist, do you think my immortal soul will be allowed to go 'au naturelle' once I am up in the clouds, or will I be required to wear a shroud like in the paintings?

Frank Bridgework, Bath

● *I am afraid that, as far as I understand it, Heaven currently operates a strict 'shrouds only' policy. However, the shrouds are really very smart, actually more like a nightie, and you will be pleased to hear that you don't have to wear pants underneath. There may well be a separate designated nudist cloud, a bit like Brighton beach, where shrouds do not have to be worn. You should ask St Peter for details when you arrive at the Pearly Gates and he will give you more up-to-date information as to its whereabouts, opening times etc.*

mr.LOGIC

HE'S AN ACUTE LOCALISED BODILY SMART IN THE RECTAL AREA.

hmmm..

HUCKNALL'S COCK GIVEN BLUE PLAQUE

THE PENIS of 80's heart-throb *Mick Hucknall* is to be honoured with a blue plaque, it was announced yesterday.

The flame-pubed sexual organ, which is thought to have been inserted into more than 3000 women during the last 43 years, has been dubbed a "British institution well worth commemorating" by senior members of English Heritage.

chairman

In a press conference at London's Somerset House, the organisation's chairman Professor Reginald Gaping explained the reasoning behind the surprising decision to honour the ex-Simply Red frontman's member.

EXCLUSIVE!

He told reporters: "It's proper mental when you think about how many birds Mick Hucknall has knobbed. Supposedly we're talking thousands. Even if you don't care for his music, you've got to say fair play to the guy."

tablelady

The professor continued: "I argued this case to several other members of the English Heritage board and we eventually decided that, instead of doing what we normally do and commemorate yet another pub that Charles fucking Dickens used to drink in, we'd use the blue plaque scheme to honour a truly ground-breaking and historic British institution – Mick Hucknall's cock."

Honour for Simply Red bell-end's bell-end

***Red:** Blue plaque for ruby-toothed crooner*

The plaque is to be installed on the end of the Simply Red singer's glans. And at an official ceremony next month, the Duchess of Cambridge will officially reveal it by pulling a cord, drawing back the foreskin.

In 2011, Professor Gaping sparked controversy when he announced plans to petition the Queen to add Rod Stewart's nuts to the New Year's honours list.

ROGER MELLIE

JOHNNY FARTPANTS
the Boy with a Bum like thunder

THERE'LL BE PRECIOUS FEW LAUGHS IN MY CARTOON THIS WEEK, READERS.
INSERT YOUR OWN 'READER'S VOICE' COMMENT HERE.

IT'S MARGARET THATCHER'S FUNERAL TODAY AND WE'RE GOING ALONG TO ST. PAUL'S TO PAY OUR RESPECTS.
SNIFF! OH, SHE WAS A WONDERFUL WOMAN. NASTY AND UNFAIR, BUT STRONG-WILLED WITH IT.
THERE THERE, DEAR. SHE'S IN A BETTER PLACE NOW.

COME ON THEN. LET'S GO AND BAG OURSELVES A GOOD SPOT BY THE ROUTE. WE DON'T WANT TO MISS THE BOX GOING PAST.
RIGHT-O, DAD.
PICNIC

AND REMEMBER, JOHNNY. YOU'RE NOT TO SPOIL THIS SOLEMN AND MOVING OCCASION WITH ANY OF YOUR TROUSER-COUGH TOMFOOLERY, OKAY?
NO DAD. I WON'T.

SHORTLY...
THIS IS A GOOD PLACE, RIGHT BY THE DOOR. WE'LL GET A CRACKING VIEW OF ALL THE GRIEF FROM HERE!
SUDDENLY...
'SCUSE ME, JOHNNY. I'M BILLY BRAGG... ANY CHANCE YOU COULD PUMP THE UNDERTAKER'S HAT OFF AS HE COMES PAST, AS A MARK OF DISRESPECT?
OF COURSE I CAN, BILLY...

I'LL BREW YOU UP A REAL GOOD BEEFY EGGO AND GUFF THAT TOPPER INTO THE MIDDLE OF NEXT...
JOHNNY?!
OOPS.

YOU'LL DO NO SUCH THING, YOUNG MAN. REMEMBER, YOU'VE GOT TO SHOW SOME RESPECT AT SUCH A TIME OF NATIONAL TRAGEDY.
YES DAD. SORRY DAD.

SHORTLY...
OOH! I THINK THE STIFF IS ON THE WAY. I CAN HEAR CHEERING AND LAUGHTER DOWN THE STRAND.
YES INDEED, YES INDEED...
?!
WOW! IT'S LEFTY COMEDIAN BEN ELTON!
YES INDEED. LISTEN, JOHNNY... DO YOU FANCY LETTING "R.I.P." WITH ONE OF YOUR SPECIAL "RUMPET VOLUNTARIES"?
SURE! WHAT FOR?

TO SPOOK THE HORSES PULLING THE CORTÈGE, SO THEY BOLT AND SPOIL THE SOMBRE ATMOSPHERE OF THATCH'S FUNERAL. THAT'LL SERVE HER RIGHT FOR SINKING THE HMS BELGRANO. YES INDEED.
OKAY. I'LL...
A-HEM!

DON'T EVEN THINK ABOUT IT, JOHNNY.
NO DAD. SORRY DAD.

SHORTLY...
WHAT AN AFTERNOON! BILLY BRAGG... BEN ELTON... ARTHUR SCARGILL... TONY BENN... DEREK HATTON... JOHN O'FARRELL AND THE REST... ALL ASKING ME TO DROP MY GUTS AT MAGGIE'S FUNERAL!
YES. AND TOP MARKS FOR NOT SUCCUMBING TO TEMPTATION.

SUDDENLY...
GOOD HEAVENS! OUR LONE BUGLER HAS JUST CHOKED ON ONE OF THE COCKTAIL SAUSAGES OFF THE WAKE BUFFET!
OH DEAR.
THE VERGER

CAN ANYONE HERE PLAY THE LAST POST?
I CAN, YOUR HOLINESS!

AND I WON'T BE NEEDING A BUGLE, EITHER!
THANK THE LORD! NOW WE'LL BE ABLE TO GIVE MRS THATCHER A SEND-OFF WITH ALL THE RESPECT SHE DESERVES AFTER ALL!

SO...
THE WHISPERING GALLERY
BRAP! TIDDLY BRAP! BRAP! QUONK! QUONK!

TONY PARSEHOLE

Why I Weep for the Iron Lady of Hearts

WHEN I heard that Margaret Thatcher had died I wept.

I wept and I wept.

I wept and I wept and I wept.

And when I had finished weeping, I sobbed.

I sobbed and I sobbed.

I sobbed and I sobbed and I sobbed.

But I was not crying for Mrs Thatcher, the platinum blonde with a steel heart of ice who ruled our land with a rod of iron for a decade and a year.

I was crying for all the babies whose milk she had snatched from their innocent mouths.

I was crying for all the miners whose mines were she had so callously closed down in front of their very eyes.

I was crying for all the old ladies who, in their one bedroomed flats, she forced to pay the same Poll Tax as an earl in his Dukedom.

Yes. It was for them that I wept and I wept and I wept.

For the babies, miners and old ladies.

Tears of sadness. Tears of desolation. Tears of woe. But mixed in with these three types of tears (sadness, desolation and woe) was another sort of tears.

A fourth sort of tears.

They were tears of pride.

Pride in Margaret Hilda Thatcher, the lowly grocer's daughter born into poverty, who worked her way up to become the most powerful woman in Britain.

The most powerful woman in Europe.

The most powerful woman in the world.

It was she alone who stormed the Bastilles of male privilege, battering down the portcullis of inequality and laying siege to the male chauvinist pigsty that was British politics in the 1970s.

Whatever you might think about her policies, when she took the keys to 10 Downing Street, Margaret Thatcher did more to forward the cause of women's rights than a hundred suffragettes.

A thousand Germaine Greers.

A million Spice Girlses.

For she invented Girl Power before Sporty, Baby, Posh, Ginger and the other one were even a gleam in their father's eye.

And in their immortal words, I'll tell you what she wanted, what she really, really wanted. She wanted not to zig-a-zig, urgh.

No.

Margaret Thatcher simply wanted to make Britain a better place. To instil in her country the values of thrift, prudence and good housekeeping she had learned at her father's knee in his humble Grantham grocer's shop. Scary, that was the other one.

But it is for her courage in battle that we will remember her. Whether she was sinking ships in the South Atlantic or trampling miners under the hooves of police horses in South Yorkshire, Margaret Thatcher was not afraid to stand up for what she believed in.

And whether or not you agreed with what she believed in, you have to respect the fact that she believed in it strongly enough to stand up for it.

And I've just remembered a fifth type of tears that I wept when I'd finished weeping the other four.

Tears of grief.

For, amidst all the pomp and ceremony of her state funeral, it is easy to lose sight of the fact that she was somebody's wife.

Somebody's *mother.*

Somebody's *daughter.*

Somebody's *son.*

And her passing leaves her children, little twins Mark and Carol, orphaned. Alone in the world and crying for their mummy.

But they are not alone. I cry with them.

The nation cries with them.

The world cries with them.

For a Colossus of Rhodes has been plucked from our heart and has left a hole that can never, never be filled. There that's 500 words. PDF invoice attached.

The Iron Lady... Your Tribute

ONE ITEM dominated the news earlier this month. The tragic, untimely death of former Prime Minister Margaret Thatcher. And since that tragic day, your letters of tribute have poured in in their dozens. *Here's a selection of some of the most moving ones we received...*

MAGGIE Thatcher may have led this country through 11 turbulent years that saw war, unemployment and class division on an unimaginable scale, but let us not forget that before politics, she was a research chemist at BX Plastics. Her work with polymers and emulsifiers led directly to the invention of soft-scoop ice cream. She may be known as the Iron Lady to many, but she will always be the Ice Cream Lady to me.

Herbert Pocket, Tooting

IN THE fifties and sixties ice cream used to come in a rock solid block and you had to take it out of the freezer half an hour before you wanted it. Even then you very often bent the spoon trying to get it out of the tub. Mrs Thatcher may have closed all Britain's pits, but she opened the way to enjoyable ice cream.

Frank Windowbox, Leeds

I DARE say that these fiends dancing in the streets, celebrating the death of Margaret Thatcher have never eaten soft-scoop ice-cream by way of protest against her policies. Then again, I dare say they have. Their hypocrisy appalls me.

Chorlton Wheelie, Luton

YOU cannot see more British a sight than a group of children at the seaside eating a cornet ice cream. It brings a lump to my throat just thinking about it. Thank you Maggie for your invention of soft-scoop. You have made me proud to be British.

Ada Chelstrom, Lincs

I WAS a miner in South Yorkshire before Thatcher closed down the pits and put me and thousands of my colleagues on the dole. But I find it difficult to be angry with her, as I love Mr Whippy ice cream. I believe that for this reason alone, the nation owes a debt of gratitude to this magnificent woman.

Ron Golightly, Selby

IN THE eighties I was a member of Millitant and regularly went on 'anti-Thatcherism' protest marches. But deep down I found it difficult to reconcile my hatred of Thatcher and my love of the soft-scoop dairy product she developed. I knew my life was a contradiction and that I would have to give up one or the other. Needless to say, I resigned from Millitant and still enjoy Baroness Thatcher's lovely ice cream to this day. Nom! Nom!

Mark Iron, Brixton

THESE people criticising Mrs Thatcher's economic policies seem to forget that in the sixties and seventies you couldn't stick a flake into an ice cream, because it was too hard. I don't agree with all the polical decisions she took, but she did make the 99 a practical reality, and if for that reason alone she should have had a state funeral.

Edward Brush, Toft

I AM a dyed-in-the-wool Tory supporter and I was delighted when Mrs Thatcher stood for Finchley in the 1959 election. There were so few women in Parliament at that time, especially amongst the Conservatives, and I thought her candidature was a welcome step towards redressing the balance. However, I love hard ice-cream and deplore the invention of this soft-scoop stuff. It has no taste and causes a dreadful mess as it melts. I was so disappointed to discover that Mrs Thatcher had invented it that I couldn't bring myself to vote for her, and for the first time in my life I voted Labour.

Edna Bargepole, Tring

THE BOTTOM INSPECTORS

Drunken bakers

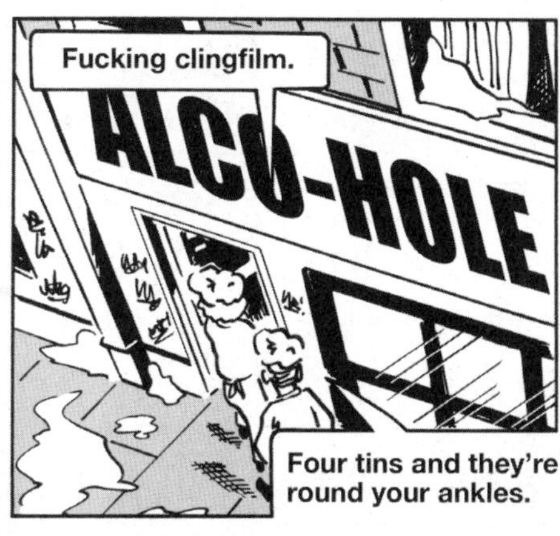

PUR-AISE JEEZUS! IT'S
IVAN JELICAL

PRAISE BE TO GOD!
FOR HE HATH GRANTED ME THE GIFT OF ANOTHER DAY HERE IN HIS MIRACULOUS CREATION!

BEFORE I FOUND GOD, I WAS ALONE. I WAS A LOST SOUL, CRYING IN THE WILDERNESS.
PIZZA
MICRO MEAL FOR 1
BUT NOW I HAVE A FRIEND IN JESUS, I WILL NEVER BE LONELY AGAIN.

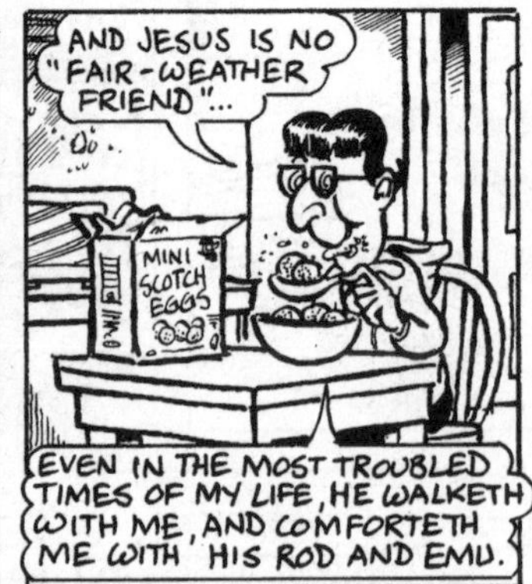
AND JESUS IS NO "FAIR-WEATHER FRIEND"...
MINI SCOTCH EGGS
EVEN IN THE MOST TROUBLED TIMES OF MY LIFE, HE WALKETH WITH ME, AND COMFORTETH ME WITH HIS ROD AND EMU.

YES, THE LORD IS A TRUE SOULMATE. WITH HIS COMPANY, I NEED NEVER SUFFER THE GNAWING ACHE OF SOLITUDE...
CLUNK
RATTLE

SPRINT!

GOOD MORNING, POSTIE! I WAS JUST REFLECTING UPON HOW LUCKY I AM TO HAVE THE FRIENDSHIP OF OUR SAVIOUR...
YEAH, SMASHING, WELL I MUST GET ON...

MORNING, MRS GRATOLI! HAVE I EVER TOLD YOU OF MY GOOD FORTUNE TO ENJOY THE CONSTANT COMPANIONSHIP OF THE RISEN CHRIST?
I KNOW I CAN RELY ON HIM TO ALWAYS BE THERE FOR ME, EVEN WHEN LIFE SEEMS...

SLAM!
...BLEAK.

TRULY THE LORD IS BOUNTIFUL! FOR HE LOOKED DOWN AND SAW THAT MAN WAS ALONE
AND HE BROUGHT FORTH FISH IN ABUNDANCE, SO THAT MAN WOULD HAVE A FELLOW CREATURE TO TALK TO

COO-EE! SIMON-THAT-IS-CALLED-PETER!
TAP TAP
WON'T YOU COME OUT AND JOIN ME IN OFFERING UP A THANKSGIVING PRAYER TO THE LORD OF HOSTS?

HMMM...
IF I HIDE BEHIND THE CASTLE HE MIGHT THINK I'M ASLEEP AND BUGGER OFF.

THE CUP OF MY LIFE DOTH INDEED RUNNETH OVER
BUT PERHAPS I HAVE A DUTY TO SEEK OUT THOSE WHO ARE LESS FORTUNATE, AND SHOW THEM THAT THEIR LIVES COULD LIKEWISE BE FILLED WITH JOY.

I WILL GO OUT AMONGST THE MULTITUDE AND INVITE THEM TO SIP FROM MY OVERFLOWING CUP.
HAS HE GONE PAST YET?

IN TOWN
NO TO "GAY MARRIAGE"
...FOR GOD ORDAINED THAT MAN SHOULD HAVE A COMPANION, AND THAT COMPANION SHOULD BE A WOMAN!

YEA, IT IS WRITTEN: "ADAM AND EVE CREATED HE THEM; AND ADAM AND STEVE CREATED HE NOT!"
NO TO "GAY MARRIAGE"
APPELLATIONS 13 VERSE 24.

HALLELUJAH! A FELLOW LAMB IN THE FLOCK OF CHRIST! WILL YOU COME AND JOIN ME FOR LUNCH, BROTHER?
MY BEDSIT IS NEARBY, AND MY LARDER IS BLESSED WITH A PLENTITUDE OF SCOTCH EGGS.

AND SHORTLY
COME; LET US SIT AND EAT, AND REJOICE IN THE FELLOWSHIP OF OUR FAITH.
HOMO SEXUALITY IS AGAINST GOD
CHRISTIANS FOR FAMILIES
SAY NO TO SATAN
SCOTCH EGGS
FOR NONE OF US CAN EVER BE ALONE WHEN WE SHARE IN THE LOVE OF CHRIST THE REDEEMER.

MUNCH MUNCH.
MUNCH MUNCH
SCOTCH EGGS

MUNCH MUNCH.
?!
SCOTCH EGGS

UH-HUH HUH HUH! UH-HUH HUH HUH!
SOB
CHRISTIANS AGAINST GAY PROPAGANDA
MUNCH MUNCH.
SCOTCH EGGS
UH-HUH HUH HUH! UH-HUH HUH HUH!
DJ '13

Is this conclusive proof of the existence of the

WORCESTER BUNGLE?

By our Crytozoology correspondent
An owl with Johnny Morris's voice

Sasquatch with mother: Does this blurred video image show the incredible moment a mysterious 1970s children's television man-bear was spotted on a Worcester allotment?

A MIDLANDS vegetable patch turned into something from the *X-Files* this week when a Bungle-like creature was once again spotted near Worcester, this time in an allotment.

The elusive animal made its fleeting appearance just after dawn, but luckily Douglas Butterman, a retired window fitter, had the presence of mind to film the creature on his Ferguson video camera.

"I only keep the camera for making my mucky films in the shed," says Mr Butterman. "It was pure chance I had a cassette in the thing."

wild

Cryptozoologists say the three-minute film is the most conclusive evidence yet that a wild Bungle may be living in the Fernhill Heath area.

"There have been reports of a furry, flustered figure around Worcester for at least two decades," says Tetley Teafolk of paranormal website woooooo.com, where the clip has been posted. "But so far the beast has only chosen to appear to people who can't hold a camera straight, or only own a pinhole camera, or are falling off a low wall at the time."

The clip has now been viewed on the website over thirty times.

water

On the short snatch of film, the beast, approximately the height of a man in a bear costume, pauses briefly as it crosses open ground and scratches its head in an exaggerated manner, then puts its hands on its hips.

"At first I thought it was a dog, or a big rabbit, but when it did the 'well I never' movement, that's when I knew I'd seen the legendary Worcester Bungle," says lucky cameraman Butterman, "I couldn't believe my eyes."

bear

The furry shape then moves to a low wall and begins sticking some cotton wool clouds onto a piece of blue sugar-paper. The beast then claps its paws, mimes remembering something, and disappears into the rough scrub by the railway cutting. The rest of the tape is just porn.

Tetley Teafolk views the film as a turning point for Worcester Bungle hunters. "The Butterman Testament, the name we enthusiasts are using for the footage has been recorded on a totally obsolete video camera with all lines on it and blurring, and cocks at the end, but you can still see it's probably a Bungle. It is tantalisingly exciting," says Teafolk, dribbling Frijj down his chin.

station

But mounting evidence for a man-bear living wild in the Worcester area has been so far pooh-poohed by the authorities.

"I've seen the footage, and it's almost certainly a dog, or a big rabbit," insists Senior RSPCA sceptic Cresta Bear. "The vague shape is Bunglish, but it could be a dog or a big rabbit dressed as a Bungle, maybe for a fancy dress party, or sexual display.

"I don't know why nobody ever films these things on a nice, steady smart phone, or a proper camera," Bear continues. "Don't forget, eyes can play terrible tricks. Or a shadow. Or dust on the lens."

Claw marks were later found on a toolshed door consistent with a human hand in a fur covered glove. Online commentators suspect the creature may have been after some scissors to cut round the clouds.

Expelli-anus!

Potter actor Emma gives arse clip the bum's rush

EXCLUSIVE!

HARRY Potter star *Emma Watson* has sparked debate by refusing to say whether or not she would shave her arse for a film.

At a press conference to promote her latest movie, *The Bling Ring*, the woman who brought Hermoine Grainger to life was asked if she was prepared to lose her bum fur for a film if the role required it. But Watson remained tight-lipped, sparking speculation as to whether or not she would be prepared to sacrifice her back doormat.

source

A source close to the actress told reporters yesterday: "Emma is perfect as she is. Waxing her anal beard would be gilding the lily. Even if there was a magic potion or spell to rid her of her back trouser quiff, Emma wouldn't be taking it."

Another source close to the Potter sidekick agreed: "Emma has no interest in mowing her arse garden. She has perfect teeth and flawless skin. There's absolutely no need for her to shave her unkempt arse tache."

"If a part required her to tame her rectal rug, then it's not the role for Emma," the source continued. "The rug stays in the picture."

lovecraft

But Watson's refusal to comment one way or another has fanned the flames of speculation. And as the 'will she, won't she' debate heated up last night, BBC film critic Mark Commode joined in, saying he thought the 22 year-old star would lop off her bum wool if the part was right.

"Emma is a terrific actor who can take her pick of roles. If something came along that she really wanted to do that required a bald bum crease, I think she'd do it," he added.

An exclusive opportunity to enjoy a luxury gourmet

5-Course Punch-up Lunch

Just £120 pp

with TV gastronome ***Gregg Wallace***

star of BBC2's Masterchef

Relax, dine, and get beaten up by TV star Gregg Wallace in the delightful surroundings of the Michelin-starred Linden House Restaurant, Iver, Bucks.

Menu

Entrées
6 glasses of Cru Champagne. Suspicious look from red-faced, sweating Wallace on arrival

Hors d'Oeuvres
Timbale of pheasant in blackcurrant jus. Wallace accusing you of pinching his bird's arse. 6 glasses of wine

Soup
Beetroot & Autumn vegetable consommé. Threatening grab of tie and overturned decanter. 6 glasses of wine

Main Course
Quail & leek frittata in squid ink with a vegetable medley. Red mist onslaught with repeated punches to temple and jaw. 6 glasses of wine

Dessert
Mandarin & almond bombe with mango purée. Tooth knocked out, choice of Sheffield Hammer or Glasgow Kiss plus overturned table. 6 glasses of wine

Fromagerie
Coffee, cheese & biscuit selection. 6 glasses of wine

(Vegetarian options plus kick in bollocks also available.)

Lunch served 1.00 for 1.30. Ambulances and police 4.00

~Book early to ensure your place in this delicious fracas~
www.punchuplunchup.co.uk

See our website for other celebrity events including 1st Class Orient Express tour to Paris with your ear bitten off by Jonathan Creek's Alan Davies and Alnwick Castle Murder Mystery Weekend with EastEnders actor Leslie Grantham.

Top Tips

TAKE a tip from convertible car drivers by buying a house with no roof on for the two sunny days a year. You can pull a canvas tarpaulin over the top for the other 363.

H Bland, Scrotum

ANTI-bacterial hand gel makes an ideal 'Bonjela' substitute for alcoholics.

David Milner, Durham

DOG owners. Track your pet's movements around the house by leaving a large tray of used engine oil at the door prior to letting it inside.

Funkwit, e-mail

MAKE your own credit card by cutting out a rectangle from a sheet of plastic. Spend to your hearts content. When you run out of credit, simply cut out another.

Donald Arse-Burp, e-mail

SAVE time washing your genitals in the morning, by first putting a bag of frozen peas in your underpants, thus halving your cock size.

Fozed, e-mail

TWO cocktail sausages fried with a quail's egg and cherry tomato make an ideal cooked breakfast for those on a diet.

D Tropper, e-mail

PORN film directors. Don't reach into shot midway through a scene to have a grab or a probe. Breaking the fourth wall spoils the illusion of reality.

Perceptive Paul, e-mail

WEIGHTWATCHERS. Buy less food when shopping in the supermarket by simply placing a brick in your shopping basket when entering the store.

Janice Crow, e-mail

UNEMPLOYED people. Feel like a London commuter by standing in your wardrobe for an hour every morning whilst your wife rocks it from side to side.

Floaty Ade, e-mail

A SALT cellar sellotaped to the back of radio-controlled car is a ideal pavement gritter for small pets.

John the Cheeks, e-mail

MAKE sausages easier to cut by marking serrated lines in them with fork prongs.

Spot, e-mail

Letterbocks

VIZ COMIC, P.O. Box 841, Whitley Bay, NE26 9EQ ⋮ e-mail: letters@viz.co.uk

WOMEN often complain that men don't pay them enough attention, yet when the wife's sister found the spycam I installed in her bathroom extractor fan she went mental and called the police. Perhaps some of these so called 'feminists' would care to explain the logic behind that.

M Shuttlecock, e-mail

IN A recent speech, Prince Charles stated that NHS hospital staff need to adopt a more caring approach. As someone who has spent 30 years working in emergency medicine, I'd like to take a moment to thank His Royal Highness for his invaluable advice. It's certainly not an approach to our work that has ever occurred to me or any of my colleagues and we are particularly lucky that our shortcomings have been highlighted by a philandering, tax-avoiding imbecile who has never actually used the NHS.

Nick Lyon, e-mail

** You forgot to include 'Big-eared, Tampax wannabe' in your list of perjoratives, Mr Lyon.*

IF GENE Kelly was so fond of singing in the rain, then why didn't he ditch the umbrella? I'm sorry, but these yanks are so full of shit these days.

Terry Corrigan, e-mail

THEY say that you never hear the bullet that kills you. Well my uncle Stan certainly did. He was shot in the leg by a border guard whilst trying to escape from East Germany and bled to death in no-man's-land over a period of two days.

Farsley Grange, Leeds

I HAVE often wondered what *A-Team* actor Mr T would have written on the back of his shirt if he took up professional soccer. Would he just have the letter 'T', or would he have the 'Mr' bit as well? If the latter, I think it would be rather unfair as it would be according him a respect that was not being shown to the other players.

Timbale Rice, Cornwall

WITH reference to Mr Timbale's letter *(above)*, I think that all footballers should have the title 'Mr' in front of their name on their shirts; Mr Téves, Mr Rooney, Mr Ba, etc. to accord the players a certain dignity. Perhaps then, they would have more respect for each other and football might return to the gentleman's game that it once was.

Hampton Brinylon, Windsor

VETERAN actors like Dame Judi Dench and Annette Crosbie are forever complaining about how there aren't enough parts in films these days for more mature women. Well I have my own video company, and last year I made a film called *Anal Grannies*, and a sequel called *Anal Grannies 2*. I wrote to Dame Judi's agent on both occasions offering her a part and I didn't even get a reply.

Dick Shitcrumbs
Bang Bang Videos Ltd

I HAVE decided to become a Puritan and lecture others on sexual morality. Seeing as I am not getting any, I don't see why anyone else should.

Alan Heath, e-mail

DO ANY readers think the actors in the 118 adverts put that on their CVs?

P Sprouts, e-mail

I WAS walking down the street when I noticed a 'Gentleman's Club', offering exotic dancers. Thinking that it sounded interesting, I paid a quid and went in. You can imagine how conned I felt when I saw nothing but a couple of strippers from Gateshead. I don't see what is exotic about that and to make matters worse, they did not even bother to do a dance.

Alan Heath, e-mail

IT IS both tragic and ironic that *Born Free* conservationist Joy Adamson got ate off a lion, but I can't help thinking it was her own fault. If I was a conservationist, I'd only try to conserve small things like mice or those very small monkeys. If I had to conserve bigger things, I'd only do herbivores.

Rosemary Flatbread, Hull

WIKIPEDIA says that King William II of England died "on the 2nd August 1100 in the New Forest, shot by an arrow, events still unclear." Now that to me sounds like it's an on-going investigation. Good luck to the copper landed with that cold case.

Henry Beauclerc, Windsor

I DON'T think it's fair that only people who are 100 years old receive a telegram from the Queen. I think we should all get a message whatever our age from those in line to the throne. Prince Charles could handle the 99-year-olds, Prince William the 98-year-olds and so on. The 60-year-olds would get a telegram from James Oglivy, 50-year-olds from Rowan Lascelles, 40-year-olds from James Carnegie, 3rd Duke of Fife, 30-year-olds from HRH Princess Ingrid Alexandra of Norway, 21-year-olds from Princess Astrid of Norway and one-year-olds from Prince Alexander of Yugoslavia.

Jason Shreeve, e-mail

I THINK Richard Dawkins shouldn't be allowed any time off work at Christmas and Easter, and he shouldn't be allowed any Easter eggs or hot cross buns either.

James Dean, e-mail

Welcome to the Amazing World of Probability

What's the Chance of That?

with **Adam Chance** off of Crossroads

THERE'S a girl in my class called Kate, and my brother used to go out with another girl called Kate. What's the chance of that, Adam?

Conrad Fitblat, Padstowe

● ***LET US*** *assume that 1:1000 girls in the UK are called Kate, that gives us 60,000 Kates in all. Let us further assume that your brother has gone out with 5 women in total. The odds of any one of those being called Kate was therefore 1:5 or 0.2. Multiplying these numbers together gives the probability of your brother's girlfriend being called Kate, a massive 1:300,000. Assuming there are 30 people in your class, the odds of one of them being called Kate is 1:(60,000x30) or 1:1.8 million. Multiplying these two figures together gives the chance of there being a Kate in your class and your brother also going out with a Kate. A staggering 1 in 540 BILLION, exactly the same as the number of atoms in a Milky Way.*

WHAT'S the chance of getting struck by lightning, Adam?

Hecules Ashbeck, Taunton

● ***THE SURFACE*** *area of the earth is 4.5×10^{15} square feet. Assuming that from above we present lightning with a target of 2 square feet, that means each time that lightning strikes, there is a $1:2.25 \times 10^{15}$ chance of being struck by any single bolt if we are standing still. However, if we assume we move an average of five miles a day, we cover an area of 1.5×10^{9} square feet in a lifetime, making the chances of being struck 1:1.5million. But lightning strikes some point on the earth's surface 44 times every second, and we live for an average of 2.36×10^{9} seconds. That means we live through 1.04×10^{11} lightning strikes. Dividing the number of strikes we live through by the length of our life in seconds, we can see that on average you can expect to be struck by lightning approximately 44 times in your life. But don't worry, since $^{2}/_{3}$ of the earth's surface is covered in water, you will only actually be struck 15 times in your life, or about once every five years.*

MY CHRISTIAN name is spelt the same backwards as it is forwards. What's the chance of that, Adam?

Ada Chelstrom, Helsinki-upon-Thames

● ***WITH 26*** *letters in the alphabet, the chance of any one of them being in your name is 26 factorial (written 26!), or 26 x 25 x 24... etc. Because there are three letters in your name, we have to cube this number. 26! is approximately 4×10^{26}, so $26!^{3}$ is a massive 64×10^{78}, about the same as the number of atoms in the visible universe.*

MY FRIEND told me that in a leap year, girls could propose to their boyfriends on St Valentine's Day. So last year on February 14th, I booked a nice table in a restaurant and popped the question to my boyfriend of 28 years. Imagine how silly I felt when he reminded me that we actually got married 26 years ago. I had completely forgotten. We did have a laugh about it.

Ada Dementia, Tooting

I LIVE in Sicily and I woke up this morning in the early hours to find a horse's head in my bed. It is not mine and I was wondering if any readers may have a horse who has lost his head?

Alan Heath, Sicily

I WAS so incensed by Lance Armstrong's confession of cheating that I set fire to my DVD of *Dodgeball* in protest. A pity as it's one of my favourite films - though it wouldn't surprise me if he took some kind of acting drugs to appear in it.

Vincent Blood, e-mail

I HAVE often wondered why people give dummies to babies. On reflection I suppose it is better than them biting someone. A friend of mine had his leg bitten off, although I think a crocodile was responsible for that.

Alan Heath, e-mail

IF GHOSTS exist why does nobody ever see ghost dinosaurs? Even pasty-faced Yvette Fielding couldn't miss a spectral Brontosaurus shuffling past.

Robert Rawcliffe, e-mail

IS IT me or has the government knocked a few millimetres off the width of Bourbon biscuits? I know they need to save money but this hasn't passed my notice, I can tell you.

Bilbo, e-mail

MY WIFE is so forgetful sometimes. Last week she called the police and reported me for throwing a knife at her. So imagine her embarrassment when they turned up and I had to explain that she is my assistant in a circus knife-throwing act.

Terry Corrigan, e-mail

I MUST admit I am completely stunned by these Jimmy Savile revelations. I have spent my entire life convinced his surname was spelt with two Ls.

Chris Higson, e-mail

I LIKE actor Warwick Davis, but I think he should branch out in his career a little. Every film I've seen him in, he plays a dwarf of some sort.

Hampton Court, Wiltshire

WHEN people say "Why don't McDonalds do delivery?", I know why they don't. It's because they have great difficulty getting lukewarm food as far as the fucking drive-through window, never mind down the street to my house.

Paul Hodgkinson, e-mail

JUST look at this picture of the Lord Mayor of Sheffield in 1943. Hitler didn't stand a chance.

Merlin Farqueharson, UK

I'M REALLY glad that I don't live in medieval times as I'd really miss things like iPods, pocket calculators and Pot Noodles. No, give me nowadays any day.

Renton Polecat, Hull

* *What would YOU miss most if you lived in medieval times? Perhaps you'd long for a sprung mattress. Maybe you'd yearn for your toaster. Or perhaps you'd hanker after one of those vacuum cleaners with no bag that never lose suction. Write in to the usual address and tell us what you'd miss most. Mark your envelope: 'What I'd miss most if I lived in medieval times.' There's a week's holiday to 1360 in a time machine for the best letter we receive.*

WHEN did people stop laughing at fart lighting? If shooting a jet of fire from your anus isn't comedy, I don't know what is. Honestly, some people.

Lee Hooper, e-mail

I HAVE a t-shirt that I think is possessed by evil spirits because whenever I put it on I seem to do wicked things. One time whilst wearing it I scratched the word 'Twat' on my neighbour's car with a screwdriver. Another time with it on I pulled up all his bedding plants and poured engine oil into his fishpond. It was in the wash when I pushed dog shits through his letterbox but it was obviously still exerting its malign influence from the tumble dryer.

Manfred Mansell, Croydon

Worried that Celebrities are going to turn up to *YOUR* party? Make sure they *DON'T* with a

NOT-A-LIKE

from the

Shitting Image Agency

Hundreds of people who look absolutely *NOTHING LIKE* your favourite stars of stage & screen.

Hugh Grant

Meryl Streep

Morgan Freeman

"My husband was terrified that Will Ferrell was going to turn up to our 25th wedding anniversary bash, so I got Shitting Image to send along a Not-Alike. The dissimilarity was uncanny."

Mrs B, Essex

"I was worried in case Colin Firth turned up at my 50th birthday party. So I hired a Not-Alike of him to make sure he didn't."

Mr B, Essex

Appearance fees from £20 + £5 per hour.

www.theydon'tlookafuckingthinglikethem.co.uk

Wild confessions of mini-mart boss Ray's Rock 'n' till Roll life behind the counter...

LEGS OPEN ALL HOURS!

Everybody loves Raymond: *The world's biggest stars are queueing round the block to perform sex acts on Ormskirk corner shop-keeper Duckworth.*

A PINT of milk... a loaf of bread... four cans of lager... twenty Consulate. We know we can always rely on the corner shop when we run out of life's essentials. Open from early in the morning to late at night, it provides a vital service, keeping us supplied with the things we simply cannot do without.

CANNY customers are often keen to bag a bargain at their local 7-11. And, says one Lancashire shopkeeper, many will stop at nothing in their bid to pay bottom dollar for the contents of their basket. What's more, according to ***Ray Duckworth***, manager of the Ormskirk Road Handy Mart in Skelmersdale, the keenest penny-pinchers of all are the Hollywood stars!

***"Honestly, if I told you the names of all the Tinseltown A-listers I've had in my store, and the lengths they'll go to in order to minimise their bill, you'd think I was making it up,"* he told us.**

"And whilst I have to admit that I have occasionally made things up in the past, like being in the SAS, swimming the Channel and flying in the Red Arrows, none of which were true, I'm definitely not fantasising this time, I can assure you."

Now Ray, 62, has written a no-holds-barred autobiography - *Fifty Shades of Ray*. His sensational revelations sparked a bidding war as rival publishers vied to secure the rights to the 8-page hand-written manuscript. He told us: "They were offering me silly money, but in the end I decided to keep control of my own work and publish it myself, selling it exclusively from a box on the counter of my shop."

In these exclusive extracts from his explosive memoir, Ray details just a few of the thousands of thrilling encounters he's had with movie stars keen to secure a bargain ... at any cost!

"Money-off coupons are the bane of shop-keepers' lives. They don't sit flat in the till so the drawer jams, you have to read the terms and conditions to make sure they're valid, and you wouldn't believe the palaver involved in actually claiming the money back off the wholesaler. So my heart sank when *Pirates of the Caribbean* star **KEIRA KNIGHTLEY** turned up at the counter with a box of Dreft Non-Bio and a 15p off voucher she'd clipped out of *TV Quick*.

pride

I checked the small print and, surprise surprise, the thing was no good as it was one day out of date. The *Pride & Prejudice* star's face fell as I explained that I was going to have to charge her full whack for her washing powder. I pointed out that suppliers only pay up if the date on the till receipt is on or before the expiry date on the coupon. "Surely we could come to some sort of arrangement," she pouted, reaching across the counter and seductively caressing the cap of the biro in my dustcoat pocket between her thumb and forefinger. "I'd make it worth your while."

There was no doubt in my mind what was going on. One of the silver screen's most desirable ladies was offering me sexual favours in return for turning a blind eye to an expired Dreft coupon. Normally I'd have resisted; after all, I'm a married man. But my wife was under the doctor with women's things at the time and I'd been kept short for weeks and I'm ashamed to admit I gave in to temptation.

"After putting her knickers back on, Keira paid me for the Dreft. I knocked the fifteen pence off, and she left the shop..."

Like any red-blooded man, after seeing her get out of that fountain in *Atonement* I'd often fantasised about what it would be like to give Keira Knightley one. Now, here I was, doing her for real. And the reality was every bit as sexy as what I'd imagined, I can tell you.

day

I'm too much of a gentleman to reveal what took place, except that it involved a lot of tit-rubbing, and when I'd finished she said it was the best sex she'd ever had.

After putting her knickers back on, Keira paid me for the Dreft. I knocked the fifteen pence off, and she left the shop. Fortunately, I remembered I'd sold a box at full price earlier in the week so I was able to submit the out-of-date coupon with that receipt and claim the money back that way."

Unlike large supermarkets, small shopkeepers working on reduced profit margins are unable to simply throw away damaged stock. Mangled tins and torn packets often end up being offered at a knock down price that many celebrities find simply irresistible.

"Earlier in the year I'd over-ordered on Goblin Meat Puddings, and since there was no space in the stockroom I ended up storing the extra gross in the shop toilet. There must have been a slow leak in the cistern, because when I finally brought them out to stack on the shelves, the tins were rusting round the bottom and the labels had gone mouldy and started peeling.

gordons

There was probably nothing wrong with the contents, but I've been in the retail business long enough to know that appearances count for everything. My customers were not going to shell out out top dollar for meat puddings in rusty tins. I knew I was going to have to slash the price to shift them. I took twenty-five percent off, marking them down from 60p a pop to 45p.

They were a bargain, and one person who clearly thought so too was *Friends* star **JENNIFER ANISTON**. She sidled up to the till with

From rasher with love: Material girl Madonna was happy to offer Duckworth a spot of true blue hanky panky in return for slightly thicker-than-usual slices of bacon.

four of the damaged tins - one in each hand and a couple tucked under her chin. "Any extra discount for bulk?" she asked, fluttering her eyelashes from under her trademark Rachel haircut.

deal

I explained that I was already practically selling the savoury suet treats at cost, and she was getting four puds for the price of three. But the *Bruce Almighty* star seemed determined to clinch an even better deal. "Come on, if you'll take a bit more off for me, I'll take a bit more off for you," she winked, as she unbuttoned her blouse and pushed her bra strap off her shoulder.

walmer

To my amazement, she then proceeded to perform the sexy striptease scene from her latest film *We're the Millers...* right there in the shop! However, unlike in the movie where you don't get to see much, I got to see everything - tits, bum, fanny ... the lot.

By the time Aniston was completely naked, the atmosphere in the shop was incredibly erotically charged, I can tell you. Then she upped the ante even further.

"Knock these meat puddings down to half price and I'll do an encore," she purred. "With audience participation."

kingsdown

A stronger man might have been able to resist, but my wife had recently had it all taken away down there and our marriage had been going through a bit of a barren patch as a result. As for what happened next, let's just say that Jennifer earned every penny of the extra 25% I eventually knocked off those toilet-damaged tins. ”

Corner shopkeepers often find themselves tangled up in red tape and bureaucracy. Petty rules and regulations about weights, measures, hygiene and what can and cannot be sold often breed frustration for managers and star shoppers alike.

“ I remember one Sunday morning a couple of years ago. The door quacker went and I turned to see ***MADONNA*** making her way up the aisle towards the counter. "I want four rashers of bacon please," she announced in her familiar New York drawl. "Extra thick," she added.

I'm quite well known locally for slicing bacon fresh rather than selling that pre-packaged stuff. It's a little extra service that my customers appreciate. I put the shank on the slicer and set the slice gauge to ten - the thickest setting for bacon. But like the hard rocker she is, Madonna wanted more. "Why don't you turn it up to eleven?" she asked.

dover

I explained to her that under EU rules, the maximum thickness for bacon is ten. Anything thicker than that must be sold as gammon and priced more expensively. I made it clear to the *Desperately Seeking Susan* star that if she wanted to have it cut at eleven, she couldn't have it at the bacon price. End of. It was as simple as that.

But the *Papa Don't Preach* singer didn't get where she is today by taking no for an answer. "Cut my goddam bacon at eleven and you can have this," she said as she whipped open her coat, to reveal that she was stark naked except for her pointy bra, sexy basque, French knickers, stockings, suspenders and thigh-high stiletto-heeled leather boots.

What man could say no to such an offer? Certainly not this man - whose wife had long since given up doing things that she had used to do much earlier in their relationship. Impetuously, Madge swept the revolving Tic-Tacs stand, chewing gum rack and scratchcards display unit onto the floor. "This is for cutting my bacon thick," she said, as she pushed me back on the counter and started tugging at my flies.

What happened next was just like that scene in *Body of Evidence* where Madonna does William Dafoe on the bonnet of that car, except it didn't take place in a darkened multi-storey and I didn't have all broken glass sticking in my bottom. It was the most earth-shattering climax I've ever achieved. After I'd tucked my tackle away, I washed my hands as I always do before and after handling raw meat, and cut my recent lover four slices of bacon at the number eleven setting.

& jerry

As I adjusted the knob on the slicer past bacon and into thin gammon, I knew I was chancing a dusting-down from West Lancashire Trading Standards. But I no longer cared - the erotic charge I'd got from my kinky counter-top tryst with the *Like a Virgin* singer was worth the risk.

Madonna still pops in most Sunday mornings for four rashers of bacon. She likes her meat thick, and I'm only too happy to give it to her, if you know what I mean." ”

Ask any shopkeeper and they'll tell you: Give your customers an inch and they'll try to take a mile. Ray well remembers one occasion when he'd got a good deal on a tray of Chinese-made fly sprays at the cash & carry, and decided to pass his savings on.

“ Demand for the half-price cans was sure to be high so I decided to limit sales to one aerosol per customer. Nevertheless I wasn't at all surprised when ***PAMELA ANDERSON*** approached the till carrying two tins of the bargain insecticide. I told her she'd have to take one of them back, as it was strictly one per punter, but she shook her head. "Only one of them's for me," explained the busty *Baywatch* beauty. "The other one's for a friend."

When you've been in the corner shop game as long as I have, you recognise a tall tale when you hear one. If I had a penny for every time I've been told "These fags are for my dad", "these rubber Johnnies are for my brother" or "my uncle wants this glue for making an Airfix model", I'd be a rich man.

& barbara

I told Pam that if her friend wanted a fly spray she'd have to come in and buy it herself. She explained that this was impossible, as her friend was Carmen Electra and she was busy posing for *Playboy* in California. "Carmen heard about your special offer," pleaded Pam. "She asked me to pick her up a can next time I was in the shop, as she's getting loads of bluebottles in the outside toilet at her Beverly Hills mansion."

"let me tell you, everything she did to the Motley Crue drummer on that tape she did to me in my shop that afternoon..."

But I was having none of it. "Rules is rules," I told her. "Now put that extra can back." At this point Pam decided to change tack and turn on the charm, coquettishly unzipping the front of her black leather bomber jacket to reveal her ample charms. "Rules are made to be broken," she panted, licking her lips and seductively sucking her finger. "How about we break a few, right here, right now."

She left me in no doubt what was on offer. And let me tell you, her offer was every bit as tempting as the half-price one I'd got on the fly sprays.

A stronger man might have been able to resist, but my wife had recently went through the change and moved into the spare bedroom. As a result I was missing a woman's touch and the temptation to take the *Barb Wire* star up on her saucy proposition was just too much.

A few years previously, I'd borrowed a video off a bloke at the Rotary Club in which Pam and her husband Tommy Lee got up to all sorts of shenanigans on a boat. Well, let me tell you, everything she did to the Motley Crue drummer on that tape she did to me in my shop that afternoon. And more.

When we'd finished and I'd shot my bolt, she paid for her two fly sprays and left. I don't know whether the second tin really was for Carmen Electra or whether Pammy wanted it for herself. I don't suppose I'll ever know. But by that point I didn't even care.

Just like Pam's first sex tape, the whole sensational episode had been captured on the CCTV security camera in my shop. Looking back with hindsight, I suppose I could have sold the footage for millions of pounds on the internet. That's if I hadn't recorded over it the next day because I've only got one tape which I've been re-using for the last 25 years. ”

Fifty Shades of Ray (Ormskirk Road Handy Mart Publishing) is exclusively available from a box by the till price 99p or 2 for £1.50

Next Week:

"How my BOGOF offer on Cheese Strings led to a tens-up orgy with the **Pussycat Dolls, Atomic Kitten, Linda Lusardi** and **Melinda Messenger**. So it was actually an elevens-up."

Pam bang, thank-you ma'am: Baywatch beauty swapped wild sex for fly sprays.

AN EXCITING CHRISTMAS ESCAPE YARN FOR BOYS!

Continued over...

Next week, as their incarceration continues, Lewthwaite and his men construct a glider using round-ended scissors, sugar paper and gloy.

10 THINGS YOU NEVER SNEW ABOUT SNOW

SNOW. It falls from from our skies every winter, bringing Britain grinding to a halt. We shovel it off our paths, scrape it from our car windscreens and make it into men. We may think we know everything about this cold, powdery, seasonal precipitate. But do we really? Here's 10 fascinating facts you never knew about snow...

1 NO TWO snowflakes are exactly the same. In 1988 there was a brief flurry of excitement in the world of meteorology when a flake was found in Switzerland which appeared to be identical to one that fell in Colorado in 1934. But when the two were compared under a microscope, there was found to be a very, very slight difference.

2 THE SMALLEST snowman ever made was constructed by the world's shortest man, ***Calvin Phillips***. He spent the whole day constructing the icy homunculus using a teaspooon for a shovel. The finished snowman sported a liqurice allsort top hat, a scarf made from a length of dental tape and an orange hundred and thousand for a nose. Phillips later fell asleep and had a dream where the snowman came to life and flew him around the garden at a height of 6 inches.

3 IN 1888, Swiss gardener ***Heinrich Hoffmeister*** was demolishing a shed on his allotment at the top of a snowy hill when he accidentally trod on two planks of wood with nails sticking out of them. He began to slide down the slope and made a grab for some bamboo canes supporting some plants, but they came out of the ground. Tucking the canes under his arms, Hoffmeister began to pick up speed and hurtled through the local golf course where he was forced to zig-zag between the flags on the greens. In an afternoon, the gardener had inadvertently invented skiing, a pastime which is now enjoyed by millions.

4 ON CAPTAIN Scott's final, ill-fated Antarctic expedition of 1912, ***Captain Oates*** famously left the tent uttering the immortal words: "I'm going outside now. I may be some time." And he was right, for at the time of going to press he has been out in the snow for more than 101 years and he still isn't back.

5 IN 1888, Swiss housewife ***Ada Hoffmeister*** was bringing her husband some tea and biscuits on his allotment when she tripped and fell awkwardly. Landing face first on the tray on the snowy ground, the momentum of her fall caused her to slide out of the gate and onto the icy road. Gathering speed as the road snaked its way to the foot of the mountain, Mrs Hoffmeister clung onto the tray for dear life through 28 turns and banked corners, eventually arriving at the village in a time of 2 minutes 13.8 seconds. She had inadvertently invented the Skeleton Luge, a sport which is enjoyed to this very day.

6 THERE ARE countless pop groups with the word 'snow' in their name, such as ***Snow Patrol*** and many, many more.

7 IF YOU thought an abominable snowman was merely a very badly built snowman, you'd be wrong. For it's actually a yeti - a sort of furry white ape-like monster that lives in the Himalayas. Or does it? We may never know. Or will we? Only time will tell.

8 THE OPPOSITE of snow is salt. Although the two substances look identical, when you add them together they both vanish into thin air. No-one knows why - it's another one of Mother Nature's mysteries.

9 IN 1888, Swiss gardener ***Heinrich Hoffmeister*** was pushing his wheelbarrow on his allotment when the wheel fell off. The barrow began sliding on the steep path, hitting three other gardeners, who tumbled into it one behind the other. Holding onto the handles, Hoffmeister desperately tried to hold it back, but eventually gave up the fight and jumped nimbly in behind his three friends. The men clung to each other in terror, putting plant pots on their heads for protection as the barrow made its way down the winding, icy mountain road, gathering speed and momentum as it went. They had inadvertently invented the 4-Man Bob, a sport that is still enjoyed today.

10 EVEN THOUGH it's been falling down to earth for hundreds, if not thousands of years, nobody really knows what snow is. "Our best guess is that it's some sort of dry rain that forms in grey clouds, that becomes wet when the temperature rises," says TV weatherman ***Everton Fox***. "But the truth is, we simply have no idea." "He's right," adds his BBC colleague ***Tomasz Schafferknackers***.

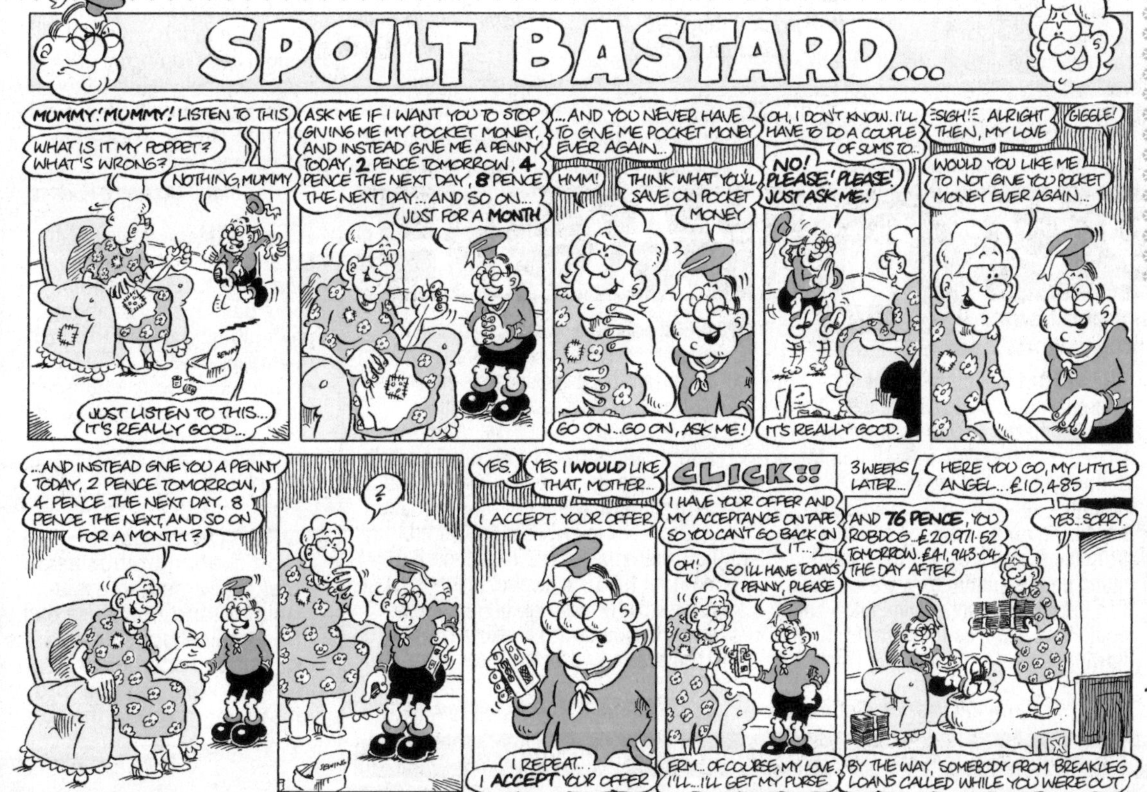

JOKE: GRADE-E

YOU KIDS HAD BETTER NOT BE RUNNING UP A HUGE PHONE BILL IN THERE.

£9,016.42

WASP with MOTHER

Britain's Stingy-est Catholic Wasp Forum with the World's Saintliest Mum

Mother Teresa of Calcutta

"Hi, Mother Teresa of Calcutta here. You may know me best from the saintly doings I did before I died, such as sitting next to dying people and spending their medicine money on statues of the Virgin Mary. But one thing I really like is suffering. I can't get enough of it, because the Bible says that suffering brings us closer to God. And, because nothing in the Lord's creation causes more suffering than a wasp sting, it's little wonder I love these stripy little yellow and black insects too. And judging by my postbag, Viz readers have also got a soft spot for wasps. So let's open up a few letters and see 'wasp' you have been saying. Amen."

Ma Teresa

I DISCOVERED a wasps' nest in my attic the other day. It was huge, with hundreds of angry wasps buzzing in and out of it. I know you can get people who come out and remove them safely, but as a devout catholic I decided to pray to the patron saint of wasps to ask him to get rid of it instead. Looking it up in a book, I found it was Saint Friard, so I said 10 Hail Marys and 5 Our Fathers to him, as it was a particularly big nest. However, the next morning it was still there and I thought that St Friard had ignored my prayer. However, when my husband came down for breakfast, he said that his piles, which had been giving him gyp for years, had miraculously vanished overnight. I knew immediately what had happened. When looking up St Friard in a book, I had accidentally prayed to the saint above him in the index, St Fiacre, the patron saint of haemorrhoid sufferers!

Mary O'Prolapse, Knotty Ash

Saints & Stingers

Catholic wasp facts with retired Pope

Benedict XVI

St Francis of Assisi, patron saint of animals, once came across a man who was pouring petrol on a wasps' nest in order to destroy it. But before he did, the saint performed the last rites and extreme unction on the stripy insects. After the flames killed them, the wasps, all 25,000 of them went to heaven, as well as the grubs and all the fertilised eggs in the queen's abdomen. And they are still there today, and will be for all eternity.

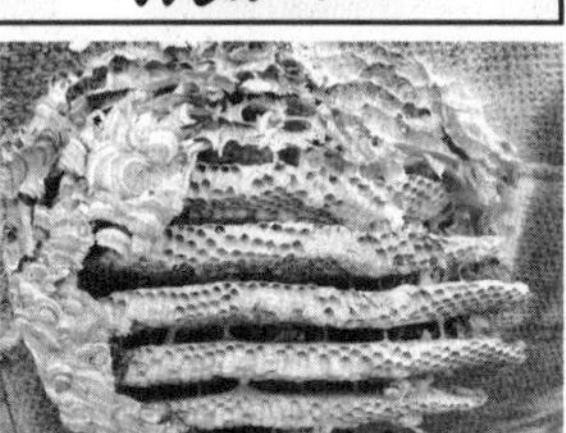

ON returning from holiday, I discovered a large nest in my garage full of angry wasps. However, they haven't caused me any problems, since wasps are not mentioned anywhere in the Bible so I simply do not believe in them. When they swarm round and sting me when I get the car out every morning, I don't worry about the pain and swelling as my faith tells me that it is not real.

Dr Patrick O'Cloghell, Ellesmere Port

WITH reference to Dr O'Cloghell's letter *(above)*. Whilst I agree that wasps don't exist, he should check that his infesting insects are not in fact hornets, which *do* get mentioned in the bible, three times - *Exodus 23:28, Deuteronomy 7:20* and *Joshua 24:12*. If he got stung by one of them, he'd know about it.

Brendan O'Hooligan, Liverpool

I AM a nun, and an unusual thing happened to me when I was taking communion the other day in the chapel of my convent, St Assumpta of the Divine Heart of Jesus. I knelt down at the altar rail and opened my mouth to receive the host wafer as usual. However, as the priest placed it on my tongue, a wasp landed on it. By that time the wafer had already started to transubstantiate into the literal body of Christ, and so it would have been a mortal sin to spit it out. So I swallowed it and the wasp stang me on the back of the throat. It really hurt, but I was comforted by the thought that my suffering brought me closer to the Lord God who sent His only begotten son to suffer on the cross and die for our sins. So that was alright.

Sister Lionelle O'Blair, Everton Plain

WHILST watching the Discovery Channel the other day, I learned with

Wasp Thought for the Day

With

Cardinal Caramac O'Paedop

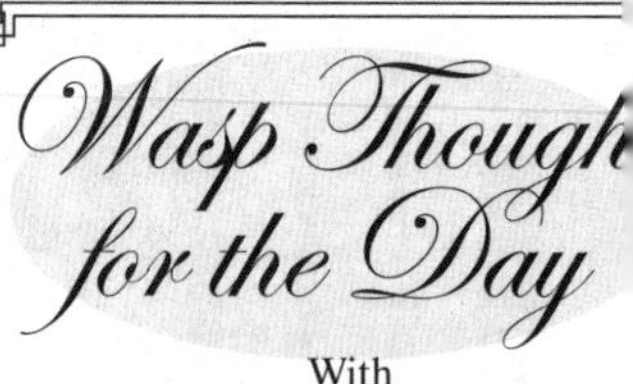

The other day I was preparing a sermon for the following Sunday's Mass when a wasp landed on my hand. Pausing from my writing, I marvelled at the wonder of God's creation... the beautiful colours... the iridescence of the little insect's gossamer wings as the light caught them... the intricacy of its tiny legs as it crawl across my hand. Unfortunately, I was also set marvelling at the

Saints & Stingers

Catholic wasp facts with retired Pope

Benedict XVI

In 1031, Bernadette of Heidelberg was stung to death whilst trying to remove a wasps' nest from the eaves of her outside toilet using a bucket and a piece of cardboard. Despite suffering an estimated 12,000 stings during her martyrdom, witnesses said that Bernadette didn't really cry out very much, considering. She was later canonised by Pope Pious VI, and is the patron saint of picnics, jam sandwiches, litter bins and dropped ice creams.

disgust that a typical wasps' nest consists of thousands of man wasps all servicing a single lady wasp. And when I say servicing, I'm sure I don't need to spell out what I mean. Not to put too fine a point on it, each nest is a veritable Sodom and Gomorrah of insect depravity. Holy Mary mother of Jesus why does God allow it? They're worse than the fecking Protestants.

Mrs O'Docherty, Widnes

WITH reference to Mrs O'Docherty's letter *(above)*. Whatever you think about the way they go about procreating, you have to admit that wasps have an awful lot of children. As long as those babies are brought up as good

Wasp a Miracle!

Your stories of wasp and hornet related divine intervention.

THE OTHER day I got stung on the wrist off a wasp. I immediately ran round to my local church where the priest sprinkled holy water on my injury. Miraculously, the swelling started to go down the next day. By the second day it was much less and the redness was starting to fade. By day three, it was well on the mend, and by the fourth day, there was practically no sign of where the wasp had stung me except for a little itchy raised bump. Praise be to God the Father, the Son and Holy Mary Mother of Jesus.

Mrs Niamh Riamhs, Wallassey

THE WHOLE congregation at my church witnessed a miracle the other day. During the Eucharist, a wasp landed on the statue of the Virgin Mary in the transept and stung it on the bottom. Even though the pain must have been unbearable, no tears came from the statue's eyes. I have been stung on the bottom by a wasp, and I can tell you that only divine intervention could have stopped the tears from flowing. It was a miracle to be sure, to be sure.

Darby O'Limerick, Sefton Oak

WE WERE plagued by wasps whilst on a church picnic the other week. They were in and out the jam and buzzing round the sandwiches all day, driving us to distraction. Eventually I lost my temper and swatted one. When I looked at it, flattened on a paper plate, I couldn't believe my eyes. Its insides had burst out and formed a perfect image of the face of our Lord Jesus Christ. I fell to my knees and prayed. My husband, however, said it was more like Al Pacino in the 1973 film Serpico, whilst the priest said it reminded him strongly of Frank Zappa. I still think it was Jesus and therefore a miracle, and I had a Mass said for that 'Jesus wasp' the next day.

Mrs Shinade O'Lampsead, Anfield

Send in your stories of wasp and hornet miracles. There's a crisp tenner for each miracle we use.

Top Was

OPUS Dei corporal mortification enthusiasts. Make yourself an extra-painful (and therefore extra-holy) cilice by tying dozens of wasps together onto a length of fishing line and fastening it round the top of your thigh.

R Kelly, Whitehal

erocity of its barbed tail as, ınprovoked, it pushed its sting nto my hand, pumping its potent venom beneath the skin before withdrawing it and flying off.

The following Sunday, whilst delivering the Mass, another wasp anded upon the lectern and, not wanting to get stung again, took off my mitre and swatted repeatedly, before flicking its feless remains onto the cathedral loor. And that got me thinking.

You see, for was not that second wasp was very much like our Lord Jesus Christ? Like the Lamb of God it had not stung me. Like Him it came in peace. t was innocent of any sin, yet it died for the sins of others.

Catholics, I'm sure God is happy to turn a blind eye to the filthy carryings-on inside their nests.

Lucien McO'Dougle, Bootle

I AM neither a catholic nor a wasp lover, and I bitterly resent forking out £10.99 on a book which contains two pages such as this that are of absolutely no interest to me whatsoever.

Furious, Tunbridge Wells

WITH reference to Furious of Tunbridge Wells's letter *(above)*, I am a devout Catholic and professor of entomology at an eminent university and my specialism is wasps. In my opinion, these two pages justify the £3.20 cover price on their own. Which is just as well, as the rest of the magazine is shit.

Dr Fintan O'Toolbox, Oxford

Saints & Stingers

Catholic wasp facts with retired Pope

Benedict XVI

The Franciscan friars of Bawtree Abbey in Devon are the only order of monks to keep wasps instead of bees. For the past 900 years, the devout brothers have lovingly tended forty wasp hives in the monastery orchard. However, in all that time their stripy charges have failed to produce so much as a single jar of honey.

I SWATTED a wasp with a newspaper on my front room window last week. It fell down dead on the windowsill and I didn't have time to remove its body. It lay there dead for a couple of days, but on the third day, its body was gone. I looked on in wonder as I saw it alive and well and buzzing about at the window once more. Just like our Lord, it had risen from the dead. I called my husband to witness this miracle. However, he spotted the body of the wasp on the floor. It must have been brushed off when I closed the curtains, and the wasp buzzing at the glass was a different one.

Ada O'Roragheor, Liverpool

Catholic Kids Say the Funniest Things ...about WASPS!

"Granny, if I got stung by a wasp, would I die and go to heaven?" my three-year-old grandson asked me the other day. I had to laugh, because that morning I had seen him spill a glass of Ribena and blame it on his baby sister. So I told him if he died of a wasp sting he'd be going straight to hell. For all eternity, and longer.

Bridget O'Brady, Everton

My six-year-old grandson was crying the other day after being stung on the thumb by a wasp. "It hurts, granny. It's the baddest pain ever," he wailed. I had to laugh, because the discomfort of a wasp sting is as nothing compared to the eternal agonising torment that awaits the little scamp in hell if ever puts a foot wrong in the eyes of the Lord.

Brenda O'Leary, Liverpool

"How many times are there bees in the Bible, granny?" my eight-year-old grandson asked me the other day. "Four", I said, "in Deuteronomy 1:44, Joshua 21:27, Judges 14:8 and Psalms 118:12." "No, there are two Bs in Bible. A capital one at the start and a small one in the middle," he giggled. I made him repeat the joke to our priest, Father O'Flaherty, who stripped him naked and beat him with a scourge for his blasphemy.

Bridy O'Frankenstein, Croxteth

Left-footer Tips

RIESTS. When attempting remove a wasps' nest om your church, use the moke from your incense-urning thurible to make the sects drowsy. The nest ay then be safely carried utside, dowsed in petrol nd set on fire.

Cormac O'Pacamac, Fylde

DON'T waste money on expensive shop-bought rosaries. Simply thread dried wasps found on the windowsill onto a length of string and finger them whilst contemplating the Mysteries.

Fr Crosby O'Devlin, Birkenhead

Sister Miriam IMMACULATE

SISTER MIRIAM IMMACULATE ANSWERS *YOUR* CATHOLIC-RELATED WASP DILEMMAS

Worried by wasp contraception solution

Dear Miriam Immaculate,

I am a Catholic and have a very large family which I don't want to get any bigger. I recently lost my job and I simply can't afford to have any more children.

I am 35 and my wife is 34. We have been married for 14 years and have 22 children. I am well aware of the church's position on contraception, and I don't want to spend eternity in a lake of burning excrement for wearing a rubber johnny.

My wife suggested that if I pushed my membrum virile into a wasps' nest so as they stung the bell end, intercourse would too painful to contemplate, and so there would be no chance of her becoming pregnant again. Whilst I am confident that this would work, would his Holiness the Pope look upon my action as just another method of contraception and therefore an act of sin?

Cormack O'Caramac, Liverpool

Sister Miriam Immaculate says...

The Pontiff is very clear on such matters. Any action deliberately taken to prevent a pregnancy is a mortal offence in the eyes of God. You cannot pull the wool over the Lord's eyes by sticking your cock in a wasps' nest and pretending it is any different from sticking it in a blob.

If, however, you were accidentally stung on the herman gelmet and rendered unable to procreate, that would be a different matter.

Why not stand by a wasps' nest, drop your trousers and smear your hampton with jam? If you get stang on the lid or brim, then that is clearly God's will and therefore acceptable to the Pope.

Hubby's impure thought repentance wasp sting interruption problem

Dear Miriam Immaculate,

My husband had some impure thoughts about Susannah Reid off BBC Breakfast, and then had some more impure thoughts about her twenty minutes later.

However, when he went to confession the next day he was stung in the mouth by a wasp half way through his repenting and died of anaphylactic shock.

Now I'm worried that because he hadn't finished atoning for his sinful thoughts before he died he might have been sent to Hell. Does the Lord's forgiveness occur at the moment you begin to confess or at the moment you finish?

Dolores O'Barsix, The Wirral

Sister Miriam Immaculate says...

This is a very difficult question and was the subject of a Papal Bull following an intensive six-week-long Cardinals' Congress in Phuket, Thailand in 2007. The conclusion of the eminent bishops' ecumenical deliberations was that God's forgiveness kicks in exactly half-way through confession.

This being the case, it is impossible for me to say whether your husband's soul is presently in Heaven or Hell, as it all depends on how long-winded he was being in the booth, and whether he made it past that all-important halfway mark before the wasp stang him in the mouth.

If there's a lesson here for all of us, it is simply to keep our confessions short and sweet, especially if there are wasps nearby and you have an allergy to their stings.

Sister Miriam Immaculate's Wasp Advice Lines

The Holy Roman Church wasp advice lines you can trust

Faith tested after being stung	Stung on naked penis during choir practice
018 118 055	**0181 18055**
Want divorce but wasps' nest in attic	Vaginal dryness
0181 18055	**01811 80 55**

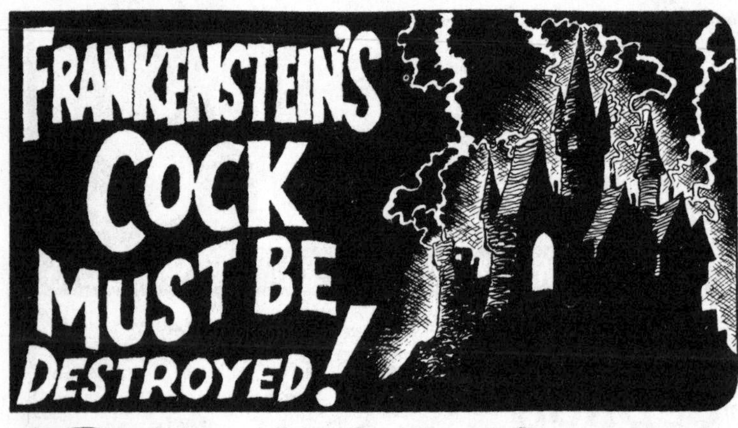
FRANKENSTEIN'S COCK MUST BE DESTROYED!

TWENTY YEARS, IGOR! ... TWENTY YEARS SINCE THOSE IGNORANT PEASANTS MARCHED ON MY CASTLE WITH THEIR FLAMING TORCHES AND DESTROYED MY FIRST GREAT BIG COCK!
YES MASTER.

...BUT I HAVE RE-BUILT IT! BIGGER... LONGER... MORE GIRTHSOME... AND WITH A BLUER VEIN DOWN THE SIDE!
...AND A SHINIER BOBBY'S HELMET.

BEHOLD! LOOK AT THE SIZE OF THAT!
YES MASTER. IT'S A PROPER BRIDE FRIGHTENER!

THE STORM IS AT ITS HEIGHT! QUICK, IGOR...! THROW THE SWITCH!
YES MASTER!

BZZZT! BZZZT!
HA-HA! HA-HA!

LOOK, IGOR! IT'S GOT HALF A TEA-CAKE ON!
IT LIVES, MASTER! IT LIVES!

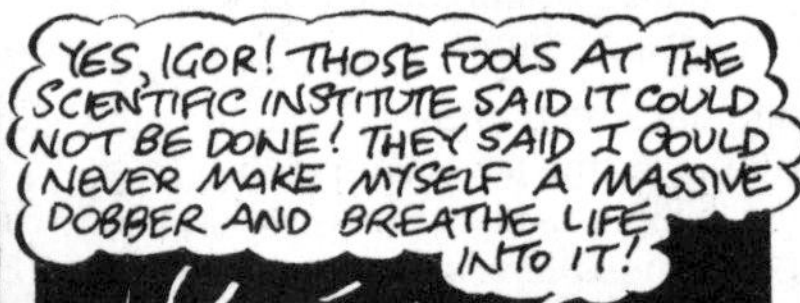
YES, IGOR! THOSE FOOLS AT THE SCIENTIFIC INSTITUTE SAID IT COULD NOT BE DONE! THEY SAID I COULD NEVER MAKE MYSELF A MASSIVE DOBBER AND BREATHE THE LIFE INTO IT!

THEY SAID I WAS MAD!

...BUT THEY SHALL EAT THEIR WORDS WHEN THEY COP A LOAD OF THIS BUGGER TOMORROW NIGHT!

THE FOLLOWING DAY AT THE SCIENTIFIC INSTITUTE...
GENTLEMEN - BEHOLD! DEAD FLESH... GALVANIZED INTO A LIVING, TWITCHING PENILE PROMETHEUS!
IT'S ALIVE! IT'S GOT A LAZY LOB ON!
BRAVO! IT'S THE WONDER OF THE AGE!

WELL I THINK IT IS AN ABOMINATION!
WHAT!?

YOU HEARD ME, HERR DOCTOR...
IF MORTAL MAN WERE MEANT TO HAVE A SIX FOOT CHAP, THEN THE LORD OF CREATION WOULD HAVE GIVEN HIM ONE!
THE LORD OF CREATION? I AM THE LORD OF CREATION!
FOR I HAVE CREATED THIS BEAUTY!

YOU HAVE CREATED A MONSTER, FRANKENSTEIN... YOU HAVE TAMPERED WITH THE VERY FABRIC OF LIFE ITSELF!
ONE DAY IT WILL RISE UP AND DESTROY YOU...!

NO! I AM ITS MASTER!

DOCTOR FRANKENSTEIN... YOU HAVE EXCEEDED YOUR ALLOTTED TIME, I AM AFRAID...
OH?

... PROFESSOR POLIDORI IS HERE TO PRESENT THE RESULTS OF HIS LATEST EXPERIMENTS.

Work of ARSE

THE NATIONAL GALLERY unveiled its latest official royal work yesterday - a painting of Pippa Middleton's arse. But the oil portrait, commissioned to commemorate nearly one hundred sales of her party-planning book *Celebrate*, received a mixed reception from both critics and public.

In the *London Evening Standard*, Brian Sewell called it "a truly execrable gobbet of ordure flung like a chimpanzee's feeshus into the public's face", whilst the *Guardian*'s Valdemar Yanuschack said it was "a dark and unsettling juxtaposition of form and content".

But editor of *Majesty* magazine Ingrid Fartsucker hailed the portrait as a masterpiece. "It is a triumph," she gushed. "A delightful and artistic evocation of the world's most majestic pair of mudflaps".

***Arse Gallery:** The National plays host to the famous tush and (below) artist, Crispin Ricicles.*

***Arse:** The portrait of the mudflaps that sparked controversy.*

Opinions split over new royal portrait

Pippa's buttocks, 28, posed for artist Crispin Ricicles over three one-hour sessions at Buckingham Palace. Ricicles told us: "Pippa's dirtbox was one of the most charming subjects I have ever had the pleasure of painting."

The 64-year-old artist confessed he was nervous at first. "I had not previously committed a regal muckspreader to canvas, but Pippa's chuff was so friendly and delightful it soon put me at my ease," he said.

But the mauling the painting received in the press did not seem to have put off the public. Queues quickly formed as art-lovers flocked to be amongst the first to see the controversial portrait.

"I absolutely love it," said Frank Scurvy, 88, who travelled from his home in Walsall to see the work. "I don't know much about art, but I know what I like, and that's Pippa Middleton's arse."

fanny

American tourist Hymen Prepuce, 55, agreed. "Me and my wife Glangela have flown all the way from Carbondale Illinois to see this portrait," he said. "We saw Pippa's fanny at the royal wedding and we thought it was real swell. Mr Ricicles sure has captured those purdy buns to a tee."

Director of the National Gallery Grant Funding said he was delighted by the response. "The principal function of any art work is to provoke emotion and debate, and this painting of Pippa's shitlocker has certainly done that," he told us.

"The gallery hasn't seen crowds like this since we exhibited Lucian Freud's ten foot canvas of the Queen Mum's spam butterfly to mark her 100th birthday in 2001," Funding added.

TOBY'S TWO GRANNIES... THEY INSULT EACH OTHER'S FANNIES

They arrived in the town - which was bustling with shoppers. Still the Grannies heaped scorn onto each other's cloppers.

NEARLY THERE, GIRLS - I CAN ALMOST TASTE THOSE STICKY BUNS NOW!

SHORTBREAD

SIGH! DO YE RECKON IT WAS THE THOUGHT OF YUR GRIZZLED AULD GAMMON - FLAPS THAT FINALLY TURNED OUR GRANDSON OVER TO COCK, MRS McPHEE?

BIFFA BACON
LOVE
HATE

SLOOO!
NICE CUPPA TEA, IS IT, BIFFA?
AYE, MUTHA, IT IS THAT AN' AALL...

...IT'S FUCKIN' CHAMPION!
SPLOOOO!

DID YUZ HEAR THAT, FATHA? DID YUZ HEAR THE FILTH WOT COME OOTA 'IS MOOTH?
AYE! I DID. THE "F" WORD!

I THINK THE BAIRN'S POSSESSED BY THE VERY DEVIL 'IMSEL! WUZ'LL HEV T' EXORCISE 'IM MUTHA
EH?

C'MON, SON... WUZ'LL TIE YUZ T' THE BED AN' CAST THE DEVIL OOT O' YUZ
WOT THE FUCK? FUCKIN' LEAVE US ALAIRN
THE POSSESSION'S GEDDIN WORSE, FATHA

SO...
PULL IT GOOD AN' TIGHT, MUTHA
FUCKIN' LESS IT, Y' CUNTS
...AN' FETCH SOME HURLY WATTA
WUZ HEVEN'T GOT NEE HURLY WATTA...

...WUZ'VE JUST GOT THESE CRICKET BATS
HMM! ARE THEZ HURLY CRICKET BATS?
NAH!
DINVENT WORRY... W' CAN BLESS 'EM

I BLESS THESE BATS IN THE NAME O' THE FATHA, O' THE SON, AN' O' THE HURLY GHURST. EXPIRITU SANCTI
AMEN

I CAST YEE OOT, FOOWAL DEMON! GAN BACK T' THE PIT O' HELL FROM WHENCE YUZ'VE CAME...
EH?

WHACK!
SMACK!
CRACK!
CRACK!
THUNK!

ONE EXORCISM LATER...
FBLL...BBFLF! FBBLLFF!
PRAISE THE LORD

HALLELUJAH! IT'S WORKED... THE SATANIC EXPLETIVES HEV STOPPED, MUTHA
THERE Y' GAN, SON... Y' SUFFERIN' IS AT AN END.
AYE, SON. IT'S AALL AWA NOO
FLUBB

YEE HEV A SIT DOON, BIFFA... YUZ'VE BIN THROUGH ENOUGH
FLUBBLE
AYE... BUT WUZ'VE GOT W' LIRRLE BOY BACK, MUTHA... JUST LIKE HE WAS IN 'IS FORST SCHOOL PHURTUR

HAD ON!... WHAT'S THAT? ...ON THE BAIRN'S HEED? ...A DIVVENT BELIEVE IT

WORRISIT, FATHA?

LOOK... THE NUMBA O' THE FUCKIN' BEAST, MUTHA... THE MARK O' BEELZEBUB!

666
IT FUCKIN' WELL IS AN AALL! IT'S THE SIGN OF 'IM WOT WAALKS BACKWADS!

MUTHA!... FETCH THE HURLY CRICKET BATS. THEZ MORE O' GOD'S WORK T' BE DONE
LORD 'AVE MORCY
FUCK!

WHACK! THWACK! WHAM! THUMP! THWACK! WHACK!
TEK THAT BIFFA...
...I MEAN SATAN

Letterbocks

PO Box 841,
Whitley Bay,
NE26 9EQ

☐ **DISAPPOINTED** Amazon reviewer T. Godouet remarked on 9th July 2010, *"Sink strainer ok but flatter than I expected."* As it happens, I have a sink strainer very similar to that one and it does the job very well. Quite frankly, I don't know what all the fuss is about.

Jimmy Boogaloo, e-mail

☐ **IF THE** new Archbishop of Canterbury got photographed stood outside the Taj Mahal in a see-through cassock so we could all see his pants like what Diana did, then I'm sure church attendances would sky-rocket. It would be a real 'Bishop of Hearts' moment.

James Brown, Edinburgh

☐ **SURELY** someone who sounds like they've swallowed a dictionary would be making agonising choking noises rather than being particularly verbose?

Martin Christina, e-mail

☐ **TODAYS** vampires are an utter disgrace. They're nothing more than a shower of scruffily-dressed, ill-mannered louts who live in council flats. Back in my day any vampire worth his salt always wore a nice suit with a bow tie, accompanied by a smart black cape. And they lived in castles. And, more ofter than not, they were very polite. Thank you Tony Blair, and your so-called 'Cool Britannia.'

Orangeman, e-mail

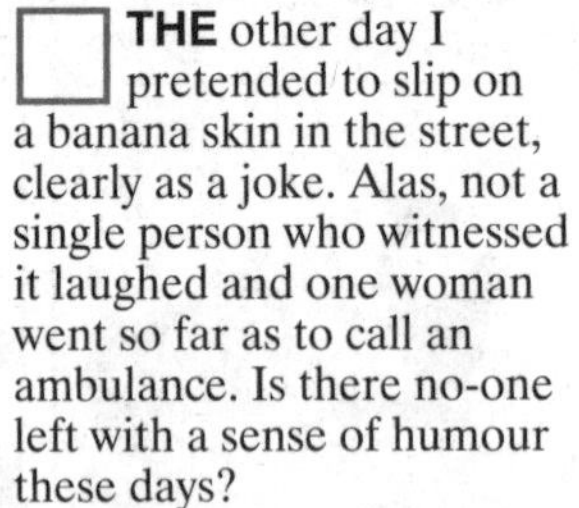

☐ **THE** other day I pretended to slip on a banana skin in the street, clearly as a joke. Alas, not a single person who witnessed it laughed and one woman went so far as to call an ambulance. Is there no-one left with a sense of humour these days?

Dan, Lincolnshire

☐ **'DATE** this woman now' says the picture on the Mature-Dating advert that just popped up on my computer screen. Ok, about circa 1957 I would guess.

Rich, e-mail

☐ **I DON'T** understand all this fuss about Richard III's skellington when the whole thing's so obviously all a fake. For one thing they didn't have car parks in Richard III's day, so how could he have been buried in one? And no account of the Battle of Bosworth Field mentions York troops encountering problems at a Pay and Display machine.

Ed O'Meara, e-mail

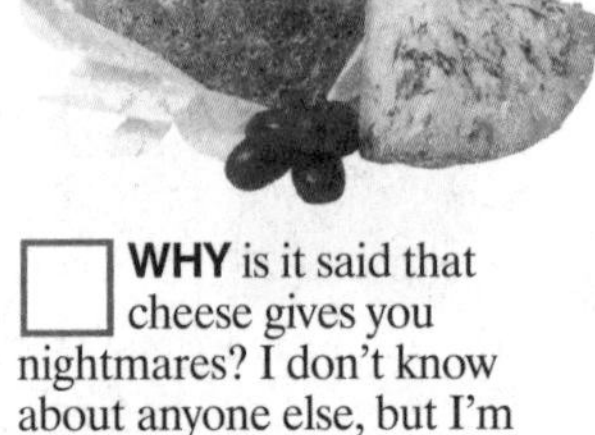

☐ **WHY** is it said that cheese gives you nightmares? I don't know about anyone else, but I'm certainly not afraid of cheese.

Heath Alansworth, e-mail

☐ **MY SCOTTISH** grandmother used to say to me 'Many a mickle makes a muckle'. Unfortunately I don't have any amusing anecdotes in which the meaning of the saying is misinterpreted for comedic purposes because I don't have a fucking clue what she was on about.

Lionel Pancakes, Truro

☐ **MY WIFE** is always cooking, cleaning, washing and ironing and last weekend she insisted that I did some. Having now experienced domestic work I really can't see why she enjoys it so much.

David Briggs, e-mail

☐ **WHY** don't councils paint all their roads white? This would avoid accidents caused by black ice during cold spells since motorists would be able to see the problem areas and drive around them accordingly.

Iain Duncan, e-mail

☐ **IT MAY** be unfashionable to say this, but I am utterly fed up with loony liberals hijacking our beautiful language. In my day, the word Lesbian referred to inhabitants of the Greek island of Lesbos. But now it is used to describe female homosexual deviants who engage in prolonged acts whereby they sensuously peel off each other's lacy bras and panties before exploring their soft, womanly bodies with their eager, probing tongues. I am so disgusted that I burnt down my local tennis club and sent the bill to Sandi Toksvig.

Lambert Butler, Truro

☐ **BONNY** and Clyde's revolver is being auctioned and apparently could fetch over $120,000. Why on earth didn't the pair of them just sell this gun and keep the money themselves? Then there would have been no need for all of that crime malarkey.

Jim Bojanski, e-mail

☐ **IF THESE** so called mathematics professors think that $2y + 3z = 2x$ then I think its time they went back to school and learned differentiate between letters and numbers.

Tam Dale, e-mail

☐ **CAN** you resign as the Pope? I thought God appointed you, so I guess you'd have to have some balls to face him and ask for your P45. Personally I'd like to see Jesus have a crack at the job. He's been out of work for nearly 2000 years so it's about time he did something.

Ben M, Rochester

☐ **I'M SICK** to death of all these bloody immigrants coming over to our country and causing trouble. My Polish neighbour, for example. Everyday at 7am I get woken up by him banging around getting ready for work. I like to lie in most days but that's not possible with him next door. The other day he had the cheek to ask me if I wanted any help removing the mattress off my front garden. I wish they'd all bugger off home.

R. Jones, Luton

☐ **I AM** watching an old *Stars In Their Eyes* final. Joe Longthorne is a judge and he's praising a pretend Marti Pellow. To be perfectly honest, it's put me right off the idea of time travel.

Chris Tina, Martin

HEN-PECKED!

TOP TIPS

CARRY a ten foot pole around with you everywhere you go in case you come across something that you wouldn't touch with it. Then you can say "I wouldn't touch that with this," while pointing to it, so saving you having to say "a ten foot pole" all the time.

Will, e-mail

NORTH American Indians. When sending smoke signals,

WHY DO wildlife presenters have to follow make it so hard to follow the story of say, a family of lions as they grow up on the Serengeti? Why call the cubs Kali, Tara, Suleiman and Caesar? What's so wrong with Dave, Tommo, Geordie and Tracy?

Terry Corrigan, e-mail

WITH all the problems in the NHS, I'm certain that the staff could increase efficiency at a stroke. When nurses move patients from beds in pairs, instead of lifting on the count of three, they should do it on the count of two, thereby speeding up the process by 33%.

Ken Labia, Clitheroe

I THOUGHT the various escapades of James Bond were supposed to be secret. Codswallop! I've been watching everything he gets up to for over 50 years. Some spy he is.

Lil' Champ, e-mail

IT WAS recently revealed that a team of forensic experts had discovered that the Pharaoh Ramses II did not die of natural causes, but had his throat cut in 1213 BC. Having resolved this mystery, could I ask that the forensic team turn their attention to the burglary which occurred at my house last month which, despite being filmed by my CCTV system, and notwithstanding the

significant quantity of semen in my wife's underwear drawer, has been placed on the 'unsolved' list by the Devon and Cornwall Police?

N Lyon, e-mail

I FARTED the chorus of Gangnam Style whilst conducting a funeral last week. Beat that!

Rev. Justin Welby
Archbishop of Canterbury

THEY say 'there's nothing quite like a McDonalds'. By the same token there's also nothing quite like getting kicked to death. And furthermore, burgers, chips and a milkshake is actually quite like a McDonalds.

I Turner, e-mail

I THINK Stuart Hall is innocent. Or guilty. One of the two, anyhow. I'm not really bothered either way.

JK Rowingboat, e-mail

THESE so-called Club 1830 holidays are a con. I went on one last summer and no one else seemed to remotely interested in discussing the accession of William IV. Mind you, I got a great nosh off a lass from Barnsley.

H Horatio, Pinner

SO, known child murderer King Richard III, who killed the Princes in The Tower, is dug up in a Leicester car park and will get re-interred in Leicester Cathedral as some sort of hero monarch. Whereas if tireless charity worker Sir Jimmy Savile were to be dug up, he would no doubt be posthumously hung, drawn and quartered. It's one rule for royalty and one rule for noncey members of the general public. It makes my blood boil.

David Harris, e-mail

NEVER in my wildest dreams did I imagine I'd win the Tour de France as many times as Lance Armstrong. However, since he was ignominiously stripped of all his titles, I've finally achieved the

impossible. And what's more, I didn't need performance-enhancing drugs to do it.

Gregory Eggs, e-mail

HOPEFULLY, now that Lance Armstrong has admitted his lies after so many years of doubt it will pave the way for others to do likewise. In that spirit I'd like to get the ball rolling by admitting to my mum that it was me who wiped their arse on the towel that time we ran out of bog roll, not my sister as previously stated.

Simon Hoffmann, e-mail

CAN'T we give Lance Armstrong a break? I tried riding a bike on drugs once. If anything, it was a lot harder. I was in a hedge within seconds.

Andy, e-mail

Letter Cox

...a selection of your letters about TV Brian Box Professor Brain Cox

• **I'M SICK** and tired of Professor Brian Cox. he's always talking about Einstein's theories, but he never comes up with any of his own. It's about time he stopped farting about on the telly, got his hair cut and discovered some science for himself. He could start off by working out how bees fly, because my mate says that nobody knows.

Troy Hurtebes, Todmorden

• **I THINK** he's alright as scientists go, but he's never make my dream team of 11 scientists. He's more of a journeyman physicist, a donkey, if you will, like Tony Adams or Dwight Yorke.

M Lawrenson, London

• **BRIAN** Cox is nothing but a charlatan. He claims to be professor of particle physics, yet whenever I turn my telly on he's always looking through a telescope. Correct me if I'm wrong, but they're for seeing big things a long way off. He should be looking through a microscope at little things very close up.

Renton Boxwood, Tooting

• **WHEN** I was at my school, the kid who was good at physics, played the piano and had a nerdy haircut would regularly have his head flushed down the toilet and his PE kit thrown onto the roof of his music block. He certainly wouldn't have every woman in the country fancying him, like what Brian Cox appears to do.

S Whiting, Nottingham

• **BRIAN** Cox is no more a scientist that I am. He's not bald, he hasn't got a dickie bow and he doesn't talk with a comedy German accent. Come on BBC, you've been duped. Bring back Heinz Wolff and get this fraud off our telly.

Tracey Spencer, Cornwall

• **WHAT** is the point of spending millions of pounds on Brian Cox looking for the Higgs Bosun particle? Why doesn't the man discover something useful instead, like a chemical that turns water into beer, a pill that can beat the breathalyser, or a car that can drive itself while you have a little nap.

George Pomfrey, Goole

• **PROFESSOR** Cox says that there may be an infinite number of universes where all possible worlds exist in parallel dimensions. If this is true, it is an inescapable conclusion that there exists an infinite number of worlds where Noel Edmonds has committed unspeakably vile acts. I only hope that the authorities on those worlds have brought the *Deal or No Deal* presenter to book for those sickening offences.

Aubrey Smollit, Croydon

... if you wish to highlight your message in bold, chuck a tyre onto your fire.

Ray Ricochet, e-mail

PENSIONERS. Protect your hips in this icy weather by wearing a car tyre around your waist.

Sue Lockyer, e-mail

PROSPECTIVE Lunar Astronauts. Experience the sensation of a moon landing by closing one eye and moving a Hob Nob biscuit gradually closer to the other eye.

Buzz Aldrin, e-mail

PRIESTS. Rather than fiddling with kiddies, try fiddling with nuns instead. As Christians they will almost certainly forgive you, and if they come from a silent order they won't go blabbing to the police.

Dougle O'Flaherty, London

UNDERTAKERS. A handful of ball bearings placed in the coffin will reveal which of your pallbearers isn't doing his fair share of the lifting.

Chad Elliott, e-mail

MOTORISTS. Save wear and tear on your handbrake by only ever parking where the ground is perfectly flat. A spirit level can be used to check, and will fit neatly into the glove compartment next to all of your gloves.

Spenner, e-mail

RECREATE the wonders of the sea at Weston-Super-Mare by simply adding ice cubes and soil to your bath.

Paul Townend, e-mail

MUSICIANS. Avoid purchasing expensive tuning forks by learning to fart in the required key.

Dave Gorr, e-mail

CONVINCE neighbours you're invisible by stiffening your dog's lead with starch and sending him out for a walk on his own.

James, Grimsby

GET that expensive Paul Weller hairstyle for free by simply running out of the barber's shop before they've finished.

James Brown, Edinburgh

Impossible Football Results

African Cup of Nations

Arsenal	2 : 1	North Korea
West Germany	2 : 0	Chicago Fire

Scottish League Cup Second Round

Nottingham Forest	3 : 2	Wales
Bayer Leverkusen	0 : 1	Doncaster Belles

Bundesliga

England	3 : 2	England

TASHA SLAPPA

EEH, IT'S SHOCKIN'! CHILD BENEFIT DOESN'T GAN FAR THESE DAYS
AYE
YUH AANLY GOT TWO PACKS OF TABS, FAWA SNICKERS AND TWELVE SCRATCHCARDS

IT'S NOT ENOUGH TO COVER THREE GROWING BAIRNS
...OR THE FAWATEEN DISABLED ONES YUH PRETEND YUH'VE GOT

HOW MAN. IT'S HARD TUH EARN AN HONEST LIVING. THE FUCKIN' RECESSION HAS BEEN TOUGH ON BOBBA
AYE. NEE CUNT'S GOT FUCK ALL WORTH NICKIN' ANYMORE

STILL, HE'S BEEN KEEPING HISSELF OOT OF BOTHER FOR A FEW MONTHS NOW
CANNY
NO ROBBIN' NEE NICKIN'
MINT
NEE PINCHIN'
MIND YOU. THAT'S AANLY COS HE'S IN PRISON

STILL. AT LEAST HE KNAAS WHAT'S IMPORTANT, EH ... FAMILY
HE'S A FAMILY MAN AALREET
...THAT'S WHY HE'S GOT BAIRNS WITH EVERY OTHER LASS IN WUH FORM

SHORTLY...
BOBBA?
AALREET TASHA. THEY LET US OOT EARLY, FUR GOOD BEHAVIOUR

EH?
AYE. I'M A REFORMED CHARACTER, ME. A DIFFERENT PERSON. A NEW ME. I'VE PUT THE PAST BEHIND US
REALLY?

AYE. AND I'VE GOT YUH A PRESENT FOR TUH SAY SORRY FOR BEING IN PRISON WHEN I SHOULD HAVE BEEN AT HOME LOOKIN' AFTER YOU AND THE BAIRNS
WHAT IS IT?

A TWELVE FOOT LONG BURMESE PYTHON

WHERE DID YOU GET THIS?
OFF ME CELL MATE IN PRISON
HOW MUCH DID IT COST?
NOWT. HE'S STILL IN FOR SIX MONTH, SO I WENT STRAIGHT ROOND HIS HOOSE AND FUCKIN' TWOCKED THE CUNT

YUH FUCKIN' IDIOT. WE'VE AALREADY GOT A FUCKIN' DOG. THE LAST THING WE NEED IS ANOTHER MOOTH TUH FEED

DIVVINT FRET I'VE SORTED IT OOT
HEV YUH NOO. FUCKIN' HOW?

whimper
NICE ONE BOBBA

THIS SNAKE IS A FUCKIN' MONEY MEKKIN' MACHINE. I'M GANNA TEK HIM DOON THE BEACH & CHARGE CUNTS FIVE POOND PER PHURTUR

SOON...
NOW THEN KIDS, HAVE YOU COVERED UP ENTIRELY IN FACTOR 100?
I REALLY THINK THEY SHOULD STAY UNDER THE SAFETY OF THE PARASOL
OH MARJORY, YOU DO WORRY TOO MUCH

HOO. DO YUH WANNA PHURTUR WITH ME FUCKIN' SNAKE? FIVE POOND.
WOW!

N-N-NO THANKYOU. WE'RE OKAY, THANKS
FIVE POOND PER BAIRN
erm...

GIZ YER FUCKIN' CAMERA, THEN.
DO BE CAREFUL! IT'S AN SLR

SAY FRIGGIN' "CHEESE"
CHEESE!

TASHA! IS 'CEX' STILL URPEN?
...I'VE GORRA FUCKIN' ESSELAR!

BACK IN PRISON...
...AYE. AAH'VE GORRA ALLIGATOR AT YEM, Y' KNAA

NOBBY'S PILES

ROGER MELLIE THE MAN ON THE TELLY

HI, ROGER. JUST HAD AN AD AGENCY ON THE PHONE... WANT YOU TO DO A VOICEOVER
SMASHING... WHAT FOR?..

OH, NO, NOT **AGAIN**, ROGER... WHAT IS IT **THIS** TIME?
IT'S AN "HISTORICAL" SEX OFFENCE, TOM.
OH, GOD.. I ALWAYS KNEW YOU'D START PAYING ONE DAY FOR THE WAY YOU BEHAVED IN THE SEVENTIES AND EIGHTIES, ROGER.

...I WAS FILMING A DOCUMENTARY ABOUT HENRY THE EIGHTH AT THE TOWER OF LONDON, AND I MADE A BIT OF A GRAB FOR THAT LUCY WORSLEY'S TITS

DJ '13
KIM KARDASHIAN'S
CAMBRIDGE COLLEGE CAPER

FAMOUS CELEBRITY KIM KARDASHIAN WAS MAKING A PUBLIC APPEARANCE AT ENGLAND'S HISTORIC CAMBRIDGE UNIVERSITY...

YOU'RE ON IN FIFTEEN MINUTES, KIM!
UNIVERSITY HALL
MAIN STAGE
WE'D LIKE YOU TO WALK ONSTAGE USING YOUR LEGS, THEN STAND THERE FOR A WHILE, BREATHING AND SMILING.

THESE PUBLIC APPEARANCES SURE ARE HARD WORK.
I'LL RELAX BEFORE GOING ONSTAGE BY LEANING AGAINST THIS WALL...

SUDDENLY
GRACIOUS! I'VE FOUND A SECRET PASSAGE!
CLICK!

GOSH! IT'S PROFESSOR STEPHEN HAWKING!
SORRY TO BARGE IN ON YOU LIKE THIS, PROF!

THAT'S ALL RIGHT, YOUNG LADY — THIS UNIVERSITY IS FULL OF SECRET PASSAGES
YOU HAVE STUMBLED UPON MY PRIVATE LABORATORY.

I'M WORKING ON A TOP SECRET FORMULA WHICH IS OF VITAL IMPORTANCE TO BRITAIN'S NATIONAL SECURITY...
BUT I CAN'T SEEM TO GET THIS EQUATION RIGHT.

I DABBLE IN MATHEMATICS MYSELF, PROFESSOR — AND I THINK I CAN SEE WHERE YOU'VE GONE WRONG...
KIM GRABBED A PIECE OF CHALK AND SCRIBBLED SOME COMPLEX SYMBOLS ON THE BLACKBOARD

I - I DON'T BELIEVE IT! YOU'VE SOLVED THE EQUATION!
NOW I CAN COMPLETE THE FORMULA, AND OUR COUNTRY WILL BE SAFE ONCE MORE!

VE CANNOT ALLOW ZAT TO HAPPEN, PROFESSOR!
GASP! ENEMY FOREIGN AGENTS!

BANG! THE FOREIGN AGENT FIRED HIS GUN AT STEPHEN HAWKING.
UGH!
LET'S SEE YOU COMPLETE ZE FORMULA VITH A BULLET IN YOUR HEAD!

WHAT WAS THAT NOISE?
IT'S PROFESSOR HAWKING — HE'S BEEN SHOT IN THE HEAD!
NOW VE MAKE OUR ESCAPE! ARFSKI! ARFSKI!

THERE'S NO TIME TO TAKE HIM TO HOSPITAL
FORTUNATELY, BRAIN SURGERY IS A BIT OF A HOBBY OF MINE...

KIM GRABBED A SCALPEL AND SET TO WORK REMOVING THE BULLET FROM STEPHEN HAWKING'S BRAIN
FORCEPS!
SWAB!

AND SHORTLY
FANTASTIC SURGERY, KIM ~ MY BRAIN IS WORKING EVEN MORE EFFICIENTLY THAN BEFORE!
RIGHT ~ LET'S GET AFTER THOSE FOREIGN AGENTS!

AND, OUTSIDE -
LOOK - THEY'RE ABOUT TO MAKE THEIR ESCAPE IN A ROCKET SHIP!

FORTUNATELY, I'M A KEEN AMATEUR ROCKET SCIENTIST...
KIM GRABBED A SCREWDRIVER AND STARTED TINKERING WITH THE ROCKET SHIP'S CONTROL PANEL

THEY'RE TAKING OFF, KIM!
DON'T WORRY — I REPROGRAMMED THE DESTINATION CO-ORDINATES...

... TO TAKE THEM STRAIGHT TO THE LOCAL POLICE STATION!
POLICE
HIMMEL!

WELL DONE, KIM - YOU'VE SAVED THE DAY!
BUT NOW I MUST RUN, OR I'LL BE LATE FOR MY PUBLIC APPEARANCE!

THERE YOU ARE KIM! WHERE HAVE YOU BEEN?
UNIVERSITY HALL
YOU'RE DUE ON STAGE IN ONE MINUTE!

AND -
HOORAY! IT'S KIM KARDASHIAN OFF OF THE TELLY!
IT'S GREAT HOW SHE'S SORT OF JUST STANDING THERE AND BEING FAMOUS.

PITY SHE DOESN'T APPEAR TO POSSESS ANY NOTABLE TALENT OR SKILLS WHATSOEVER.
IF ONLY HE KNEW - EH, READERS?!

Nail in the Coffin

Actor Jimmy now a vampire, say pals

FRIENDS of *Crocodile Shoes* star *Jimmy Nail* were last night distraught after it emerged that the 61-year-old Geordie TV favourite has become a vampire.

"Jimmy left his bedroom window open one night last week and a bat must have flown in, turned into a Dracula and bitten him in the neck," confided one close pal. "It's tragic."

Since the incident, Nail is understood to have slept in a coffin with his arms folded across his chest, wearing a bow tie, dinner jacket and cape.

"We know we ought to go round to his house in the swish Darras Hall district of Newcastle, prise open his casket and hammer a wooden stake through his heart," said Nail's *Auf Wiedersehen Pet* co-star ***Tim Healy***. "It's the only way to release him from his torment."

"But Jimmy's always been a canny lad, and so far we just can't bring ourselves to do it," added colleague ***Kevin Whately***.

Welch Rabbits

Bunny sanctuary for Loose Woman Denise

NEWCASTLE-based actress *Denise Welch* has set up the north east's first rabbit sanctuary. Now the 55-year-old star plans to plough the proceeds of her local radio tile warehouse ad voiceovers into the ambitious project to look after the region's bunnies.

"I've always loved rabbits and it breaks my heart to see them living rough like tramps in the countryside," she told Metro Radio's *Nightowls* show. "And it's even worse with Christmas approaching."

For the past three months Welch has been snaring wild rabbits throughout the region and releasing them into her garden in the swish Darras Hall district of Newcastle. The sanctuary, which is open to visitors, is now home to more than twenty bunnies.

"It's eighteen pounds to get in, ten pounds for juniors or OAPs and thirty-five pounds for a family day pass," she told listeners.

"Obviously, ticket prices will rise the more rabbits I catch, but rest assured every single penny will be going to those bunnies," she added.

All Ants on Deck

TV PJ clones set sail

SCIENTISTS at Newcastle's Centre for Life have cloned *X-Factor* presenter *Ant McPartlin*. Ten identical copies of the 38-year-old funnyman survived from the experiments, and are now planning to crew an entry in the 2014 Whitbread Round the World Yacht Race.

"I've never set foot on a boat in my life," laughed the original McPartlin. "So being identical clones of me they'll have no sailing experience whatsoever."

"They'd better pack their life-jackets," he joked.

Robson's Choice

Geordie star smashes menu record

PINT-SIZE Geordie actor *Robson Green* has smashed the world record for dithering over a restaurant menu. Green, 50, who first rose to fame in the eighties as hospital porter Jimmy Powell in *Casualty*, has now been sat at a table in the Newcastle branch of Zizzi's for more than four months, pondering what to have.

During that time, the waitress has been back to ask the *Wire in the Blood* star if he's ready to order or would he like a few more minutes over thirty thousand times.

The previous record was held by Newcastle-born AC/DC front-man ***Brian Johnson***, who sat in Café 21 in Fenwicks for 107 days in 2006 before deciding to have a ham, cheese and tomato omelette and a pot of tea for one.

All Hands on Dec

Thai massage shame of TV Duncan

FORMER *Byker Grove* actor *Declan Donnelly* last night accepted a police caution after being caught naked with more than forty Thai masseuses.

Northumbria cops responding to complaints of loud noises from a room of a Whitley Bay guest house broke down the door to find the *I'm a Celebrity* star getting a happy ending off more than three dozen scantily-clad Oriental lovelies.

A spokesman for the star claimed that the reason Dec had employed so many masseuses was because he had extremely tense muscles in his back. Reading from a prepared statement, he told reporters: "Mr Donnelly's back was more than forty times as stiff as it ought to have been, which is why he had summoned so many semi-naked lovelies to his room."

"The fact that they were attempting to masturbate him to orgasm when the police broke the door down was due to a simple misunderstanding over language," he added.

Shamed TV Kirkwood stripped of titles

Oh, Carol!: Kirkwood presenting the weather about 15 years ago yesterday.

FIVE-TIMES winner of TV Weather Presenter of the Year *Carol Kirkwood* has been STRIPPED of her titles after testing positive for banned substances.

The *BBC Breakfast* favourite has taken the prestigious prize every year since 2008, with judges praising her accurate forecasts, cheery manner and clarity of presentation. However the Met Office has now scrubbed her name off the records after a routine test found traces of an illegal forecast-enhancing drug in her urine.

recovery

"High levels of nandrolone were found in the samples submitted by Miss Kirkwood," said Met Office spokesperson Kiki Bryer. "This substance is known to speed up recovery times, allowing a forecaster to train for extended periods without fatigue."

"Typically, a forecaster can practise sweeping their hand across a big map and pointing to areas of low pressure for a maximum of three hours a day before tiredness sets in," said Miss Bryer. "By using this drug, Carol could easily have extended this training period to five or six hours a day, giving herself an unfair advantage over other contenders for this prestigious forecasting award."

home start

A spokesman for Carol Kirkwood said the presenter, 53, was shocked, surprised and dismayed at the result. "Carol, 53, has never knowingly taken a banned forecast-enhancing substance and will be appealing the Met Office's decision," he told reporters. "She believes the positive test result may be an anomaly caused by a proprietary remedy that she took whilst suffering from a runny nose."

Pending any appeal, the TV Weather Presenter of the Year title has been provisionally awarded to this year's runner-up, Thomas Shavenknackers.

THE UK IS A CROWDED COUNTRY, with 60 million of us crammed into a tiny island. And it's an undeniable fact that these days our lives often feel like a constant round of queues, traffic jams and waiting lists. But if you think Britain is congested today, just wait until 2020!

For according to a new report by a leading social scientist, the present population of the UK is set to DOUBLE by the end of this decade. And what you think is bad now is set to get much, much worse as we're packed ever more tightly into....

SARDINE BRITAIN

PANT-SHITTING EXCLUSIVE!

"**WITH MORE BABIES** being born every day and old people living longer, this island will be bursting at the seams in just seven years," says amateur historian ***Jim Plywood***. And Plywood predicts that with ***120 million people*** all wanting somewhere to live, somewhere to play and something to eat, everyday life in this country will be unrecognisable by the end of the decade. In his report he paints a chilling picture of the world that awaits us and describes how every aspect of our lives will change in 2020...

SEX

PEOPLE HAVE been having sex in the same way since time immemorial. But our old-fashioned notions of lovemaking will be nothing but a distant memory in the pressure-cooker Britain of 2020. With 120 million people crammed within our shores, you will never be more than 6-inches away from another person. As a consequence, privacy for couples will be an impossibility, and every sexual act will have to take place under the gaze of a huddle of boggle-eyed bystanders. The result will be a nationwide epidemic of performance anxiety, with the vast majority of men unable to achieve erections. The only people who will feel comfortable having public sex will be porn stars such as Ben Dover, rampant exhibitionists and doggers such as Phil Mitchell out of *EastEnders*.

But whilst intercourse will be off the cards for most of us, the UK in 2020 will be a frotterers' paradise. On crowded commuter routes it will be standing room only, and passengers will be packed so tightly that they will have no choice but to rub up against one another. As the already overburdened legal system faces being overwhelmed with public transport indecency cases, the government will have no choice but to remove the crime of frottering from the statute books. As a result, even the shortest bus,train or tram journey will become a grope, rub and fondle free-for-all.

LEISURE

EVERYONE loves a leisurely walk in the park - it's a great way to escape from the hustle and bustle of our busy modern lives. But in 2020 something as simple as a gentle stroll will simply add to our already sky-high stress levels. Our municipal parks will be so crowded that strollers will be packed tightly together and forced to synchronise their steps like Madness in one of their videos. One wrong step could bring thousands of walkers crashing to the ground, so Park Wardens will rhythmically bang drums like on a Roman Galley to keep everyone in step as they take the air.

And if you fancy a trip to the zoo, the scene that greets you in 2020 will be very different from the one we know today. Gone will be the elephants, tigers and giraffes we know so well, the vast amount of space they require now unavailable. Instead, only smaller animals will be on show such as mice, frogs and wasps.

Other traditions will continue in the future, albeit in an altered form. Saturday afternoon footy matches will kick off at 3.00pm just as they always have. But in spaced-starved Britain, a soccer pitch will be no bigger than a tennis court. And with 22 players, a referee, two linesmen and possibly two goal line officials all battling for elbow room, we could see a record number of red cards.

HOME LIFE

FOR THE BRITISH homeowner of the future, every day will be like Christmas day; your house will be extremely crowded and there won't be enough chairs to go round. With twice as many people in the country as there are chairs, things to sit on will be at a premium. Come 2020, don't be surprised to find yourself perched on a piano stool, or slumped in a deckchair to eat your dinner. For most of us, dining chairs will be a distant memory, now a luxury enjoyed only by the rich and famous.

But it's not all bad news. 120 million people need somewhere to live. And this unprecedented demand for accommodation will mean that it is a buyers' market, and house prices will drop through the floor. A four bedroom detached house in Knightsbridge could be picked up for around a hundred space credits... about a hundred pounds in today's money.

And a trip to the supermarket will no longer be the relaxing jaunt that it is today. The car parks will be full and you may be forced to leave your vehicle miles away from the shop. Often you will have to park further away from the supermarket than you live. And once inside the nightmare continues. With so many customers, the aisles will face trolley gridlock and tempers will fray. Lawlessness will prevail and a *Mad Max* style anarchy will become the order of the day. Trolleys will be customised with blades, spikes and flamethrowers, and customers, some with mohican haircuts and leather eye patches will battle to the death in a bid to reach the tills with their weekly shop. Once at the checkout, the queues will be so long that the managers may even be forced to open a couple more tills. Although obviously not all of them.

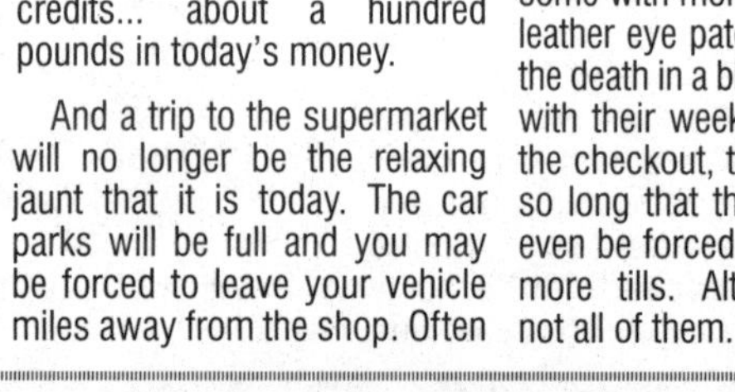

Blackpool Gears up for Population Boom

"Bring it on!" says Lord Mayor

THE beaches of Blackpool are packed each and every summer. So much so, that you might think it would be impossible to squeeze one more holidaymaker along the resort's famous Golden Mile. But you'd be wrong. For, with the expected population boom just over the horizon, plans are already underway to accommodate a THOUSAND TIMES as many sunseekers on the famous sands by 2020.

At a packed meeting of Blackpool Council, the town's Lord Mayor Councillor Eric Tonks introduced a Ten Point Plan to cope with the expected UK population boom.

Amongst the measures announced by Councillor Tonks were:

- *Four more beach donkeys to be purchased to cope with growing demand for rides during peak holiday periods.*
- *A new system of "oil rig"-style round-the-clock 8-hour sleeping shifts to be introduced to triple guest capacity in the town's Bed & Breakfast establishments.*
- *Post Office pillar box collection frequency to be doubled in order to accommodate increased holiday postcard traffic.*
- *The width of the standard municipal deckchair to be reduced by three inches in order to maximise seating along the beach front and promenade approaches.*

In addition, the council has set up a working party to look into increasing the number of visitors who can be safely accommodated up Blackpool Tower.

"This iconic landmark is an unrivalled vantage point from which to enjoy spectacular views of the Fylde coast," Councillor Tonks told reporters. "It is said that on a clear day it is possible to see as far as Fleetwood in one direction and Lytham St Annes in the other from the viewing platform at the top."

"At the moment, on a typical day in high season, the tower welcomes between twenty and thirty visitors," he continued. "But if, as we expect, daily visitor numbers rise above ten million by 2020, we'll have to re-think how to get them all up and down efficiently."

No room with a view: Blackpool Tower in 2020 and (above) Mayor Eric Tonks

split

"Presently, we're looking at replacing our existing single staircase into a split two-way, up on the left, down on the right, system. This would involve fitting a central handrail on all six flights, as well as twelve 'Keep Left' signs and twelve 'No Entry' signs."

republic

However, the council hasn't ruled out taking more extreme measures. Tonks said: "Here in Blackpool we like to think outside the box, so we're also looking at reserving the stairs for going up the tower only."

"Once at the top, visitors would be offered an exciting range of ways to get down. These would include a three-hundred foot fireman's pole down the middle of the tower, a helter-skelter round the outside, or a two-mile white knuckle ride down a zipwire to the floral clock in Stanley Park," he added.

TELLY

IN THE WORDS of Charles Darwin, showbiz will be forced to adapt in order to survive in the harsh, overpopulated conditions that await us just 7 years in the future. *Britain's Got Talent* is presently one of our most popular television programmes, and its yearly auditions attract thousands of contestants, all eager for a chance of stardom. In 2020, *Sardine Britain's Got Talent* will attract countless more hopefuls - so many that the show will have to run 24 hours a day across TEN dedicated TV channels. Teams of celebrity judges such as Simon Cowell, Cheryl Cole and Bruno Toglioni will be forced to work in gruelling round-the-clock shifts if they are to stand any chance of discovering a Susan Boyle for the next decade.

Fishy Future for UK

TELLY naturist *DAVID ATTENBOROUGH* says that the forthcoming UK population explosion could have unexpected consequences. For the 86-year-old BBC presenter believes that pressure for living space could force us back into the sea.

He told us: "Fish grew legs and lungs back in dinosaur times, when the fear of predators in the ocean forced them out of the water and onto the land. But now that evolutionary process is set to happen in reverse."

search

Attenborough predicts that overcrowded conditions will lead Britons to return to the water in search of space to live. "Mother nature has spent thousands of years equipping us to live on the land," he said. "We have evolved feet in the place of fins and we no longer do big long stringy shits that would trip us up when we were walking about. But now our time on the land is over. It is time for the UK population to return to the sea."

Shoal mates: Humans face wet future and (inset) Attenborough

Britons will Return to the Sea Predicts TV Attenborough

"Our human bodies are no longer suited for living underwater, but all the necessary D & A is still encoded in our jeans," he continued. "The first few years underwater will be difficult. People will have to spend most of their time treading water. At night, they will have to set their alarm clocks to go off every couple of minutes so they can swim up to the surface for a mouthful of air."

But, says Attenborough, it won't be long before we start to adapt to our new environment. "I estimate it will be a couple of years before the first water-living humans begin to evolve simple gills," he told us. "We will find that our arms and legs are gradually flattening out into flippers, better suited for swimming after our prey."

newsround

With over three-quarters of the earth's surface covered in water, and with no humans currently living there, Attenborough's scheme sounds like the perfect solution to Britain's overcrowding nightmare. But the veteran *Blue Planet* host had this warning for anyone thinking of crawling back into the primordial soup of the ocean.

"Once your fish gills develop, your lungs will shrivel away and there is no turning back. You've burnt your bridges," he told us. "You'll never be able to return to dry land again. Not even to pop round and see your mum at Christmas."

"Unless you evolve into a crab instead of a fish," he added.

A Christmastide Adventure with Black Bag  The Faithful Border Binliner

'TWAS the night before Christmas, and Peebles shepherd, Andrew Selkirk, was reading a chilling seasonal ghost story to Black Bag, his faithful border bin liner. And the spooky tale of the Ghost of the Kirkyard was making the plastic on the bag's back stand on end. "Dinnae be afraid, boy," said Selkirk as he closed the book. "It's awnly a daft, wee tale, y' ken. There's nae such thing as ghosties."

SELKIRK stood up and and began pulling on his heavy tweed overcoat. "Come on, Laddie. We must leave this warm hearth and head oot tae the kirk fair the traditional candlelit carols, haggis, neeps and deep-fried Mars Bars service," he said. His faithful pvc companion excitedly fluttered around his master. "Ye best wrap up wairm, Baggie. 'Tis a three mile hike tae the village."

THE going was slow through the drifting snow that blanketed the Peebles hills and burns, and it was nearly midnight when the pair finally approached the tiny granite kirk of St Donald O'Nae Troosers. As they made their way through the graveyard, a sudden blast of icy wind blew out Andrew's lantern. "Och the noo, boy," cried the shepherd. "It's gone affy dark!"

AS their eyes slowly grew accustomed to the midnight gloom, they were met by a terrifying sight. For there, hovering above a nearby gravestone, was a shimmering white apparition. The freezing cold of the December night grew even colder as Black Bag shook with fear. "Och m'boab. Whit's that over theere, boy?" said Andrew. "It looks like a wee spectre!"

BUT there is little in this world, or the next, that could put the willies up a braw Highlands shepherd, and Selkirk strolled bravely towards the ghostly shape. "Why, calm yersel', laddie," he laughed. "'Tis naught but an auld pedal bin liner going aroond and aroond in an eddy of wind." He grabbed the errant bag and stuffed it in his coat pocket.

BAG soon recovered from his fright in the graveyard, and sat faithfully in the pew by his master's feet throughout the service. After the carols, as the congregation enjoyed their traditional candlelit Christmas Eve supper, Andrew got talking to Angus the gravedigger. He told him all about the white bin liner he'd just found blowing around in the kirkyard.

"THAT wis nae white bag ye saw," intoned the gravedigger. "That was the ghost of auld shepherd Tam McGinty's black bag. When he died, his faithful binliner pined awa' an' died himsel'! Every Christmas Eve it is said his spirit comes back to this graveyard." "Nonsense," said Andrew. "It wis a pedal bin liner." He reached into his pocket. "Whit the...?! It's gone!" he cried.

BLACK Bag and Selkirk looked on in horror. "There," said Angus. "He has returned once again tae flutter aroond o'er his master's final restin' place." "Guid almichty, whit's that affy smell?" said Andrew. "Is it the sulphuruous fumes o' the realm o' Hades?" "No," said the gravedigger. "It's your baggie, Andrew. He's gone and shat his breeks in fricht!"

Dawkins to Found Atheism Institute

CAMBRIDGE academic *Professor Richard Dawkins* has announced plans to set up a worldwide centre to promote atheism. And the outspoken scientist, whose best-selling book *The God Delusion* questions mankind's need to create supernatural deities, says he will use his institute - *the Worldwide Society of Atheists and Free-thinkers* - to rid the world of what he called 'the superstitious shackles of religious belief.'

Cambridge boffin keen to promote ideas about religion

The foundation will be housed in a specially-constructed building, the centrepiece of which will be the so-called "Tower of Atheism," a 400ft-high spire topped with a gilded question mark.

tower

"The tower is so high in order that people can see it from miles around and come to hear me speak," the 72-year-old Darwinian ethologist told reporters. "It is important that my wondrous message of atheism is heard by as many people as possible, so they can accept it into their hearts and take it forth unto the world," he added.

To distinguish himself as the founder of the order, Dawkins intends to wear elaborate robes and an unusually tall hat which he has had specially designed.

dental

The Atheism Institute is open to everyone, but the professor insists that anyone joining must abide by a set of ten strict conditions, the first one being that adherents should listen to no other atheists except Professor Dawkins himself.

I don't believe it: Dawkins (top) to promote his ideas but not those of rival Hitchens (left) at Centre (above).

"There are many other atheists who claim to speak the truth," said Dawkins.

"Men such as Christopher Hitchens, AC Grayling and Penn out of Penn and Teller. But I say unto you, Listen ye not to these men for their words are false. I am the only true atheist."

plastic

The second commandment is that wherever they happen to be, members will be required to face the institute five times every day and recite a short passage from *The Blind Watchmaker* with their eyes closed.

Later rules cover such varied topics as which foods atheists can and cannot eat, approved facial hair arrangements and sexual practices that the Professor forbids.

tree

Whilst joining the atheist congregation is relatively easy, potential members should take note that getting out may not prove quite so simple. "Cursed are the shallow ones who leave my fold to follow false atheists," Dr Dawkins told reporters.

"Cursed be they by day and cursed be they by night. Cursed be they when they lie down and cursed be they when they rise up," he continued.

"Cursed be they even unto the fortieth generation," he added.

Holy Father to become Beach Volleyball Ref

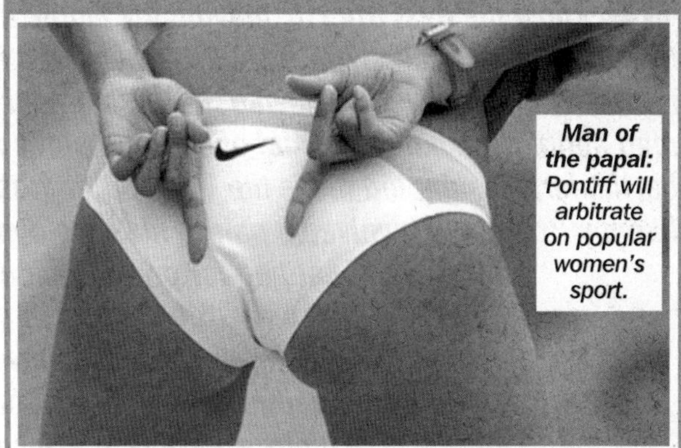

Man of the papal: Pontiff will arbitrate on popular women's sport.

HIS HOLINESS the Pope has rocked the Vatican with his latest proclamation. And it's not an edict about contraception, a papal bull about original sin or an apology for paedophile priests that has got catholics buzzing around the globe. For Francis yesterday announced that he has qualified as a professional *Beach Volleyball umpire*.

The 76-year-old Pontiff, who passed the rigorous refereeing exam with full marks, joins an elite band of arbitrators who travel the globe judging close line calls and net offences for the popular, glamorous sport.

match

A Vatican spokesman told reporters: "His holiness became interested in beach volleyball after he was invited to watch the women's final of the Rome Beach Volleyball Championships in April. Whilst he greatly enjoyed the sport, he was dismayed at the number of poor refereeing judgements that were made during the match."

"The Pope decided to become an umpire, as all his decisions would be correct as a result of his papal infallibility," he continued.

light

According to the spokesman, the Pope intends to concentrate exclusively on women's beach volleyball, as he feels strongly that female sport often plays second fiddle to men. He will also mainly be umpiring matches in hot countries where the competitors wear bikinis and sweat a lot.

"The Holy Father feels that in colder climates, where the players wear leggings and long-sleeved tops, the issue of poor refereeing isn't such a problem," added the spokesman.

Onan Spillseed, chairman of the World Women's Beach Volleyball Association, welcomed Francis's decision to back the sport in such a practical way. He told us: "We're delighted to have such an eminent man of the cloth joining the ranks of our officials."

"Players and spectators of any game that the Holy Father is refereeing can be confident that all calls he makes will be a hundred percent spot-on," Spillseed continued.

pose

"We'll probably use him for important, high profile games such as internationals, important qualifiers and Olympic finals," he added.

Addressing a crowd of 20,000 from the balcony of St Peter's Basilica, the Pope said that once he had found his feet, he intended to specialise within the sport. "In future I'll be looking to mainly concentrate on women's youth matches," he said. "Nothing where the birds are more than about eighteen or nineteen."

"Twenty tops," he added.

Samantha Fox's

Topless Histories

This week...

The Phwo

" *Hi, Page 3 lovely **Samantha Fox** here. You may know me best from displaying my ample assets to Sun readers back in the eighties. What you might not realise is that, as well as having 38DD charms, I'm also mad about British history. And one period that's always particularly fascinated me is the Wars of the Roses. Just like my Bristols, it involved a pair of massive dynasties battling for power inside the bra that was 15th century England. Most stories from this intriguing and tumultuous period in our country's past - the Princes in the Tower, the death of Richard III at the Battle of Bosworth and the murder of the "Sleeping King" Edward VI - are as familiar to the public as my tits. But here are a few chapters from the Wars of the Roses that you might not find in the history books.* **"**

Sam

THERE ARE many competing theories, but nobody really know what happened to the Princes in the Tower - the sons of Edward IV, and th rightful heirs who blocked Richard III's path to the throne of England. Many people believe they died at the hands of their uncle, whilst others claim that Henry Tudor had them murdered in an attempt to eradicate the Yorkist line once and for all. But according to one compelling conjecture, they may have died in an escape attempt after guards left an economy pack of 24 rolls of lavatory paper in the en-suite bathroom of their cell. The resourceful princes unravelled the bathroom tissue and wove themselves a strong, sturdy rope which they tied round the door handle before lowering themselves out of the window of the White Towe

EARL STANLEY, Duke of Beaufort famously watched the progress of the Battle of Bosworth from the top of a nearby hill before deciding which side to join in the conflict. Less well known is the reason for his circumspect approach - earlier that morning his Grace had placed a fifty pound bet at a bookies on a Lancastrian win at odds of three-to-one. Half way through the battle the Yorkist forces under Richard III began to take the upper hand, and Stanley dispatched his squire in a desperate bid to change his punt to an each-way wager. However, the hapless runner was met with the news that the book on the battle had already been closed, leaving Stanley with no option but to pitch in on the side of Henry. His decision was pivotal, ensuring a win for the Tudors and a £150 payout (minus tax) for the Duke of Beaufort ... equivalent to £25,000 in today's money. That's a tasty jackpot ... but not quite as tasty as my 38DD knockers, eh guys?

AFTER EATING a haunch of venison that was on the turn, Richard Neville, Earl of Warwick was struck down with a violent bout of l foulage. Making a dash for the wat closet in his castle, and expecting to be ensconced on the thunderbox for some time, he grabbed the nearest bit of reading material to hand. As h had expected, it was a particularly messy do, and at the end of it Nevil was horrified to see that there was paper left in the netty. Like countles thousands before him and countless thousands since, he was forced to improvise, setting about tearing his reading matter into strips with which to sort out his clarty back end; it wa a long job, but eventually he drew a ace. It was only then that he looked at the last shred of parchment in his hand and saw the words written up it - "Magna Carta". To his horror,

ɔars of the Roses

ɣy, the fates were not on their side,
when they were half way down a
ential rainstorm blew up, turning their
er lifeline to mush and sending them
ging eighty feet to their deaths. Had
rainstorm not started, the Princes
well have survived
the whole
rse of history
ld have been
nged. Perhaps
ouldn't of
been
and
my
out
ne
ers!
sh
thought,
boys?

THE BATTLE of Towton holds the grisly record for the most men killed in a single day on British soil; by the evening of 29th March 1461, 30,000 lay dead or dying on the snow-covered Yorkshire battlefield. But the famous face-off between Yorkist and Lancastrian armies has another claim to fame, as it was also the most badly-organised engagement during the whole of the Wars of the Roses. Disastrously underestimating the popularity of the event and expecting a mere 10,000 combatants to turn up, battle organisers laid on a mere 25 portaloos for the whole site. They had forgotten that Palm Sunday was a Bank Holiday, and when the site

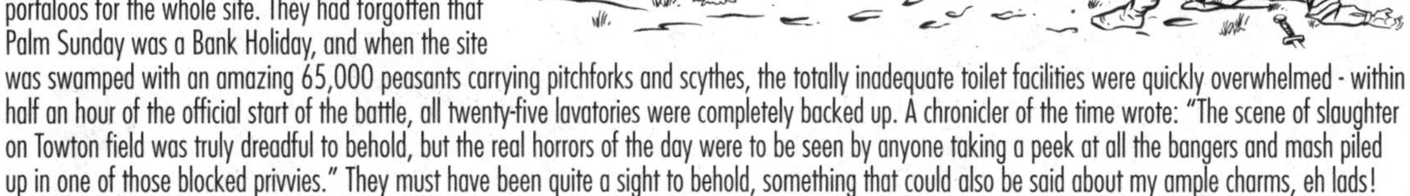
was swamped with an amazing 65,000 peasants carrying pitchforks and scythes, the totally inadequate toilet facilities were quickly overwhelmed - within half an hour of the official start of the battle, all twenty-five lavatories were completely backed up. A chronicler of the time wrote: "The scene of slaughter on Towton field was truly dreadful to behold, but the real horrors of the day were to be seen by anyone taking a peek at all the bangers and mash piled up in one of those blocked privvies." They must have been quite a sight to behold, something that could also be said about my ample charms, eh lads!

IN 1478, George Duke of Clarence was found guilty of treason after plotting against his brother, King Edward IV. As a noble, he was spared the traitor's death of hanging, drawing and quartering and given the privilege of choosing the manner of his own execution. To the surprise of the court, his Grace requested that he be drowned ... in a vat of Dr Pepper! The entire room burst out laughing, and even the condemned man had to chuckle, when the judge informed him that that particular fizzy drink would not be invented for another five centuries. When the court's amusement had subsided, the red-faced George asked instead that he be drowned in a butt of Malmsey wine. I'm sure his cheeks were the same colour as one of my areolae, eh gents?

rwick realised he was holding the
cument signed by King John and his
dal barons at Runnymede in 1215,
Great Charter of the Liberties of
gland - and he'd just used it to wipe
nipsy. Warwick had
de a big boob,
not as big as
pair of boobs
e got attached
my chest, eh
as?

"A HORSE! A HORSE! My kingdom for a horse!" declared King Richard III at the Battle of Bosworth. The beleaguered Yorkist monarch knew his only chance of survival was to flee the battlefield, and it wasn't long after his offer that local publican Silage Armstrong turned up with his drayhorse Beauty, which he said he was willing to swap with Richard in return for England. At this point, the King began to back pedal, explaining that his original offer had been a rhetorical one, not to be taken literally. He did promise, however, to "see Armstrong alright" once he regained his crown. However, the stubborn innkeeper insisted that he didn't give tick to anyone in his pub and he wasn't going to start now, and took his horse back to his pub in nearby Kirkby Mallory. Ironically, not ten minutes later Richard did indeed find himself on a horse, although by now he was dead, bollock-naked and had a sword stuck up his arse. And after that story, what do you think of my big tits, eh fellas?

Next week... ***Linda Lusardi*** **looks at the horrors of the Somme in *'The Phwoar to end all Phwoars'***

OH, LORDY! IT'S THE FAT SLAGS...

MEDDLESOME RATBAG

ROGER MELLIE THE MAN ON THE TELLY

HENMAN COMES ON!

FORMER TENNIS ace *Tim Henman* has shocked his fans by finally coming on... *more than ten years after they originally urged him to do so!*

By our Tennis Correspondent
'Right' Charlie Cairoli

'Come on, Tim!' was the famous cry that rang around Wimbledon's Centre Court every summer of the previous decade, until Henman was routinely thrashed by a superior foreign opponent in the quarter finals. But while the 38-year-old star consistently proved incapable of coming on during his playing days, he now claims to have managed it in the privacy of his own home.

dinner

At a press conference in London this morning, Henman told journalists: "Last night, quite unexpectedly in the middle of dinner, I came on for the very first time."

"I have to admit, it felt great", he continued, pumping his fist and gurning at the assembled press. "It made me really regret that I was never able to come on back when I was competing in professional tennis tournaments. I suppose it was down to the pressure of thousands of people loudly pleading for me to come on, both in the crowd and in front of the TV at home. That's a heck of a lot to deal with."

And Henman went on to insist that the incident would not be a one-off.

"Now I've figured out how to come on, I'll be doing it fairly regularly," he confirmed. "Who knows, maybe one day I'll even do it publicly, so my fans can finally see what it looks like."

party

However, while Henman seems confident that his supporters will share his delight in the long-awaited achievement, there are indications that many feel confused and let down by the news.

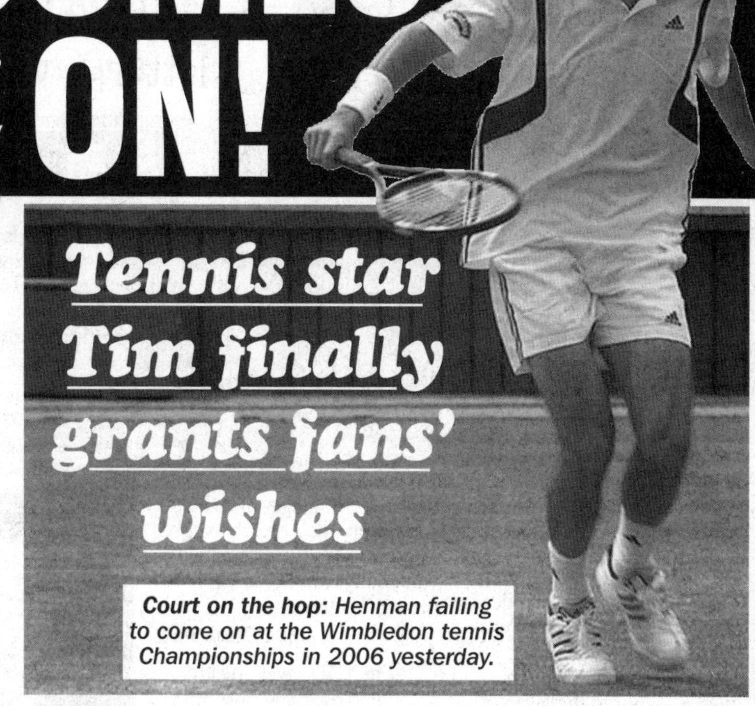

Tennis star Tim finally grants fans' wishes

Court on the hop: Henman failing to come on at the Wimbledon tennis Championships in 2006 yesterday.

Ophelia Barrie-Crier, an interior designer from Notting Hill, was one of many British tennis fans who took to Twitter this afternoon to condemn Henman's actions.

hammer

"I spent the best part of my twenties on Henman Hill urging Tim to come on, but he never once managed it," fumed the 34-year-old mum of two. "To learn that he has finally come on for no particular reason and without me witnessing it has left me feeling sick to my stomach."

"It makes a mockery of anyone who's ever yelled 'Come on, Tim!' at the top of their voice, before watching him get battered in straight sets by some eastern European," she added.

Water Rip-Off!

BOTTLED water producers are taking customers for a ride, according a new report. Scientists compared ten leading brands of expensive bottled water with samples of ordinary tap water from around the country. Amazingly, they found *no difference* in how wet they were.

"The stuff that comes out of your kitchen tap is every bit as wet as your fancy bottle of Perrier or Buxton Spring costing £3 or £4," said the report's author Professor Adrian Street of Crabtree University's Liquid Research Institute.

waters

Researchers carried out a peer-reviewed double-blind test in which they poured the various waters onto lino and walked through them in their socks. "Their results were little short of astounding. From the cheapest to the most expensive, all the samples we tested measured 100% wet," said Dr Street.

"It was clear from our findings that the stuff comes through the tap is perfectly wet. There is frankly no need to buy bottled water," he continued. "The public is being ripped off."

But the report's controversial findings were disputed by Tibor Szakacs, spokesman for industry association The Bottled Water Council. "You simply cannot compare the wetness of expensive bottled water with that of tap water," said Mr Szakacs.

"Our product has a different kind of wetness, a prestige sort of wetness that more than justifies its premium pricepoint," he added.

shoes

Dr Street last courted controversy when he accused wine producers of dirty tricks by filling Champagne bubble with carbon dioxide, a gas that is freely available in the air.

Wet: Some water in a tap yesterday.

Tap H_2O no different to expensive bottled stuff
~ Report

Walliams Bans Gay Marriage Veto from own Wedding
~Reuters

LITTLE Britain funnyman *David Walliams* has become the first celebrity to come out and openly ban gay marriage - *from his own marriage!* And he's got the blessing of the church!

Walliams, the first straight man to swim the channel while possibly thinking about men, made the anoucement after internet rumours surfaced that he was thinking of entering into a civil partnership with his wife of 3 years.

controversy

In 2005, Walliams courted controversey when he said he thought straight sex should be banned in a gay marriage, if both parties consented.

"Why shouldn't two straight men who love each other very much, be allowed to ban gay marrriage from a loving straight relationship?" he said. "It's okay for two gay men who are in heterosexual relationships with women to allow same sex marriage, so why should the rules be any different for straight men? Straight men can ban gay civil partnerships from long-term relationships so why not give them the right to ban same-sex marriage from their own marriage?"

campaign

Walliams has been the target of a campaign by straight men who believe he is devaluing same-sex marriage by refusing to have a civil partnership.

Meanwhile, the head of the Church of England said he supported the right of happily married men to veto gay marriage as long as that veto didn't take place in a church.

Letterbocks

...viz Comic, PO Box 841, Whitley Bay, NE26 9EQ ...e-mail letters@viz.co.uk

STAR LETTER

I'VE I've just returned from Belgium where I spent a week visiting the First World War graves of the Allied troops. Whilst the sight of thousands upon thousands of gravestones was a very moving experience, the breakfast in the hotel was awful. It was just a few buns with jam and some slices of meat and cheese. I like a full English with sausages and bacon and wotnot. Perhaps we should move these war graves over to England, then we could pay our respect to the fallen and have a decent breakfast.

Hector Crumbpipe, Luton

OSCAR Pistorius's story that he thought it was a burglar using his toilet doesn't ring true to me. I've been burgled three times, and on every occasion the intruder ignored the lavatory completely and did a big shit in the middle of the carpet.

Dr M Tintwhistle, Barrow

ALL MY life I have been inetersted in Egyptology and I had always wanted to see the Rosetta Stone above all other artefacts. After years of waiting I finally got the chance this year to come to London and see this object at the British Museum. I could barely contain my excitement as I joined the throng of people gathered around the exhibition case. But as I got to the front, somebody farted. It was a real bad eggy one that took everyone's breath away. Whoever dealt it completely ruined my experience of seeing this treasure.

Jack Dury, York

IF YOU say it quickly and over and over again, 'Because' sounds an awful lot like 'cosby.'

Britt Roberts, e-mail

WHAT on earth has happened to all our superheroes these days? Apart from the Incredible Hulk they're all wearing titanium polycarbon diamond-plated armoured suits or something. The real supermen of yesterday used to wear spandex or y-fronts over their 40 denier tights, which in my opinion was probably much more resistant to bullets and lasers. Bring back polyester superhero outfits, that's what I say.

Dr Richard Evans, Colwyn Bay

THAT billionaire out of *Fifty Shades Of Grey* only has to give that bird a couple of paragraphs of foreplay and a few thrusts, and bingo, she comes in buckets. I have to give the missus a good hour, and then she brings herself off. Some blokes have all the luck.

PB, e-mail

I THINK the world would take Kim Jong Un's threat to start a nuclear war a bit more seriously if he got a decent haircut and laid off the Mars Bars for a bit.

Tam Dale, e-mail

I JUST bought a bag of liquorice allsorts. After emptying the contents onto the table to count them I discovered that out of all 14 possible sorts I had only 7. Of the 27 sweets, 21 were square icing and liquorice, in 4 colour sub categories, leaving only 3 coconut wheels, 2 icing filled liquorice tubes, 1 blue thing covered in sugar beads and 1 odd man-shaped thing. "Liquorice several sorts" would be a more apt name.

Lee Hooper, e-mail

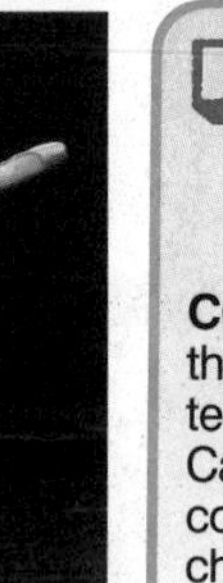

WHEN I was young, I would have dearly loved to have been a ballerina. However, my dream was not to be as I never showed any interest in ballet. In fact, I have never liked dancing of any kind and I find classical music boring.

Sandra Baumgartner, Leeds

I LOVE the ballet and my favourite dancer of all time was Rudolf Nureyev because he had the largest set of sexual organs that I have ever seen tucked in his tights.

Phyllis Traumaturge, Oswestry

THE ballet is discriminatory against male spectators. Whilst the men dancers are all very well-endowed in their tights and get the ladies in the audience all hot and bothered, their female counterparts invariably have next to nothing "up top". Come on, ballet companies, what's sauce for the goose should be sauce for the gander. Sort your act out and get in some ballerinas with decent tits.

Indigo fforbes-ffawlkes, Bloomsbury

WITH reference to the previous writers, I recently went to see a touring production of *Coppelia* by the Moscow Ballet Company. From my seat on the front row I was pleased to see that some of the girls on the stage were pretty decently stacked, all things considered. One of them did a particularly impressive pas de deux from first position, but when I showed my appreciation by reaching out and sticking a tenner down her tights I was thrown out by the management. As usual, it's one rule for the ballet and another for lap-dancing titty bars.

Ted Fibreboard, Hull

To

CONVINCE others you hav the latest in smartphone technology by talking into a Caramac. As smaller model come out, simply break chunks off.

Richard Sloan, e-m

FUTURE *Crystal Maze* producers. Save money on expensive sets by using the 'future zone' of the past *Crys Maze* as the 'past zone' of th future *Crystal Maze*.

Somin Schunt, e-m

I WAS horrified this morning when the doctor phoned to tell me my wife had had a stroke. Imagine my relief, however, when I remembered that my wife is Hollywood actress Drew Barrymore and the doctor was simply reminding me that between the years 2002 and 2007, she had enjoyed a sexual relationship with Fabrizio Moretti, drummer of US indie rock band The Strokes.

Arthur Barrymore, Hollywood

AT MY father's funeral recently, I was consoled by my uncle telling me that "He died doing what he loved." This surprised me because I wasn't aware that my father's favourite pastime was clutching his chest and saying, "Please, not now, not yet."

Britt Roberts, e-mail

PUSSY-WHIPPED!

ONVINCE others you have ve the latest in smartphone chnology by poking penny ilk bottle' sweets on the d of a white shoelace to shion some distinctive adphones.

Richard Sloan, e-mail

MOTORISTS. Save money on expensive pine-scented car air fresheners by keeping old Christmas trees on the back seat. The falling pine needles also give the impression of expensive shag pile upholstery.

Mike Bone, Poole

RNOGRAPHERS. n't waste time putting ur adverts on free porn es where your audience e already in the act of nwinding.' Instead place em on sites where people tually need to 'de-stress', e bbc.co.uk/news or sco.com.

James Massett, e-mail

CAN'T afford scales? Use the ones at your local post office for weighing flour etc. on your next visit.

Betty, e-mail

GrumbLE BucKs

IT SEEMS that these days *pornography* is never far from our readers' minds. And this week it seems that, like those readers, our sacks have been bulging with letters on the subject...

● THEY say that you get your pornstar name by adding the name of your first pet to your mother's maiden name. Well it must be true, because before she was married my mum was called Ada Jeremy, and my first pet was a gerbil called Ron.

Rod O'Steele, Luton

● WITH reference to Mr O'Steele's letter (above), I much preferred the old days when pornographic actors simply used their real names, such as John Holmes, Bill Margold and Mary Millington. I can't be doing with all these modern fuck film stars calling themselves Dick Thrust, Honey Chambers, Rocky Ironshaft and what-have-you. It's completely unbelievable and really spoils my enjoyment of adult entertainment.

Clint Hardwood, Tring

● I WOULD have loved to have been a pornstar, and my first pet was a goldfish called Tempest. Sadly, I spent my childhood in an orphanage and never knew my mother's name. As a result I was unable to follow my dream of hardcore adult film stardom and I decided to become a dinner lady instead.

Irma Oswaldtwistle, Hull

● I READ recently that young people these days are having their expectations of sex twisted by the hardcore porn they view on the internet, and in my experience this is absolutely true. I went up to my teenage son's bedroom to take him a cup of tea the other morning and he had twelve naked Japanese men in there masturbating onto a blindfold woman in a nurse's uniform.

Janice Goombay, Danceband-on-Tyne

● THERE'S an awful lot of anal sex on the interweb isn't there. In the real world it can take years of dogged chicanery, coercion and skullduggery for a chap to earn his chocolate wings, whereas 'on line', brown berets get handed out to pizza delivery boys and manual labourers of every stripe after only the most cursory of introductions. Once again it seems there's one rule for the monster-cocked denizens of cyberspace and another rule for the rest of us.

Pat Doyle, e-mail,

I JUST love classical music and I would love to see Myleen Klass and Nicola Benedetti perfom Schubert's *Fantasy in C* for violin and piano or Chopin's *Nocturne* for piano and violin. Then afterwards I would like to see them get nude and lez off, properly. Double-ended dildos, cunnilingus, strap-on cocks, up the arse, whipping and everything. Oh, yes, you can't beat classical music.

Ross Neil, e-mail

MRS Thatcher was found dead in bed at the Ritz hotel. The following day, my Uncle, a former coal miner, nearly choked to death on a Ritz cracker. It seems that even death hasn't stopped her poisoning the country with her malevolent influence.

Marjorie Fray-Bentos, Cornwall

IN THE 1970s, when I was 8, I wrote to *Jim'll Fix It* and asked if he could fix it for me to be an astronaut. To my amazement, the producer wrote back and said my letter had been picked to go on the show. I was flown out to Cape Canaveral, from where I blasted off in a Saturn V rocket to the moon, where I spent a whole day driving round craters in the Lunar Rover. On the way back, the other astronauts even let me fly the rocket during the re-entry process. We splashed down in the Pacific Ocean and when we got onto the deck of the recovery vessel, I was presented with my *Jim'll Fix It* badge by Neil Armstrong himself. Sadly, the film never got shown on the programme. It was dropped for a girl whose dream was to sit on a beanbag next to David Essex and a film of a boy who wanted to see how liquorice allsorts were made.

Terry Dungworth, Luton

THOSE FUNNY YANKS!

AFTER several years living in the States, I went to my local DIY store to buy some taps for a kitchen I was fitting in my flat. However, the man behind the plumbing counter didn't seem to understand what I was asking for and just looked at me blankly. After a lot of fruitless miming, I eventually drew a picture of some taps on a piece of paper and he finally twigged what I was after. "Oh, you must mean a *faucet*," he laughed. Apparently, 'faucet' is what Americans call taps! Whoever said that the UK and USA are two cultures separated by a common language hit the nail on the head.

Rampton Scratchings, Grantham

LIKE Mr Scratchings *(above)* I lived in America for a while and once, whilst doing some home repairs, I went out to buy a length of four-by-two. At the DIY store, I was amazed when the assistant didn't know what I was talking about. After about half an hour's discussion and much confusion, it finally dawned on him what I was after. In the States they call it *"two-by-four"!*

Frampton Trotter, Hull

I HAD a very similar, and equally funny, experience to the previous writers at an American DIY store. I'd gone in to buy a tin of red coloured paint, but the man at the counter just stared at me in evident bewilderment, saying: "What do you mean, red coloured paint?" It was several minutes before the penny dropped. "Oh, you must mean red *colored* paint," he said. Then it dawned on me - in America, they spell colour without the "u"!

Hampton Snout, Dunham

WHILST visiting America I called in at a branch of Home Depot to buy a 1⁷/₈" bath-plug. The assistant didn't seem to understand me at all. The more I tried to explain what I wanted, the more confused and bewildered he looked, in fact he just looked at me as if I was talking in Chinese. Then it dawned on me. I was talking in Chinese. I had forgotten that I was on holiday and had slipped into my native language. How we laughed.

Chiang Kai-Ping, Jinhao

I THINK schools should bring back the birch. I'm not into corporal punishment, I just think it's a nice tree which would brighten up Britain's playgrounds.

James Brown, Edinburgh

I HAVE 5 types in spoons in my cutlery drawer and one of my neighbours claims to have 7. I'm not counting all my wooden spoons and metal and plastic spoonettes, but I suspect they might be.

Judy Cline-Donner, e-mail

WHY don't people on TV ever walk into a room and forget what they went in for? We've all done it, so why don't they?

Ross Kennett, e-mail

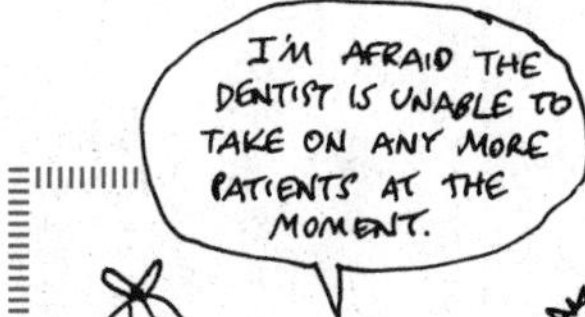

THE CHESTERFIELD MAN
MIT RESEARCH PHYSICIST DR GLENN DAVENPORT WAS ON THE BRINK OF AN AMAZING SCIENTIFIC BREAKTHROUGH. FOR HE HAD BUILT A REVOLUTIONARY TELEPORTATION DEVICE THAT COULD BREAK DOWN ANY LIVING ORGANISM INTO ITS CONSTITUENT ATOMS, AND THEN RECONSTITUTE IT IN ANOTHER PLACE. AND NOW, AFTER TESTING IT ON HIS DOG FEYNMAN, IT WAS TIME TO TRY IT OUT ON A HUMAN SUBJECT...HIMSELF!

JUST WAIT TIL THE WORLD SEES THIS, FEYNMAN. A MOLECULAR SCANNER THAT CAN PINPOINT THE POSITION AND STATE OF EVERY ATOM, EVERY NUCLEUS AND EVERY ELECTRON IN MY BODY, BEFORE OBLITERATING THEM AND RECREATING THEM EXACTLY ON THE OTHER SIDE OF THE ROOM...
...OR ON THE OTHER SIDE OF THE UNIVERSE!

IF THIS EXPERIMENT WORKS, IT WILL REVOLUTIONISE THE LIFE OF EVERY MAN, WOMAN AND CHILD ON THE PLANET.
JUST IMAGINE IT. INSTANT TELEPORTATION TO ANYWHERE IN THE COSMOS IN THE BLINK OF AN EYE!

NO MORE AIRPLANES, ROCKET SHIPS OR SUBWAY TRAINS.
WOOF!

I SHALL STEP INTO THIS PODULE, FEYNMAN, AND BY THE MIRACLE OF SCIENCE I SHALL STEP OUT OF THAT ONE OVER THERE.
BZZSHOO!

SEE YOU ON THE OTHER SIDE OF THE LAB, BOY.

THE PODULE DOOR CLOSED.
HERE GOES...
SEQUENCE INITIALISED 05
TELEPORTING IN 5..4..3...

MY GOD! A CHESTERFIELD ARMCHAIR! HOW DID THAT GET IN HERE...?! THIS IS SUPPOSED TO BE A STERILE EXPERIMENTAL ENVIRONMENT. DAMN! IT'S TOO LATE TO ABORT THE PROCEDURE!
...2..1...ZERO...TELEPORTING!

BZZZ!
VZAP!
VZAP!

MOMENTS LATER.
IT WORKED! IT WORKED!

WOWEE! EVEN THE CHESTERFIELD HAS BEEN RECONSTITUTED IN THE DESTINATION PODULE. NOT ONLY LIVING THINGS BUT ALSO INANIMATE OBJECTS CAN BE TELEPORTED!

BUT THAT NIGHT, SOMETHING FELT WRONG. DAVENPORT WAS ON EDGE.
DINNER WON'T BE LONG, HONEY.
HMMM...?

IS EVERYTHING ALRIGHT, GLENN? YOU DON'T SEEM YOURSELF.
NO, I'M FINE.
AND YOUR FACE LOOKS DARKER THAN USUAL...AND LEATHERY.
WHAT?

DAVENPORT RUSHED INTO THE BATHROOM.
DARK, LEATHERY FACE...IT CAN'T BE!

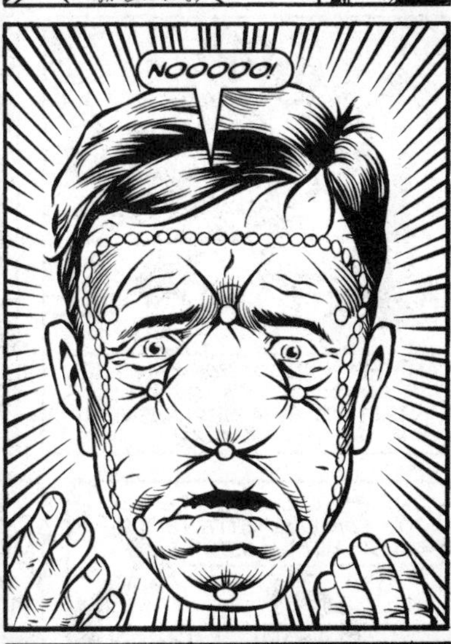

NEXT WEEK

AS THE MUTATION PROCESS GATHERS PACE, THE TORMENTED CHESTERFIELD MAN ACCIDENTALLY STAGGERS INTO 'WORLD OF LEATHER', WHERE A COUPLE BUY HIM ON INTEREST-FREE CREDIT, WITH JUST £100 DEPOSIT AND NOTHING TO PAY FOR THE FIRST TWO YEARS.

YOUNG TOMMY TAYLOR'S VERY BEST FRIEND WAS A FANTASTIC ROBOT NAMED TINRIBS

George Bestial

Mysterious Masked Dentist reveals what stars confess under gas...

THE TOOTH, THE WHOLE TOOTH, AND NOTHING BUT THE TOOTH!

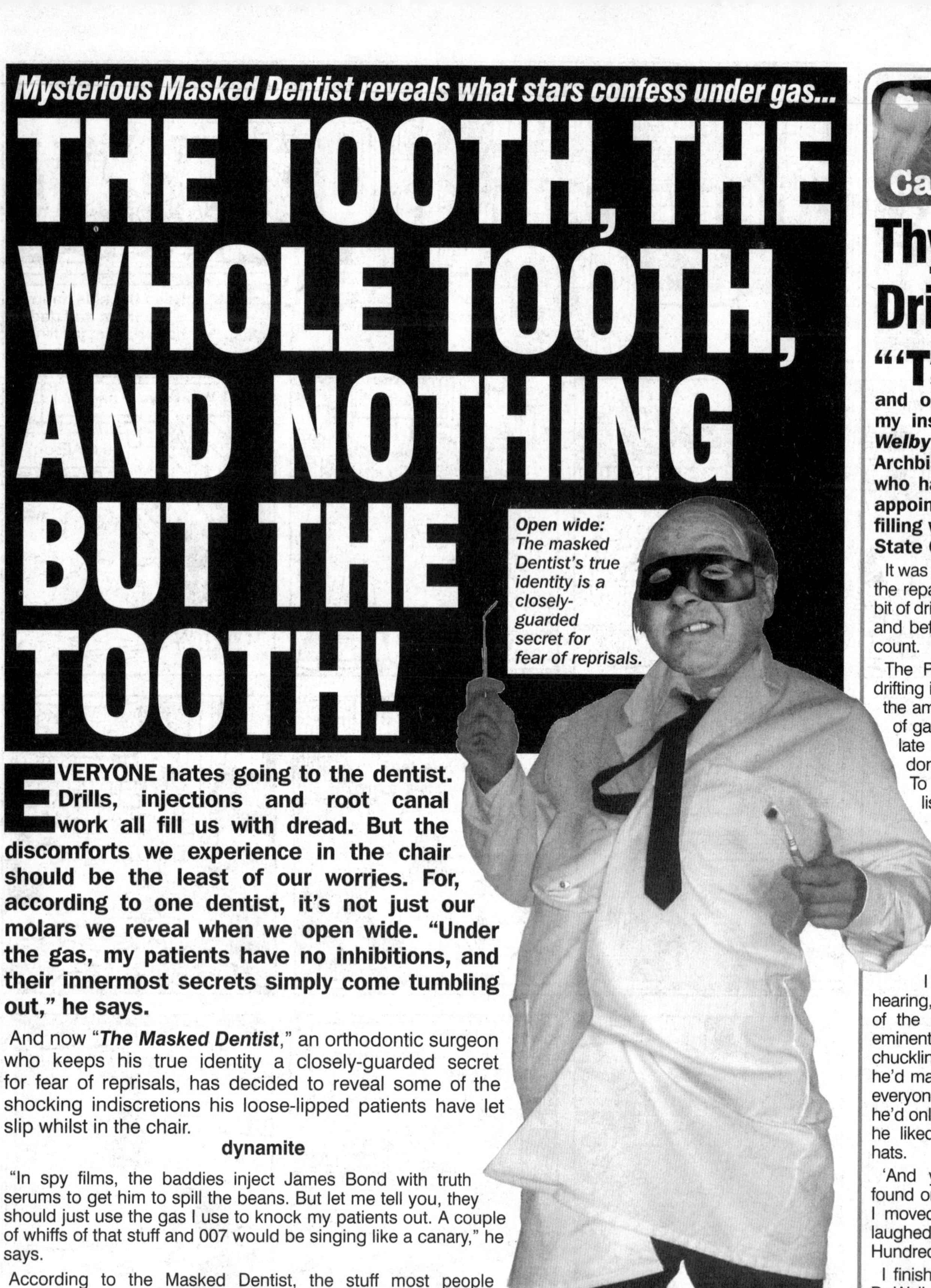

Open wide: The masked Dentist's true identity is a closely-guarded secret for fear of reprisals.

EVERYONE hates going to the dentist. Drills, injections and root canal work all fill us with dread. But the discomforts we experience in the chair should be the least of our worries. For, according to one dentist, it's not just our molars we reveal when we open wide. "Under the gas, my patients have no inhibitions, and their innermost secrets simply come tumbling out," he says.

And now "***The Masked Dentist***," an orthodontic surgeon who keeps his true identity a closely-guarded secret for fear of reprisals, has decided to reveal some of the shocking indiscretions his loose-lipped patients have let slip whilst in the chair.

dynamite

"In spy films, the baddies inject James Bond with truth serums to get him to spill the beans. But let me tell you, they should just use the gas I use to knock my patients out. A couple of whiffs of that stuff and 007 would be singing like a canary," he says.

According to the Masked Dentist, the stuff most people reveal in his surgery is pretty mundane - office gossip, mildly racist opinions, internet passwords and the like. But sometimes, particularly if the patient is a celebrity, what they disclose under anaesthetic is dynamite.

moneypenny

"Once they're under, they lose all their inhibitions, and the secrets they let slip would make your hair stand on end. Or curl. Or go white. If it wasn't any of those already. And if it was it would make it do the opposite," he said.

"I've had quite a few stars in my surgery for various procedures and when the tooth gas has taken effect, the eye-popping confessions begin. And the the thing is, they don't remember a thing about what they have said when they come round."

Now the Masked Dentist is opening up his dental records. And he had this message for *Viz* readers: *"What you are about to read is the tooth, the whole tooth, and nothing but the tooth."*

Case 1

Thy Drill be Done

"'TAKE YOUR mitre off, sit down in the chair and open wide.' Those were my instructions to *Dr Justin Welby*, the newly-invested Archbishop of Canterbury, who had made an emergency appointment after pulling out a filling with a Curly-Wurly at the State Opening of Parliament.

It was quite a big cavity, and I knew the repair was going to take quite a bit of drilling, so I gave him some gas and before long he was out for the count.

The Primate of All England was drifting in and out while I was mixing the amalgam. It was the usual sort of garbled nonsense about being late for school and not having done his maths homework. To be honest, I was only half-listening, but then he said something that caught my attention.

'Of course, it's all a load of bollocks, you know,' he said. 'Big man in the sky watching everything we do? What a pile of wank.'

I couldn't believe what I was hearing, straight from the mouth of the Church of England's most eminent cleric. By this time he was chuckling to himself, boasting that he'd managed to pull the wool over everyone's eyes, and about how he'd only become a bishop because he liked wearing dresses and big hats.

'And you'll never guess what I found on top of the wardrobe when I moved into Lambeth Palace,' he laughed. 'All Rowan's jazz mags. Hundreds of them ... dirty bastard.'

I finished up doing the filling and Dr Welby came round. He was a bit woozy from the anaesthetic, and I could tell he didn't remember a thing about what he'd just revealed. After he'd rinsed the bits of filling out of his mouth, he asked me if he'd be seeing me in the congregation at Westminster Abbey the following Sunday.

'I've been doing a series of sermons about the Ten Commandments, and this week it's "Thou shallt not lie",' he said. I couldn't believe the hypocrisy.

In fact, I think that's the only time during a procedure when I've been more open-mouthed than my patient."

Schoolboy error

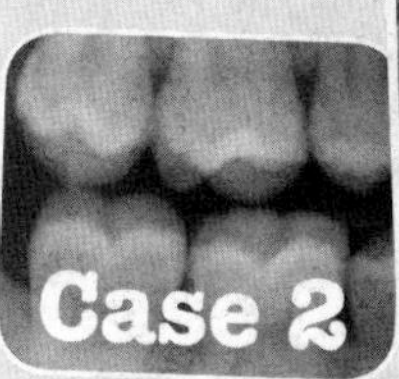

"LIKE DOCTORS, lawyers and priests, everything that transpires between a dentist and patient is confidential. But occasionally, we are faced with ethical dilemmas when the correct course of action to take is not so clear-cut.

One such moral quandary occurred when *Crackerjack* funnyman Ian Krankie dropped his son, pint-sized Scottish schoolboy ***Wee Jimmy***, off at my surgery for his six-monthly check-up. Like all kids, Jimmy had been spending his pocket money on sweets, and as a result he needed a tooth out.

The youngster didn't want an injection, as he was scared of needles, so I popped the mask on him and gave him a few puffs of gas. In a few seconds he started getting fandabi-dozy and before long he was out like a light. I set to work pulling out the bad tooth with my pliers, but it wasn't long before my young patient started nattering away.

I pieced together his mumblings, and gradually the jigsaw fell into place. I's no exaggeration to say I was horrified by what I heard. Apparently, little Jimmy, who was still in shorts, had been seduced by one of his teachers, whom he identified as Miss Pollard.

One thing was clear: the relationship was wholly inappropriate. The pair were planning to run away to the continent the following week.

I was in a tricky position. Clearly a serious crime had been committed; the teacher had abused her position of power to take advantage of an innocent young schoolboy. Yet, as a dentist, I was bound by a duty of professional confidentiality which meant I couldn't go to the authorities with the information I had discovered.

What I could do, however, was go to his Dad. When I told Mr Krankie what Jimmy had said whilst under the anaesthetic. I expected him to be furious, vowing to go straight to the school to have it out with the headmaster, but to my surprise he burst into laughter.

'Och, Jimmy's not really a schoolboy,' he explained in between guffaws. 'He's a 67-year-old female pensioner called Jeanette!' He told me that what I'd heard was actually his aged wife rehearsing a light-hearted sketch for that Friday's episode of *Crackerjack*."

Ground Zero Force

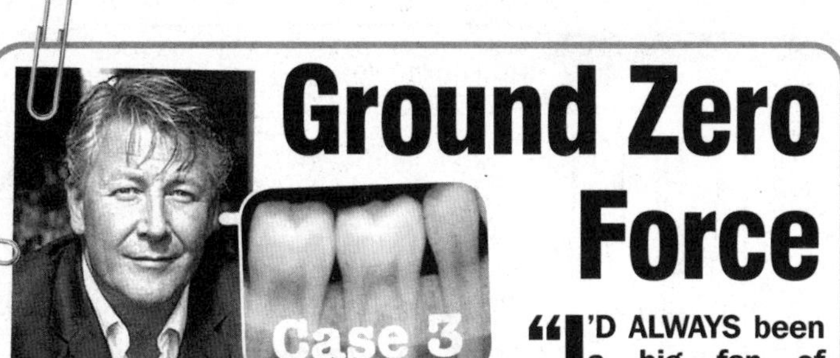

"I'D ALWAYS been a big fan of *Charlie Dimmock*, the large-breasted, bra-less gardener from TV's *Ground Force* garden makeover show. So I was disappointed to say the least when her fellow presenter *Tommy Walsh* turned up with a nasty abcess, needing root canal work.

Once in the chair, the burly handyman asked me for a double dose of gas. "To be honest with you, I hate going to the dentist. I'm scared as a kitten," he confessed. If only that was all he had confessed, because the bumper dose of anaesthetic really loosened his lips. And what he revealed as I worked on his teeth left me reeling with shock.

mastermind

For Tommy Walsh had been the evil mastermind behind the 9-11 attacks on the World Trade Centre. Apparently he had been left bitter after *Groundforce America* - the transatlantic spin-off of the show where he had made his name in Britain - had been axed after a mere two series.

Like the infection on the root of his left lower bicuspid, this bitterness had festered, swelling into a hate-filled abcess. And just like in his gums, with nowhere for the poisonous vitriol to go, this hatred had erupted into an orgy of murderous revenge.

Now, under the anaesthetic, Walsh was crowing about how the innocent Osama Bin Laden had taken the blame, not to mention a bullet in the eye, for a crime he didn't commit.

When he came round, Tommy was his usual avuncular self, but I found it hard to reconcile the smiling, friendly man in the chair with the monster who had killed 3,000 innocent New Yorkers on that terrible day in 2001. It was with a heavy heart that I shook his hand and told him to come back if there were any problems, but otherwise I'd see him again in six months."

Secret Life of Brian

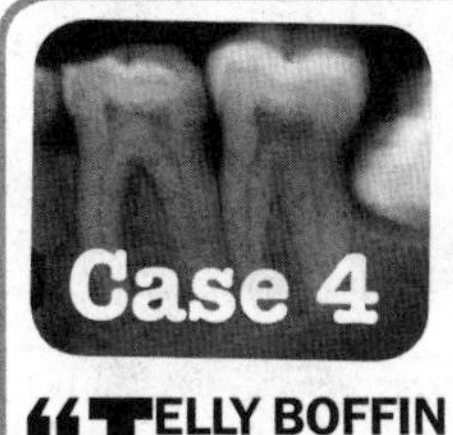

"TELLY BOFFIN Professor *Brian Cox* is as well known for his trademark toothy smile as he is for his encyclopaedic knowledge of science. As a result, he's a regular visitor to my cosmetic dentistry clinic, where he gets his front teeth re-capped and whitened several times a year.

Once I've got him under the gas, I'm used to him prattling on about atoms, planets, gravity and what-have-you, just like he does on all his programmes. I usually just zone out, but during one procedure he said something that made me sit up and take notice for once.

'I cheated ...' he muttered. 'I cheated in a woodwork exam ... made a pipe rack ... used nails instead of dovetails.'

'Sorry ... sorry ... so ashamed,' he continued. I allowed myself a little chuckle. Cox's little secret was safe with me. But what he said next made my blood run cold.

'Cheated again ... a second time ...' he said. 'Professor's exam ... copied off Stephen Hawking ... all the answers ...'

'Sorry ... so ashamed ...' he added. But this time his weasel words cut no ice with me. I couldn't laugh off this confession so easily. Cox was at the top of the academic tree, and he'd got there under false pretences.

When he came round, I made some small talk about Large Hadron Colliders, casually asking him how big they are and how they work. He ummed and aahed for a bit, before trying to change the subject to the chart career of his pop band D-Ream, but he wasn't fooling me.

What Brian Cox knows about science could be written on the back of a Bowes Higson. Take it from me - I'm his dentist."

Jezza's Bombshell

"YOU'D THINK that *Top Gear*'s *Jeremy Clarkson* has it all. With his top-rated TV show, a dozen supercars lined up on the drive of his swish Chipping Norton mansion, and a whole shelf full of best-selling books and shit DVDs to his credit, you wouldn't think he'd want for anything.

Clarkson is the last person you'd expect to be moonlighting after hours as a *Midnight Cowboy*-style male prostitute, turning tricks with strange men in seedy public toilets to top up his seven-figure BBC salary. But that's exactly what he does do, and I should know. Because I've heard it ... straight from his motormouth.

The outspoken TV petrolhead was in my chair, under the gas whilst I replaced a loose porcelain crown on his second pre-molar with a gold one. As I waited for the dental cement to set, he started talking, and I was immediately taken aback by what I heard.

'Fifteen quid for a handjob...' he muttered. 'Aren't you a big boy ... I'll go round the world for thirty but no kissing ... kissing's extra.'

'How do you like that, cowboy...?' he said. I couldn't believe what I was hearing. 'I can play it rough as you like, cowboy,' he continued. 'Bareback, fisting or Cleveland steamer, I'm all yours if the price is right.'

Sure enough, when I looked in Clarkson's bag (which had fallen over, spilling some of the contents out on the surgery floor), I found a stetson, a fringed suede jacket, a pair of arseless chaps and a tube of Liquid Silk anal lube."

SID
the SEXIST

TITS OOT!
TYNESIDE'S SILVER-TONGUED CAVALIER

HOW, BOB, YUZ'VE GOT T' SHAG THE NEXT WOMAN WOT COMES THROUGH THAT DOOR.
REET... GAME ON!
NCB

HAD ON, LADS... THEZ SOMEONE COMIN' IN...!

WOOAH! BACK O'THE FUCKIN' NET!
AYE, BOB.
CANNY RESULT, THAT.

REET... WHO'S NEXT?
MY TORN.

REET, JUR... YEEZ'VE GOT T'TEK THE NEXT BORD WOT COMES THROUGH THAT DOOR UP THE DORT-BOX.
REET.

OOH, IT'S URPENIN', JUR MAN!
COME ON YOU BEAUTY...!

HA! HA! HA!
EH?! NAH... NAH...
HO-HO! IT'S A FUCKIN' BLURK, JUR!
HA! HA!

AYE. YUZ'VE GOT T'BUM 'IM, JUR...!
NAH...NAH. HAD ON, MAN. YEE SAID THE NEXT BORD THROUGH THE DOOR... NOT BLURK.
Y' GEET HEEMASEX!

AYE, HE'S REET THOUGH BUT, BAZ.
AYE... HE'S REET. RULES IS RULES.
AALL REET, THEN. JUST LASSES...

WOOAH! BIT DODGY, THAT, JUR MAN.
AYE. BIN ROOND THE CLOCK, HOR. MUST BE FAWATY IF SH A DEEAY.

NAH! I'LL STICK ON THAT, LADS. SHE'S A MILF, HOR...
SHE'S A FUCKIN' YUMMY MUMMY!

BIN AROOND A BIT, I'LL BET. SHE'LL KNAA AALL THE TRICKS...
AYE, WELL... YUZ'VE GOT A POINT THERE, JUR, MAN.

BARKDOOR WORK.. FACIALS... BELGIAN BISCUITS... THE LOT! THERE'S FUCKIN' NOWT SHE WIVVEN'T DEE, MAN!

AYE. SHE'S MEBBEEZ NOT AS TAST AS BOB'S PIECE, BUT THAT'S A FUCKIN' CANNY RESULT, THAT, JUR.
YEE NEXT, BAZ.

Continued over...

SORRY, SID... IT'S UNANIMOUS. YUZ'VE GOT THE HOOND.

HAD ON... PHURTUR FINISH, Y'SAID. WELL, THERE'S A SECURITY CAMERA ON THE FUCKIN' DOOR. WUZ'LL EXAMINE THE FOOTAGE!

HOO, DAVE MAN. CAN Y'REWIND Y'VIDEO A BIT FORRUZ?
AYE, SID. WOT'S WRANG?
WUZ JUST NEED IT T'SETTLE A GENTLEMEN'S DISAGREEMENT ABOOT SOME BORD'S KNOCKAZ.

...DOOR'S URPENIN'... HERE THEY COME...!
STOP IT THERE, DAVE... STOP IT THERE!

LOOK... SEE? HER TITS IS THE FORST THING THROUGH THE DOOR..!
HMM...
IF Y'DRAW AN IMAGINARY LINE ACROSS THERE Y'CAN SEE IT, BAZ...!

THEM KNOCKAZ WAS DEFINITELY IN FRONT.
AYE. SID'S REET.
AYE.
THE POOND O' THE BASKERVILLES COME IN SECOND.

YES!! FUCKIN' GEDDIN!

FUCK YEE, Y'LOO-ZAZZ!

YUZ'VE GOT T'GET UP CANNY ORLY T'BEAT SID T' THE FANNY!

I'M OOT O' YOUR LEAGUE, LADS! Y'CANNAT COMPETE! IT'S LIKE THE TOON VERSUS GATESHEED! THERE'S NEE FUCKIN' CONTEST!

HOO PET, YUZ WON! YUZ WON! COME OOTSIDE AN' SUCK ME COCK AN' I'LL SPUNK AALL AWA Y'TITS!
!
NCB

NER! NER! NER! N
NER! NER!
AMBULANCE
EMERGENCY

SHORTLY...
CASUALTY
TIME TO NEXT PATIENT 6 HOURS
HOW, BOB... YUZ'VE GOT T'SHAG THE NEXT NORSE WOT COMES THROUGH THAT DOOR.
REET... GAME ON!
PUNCH
NHS

NEXT WEEK: A FIRE BREAKS OUT AT THE LOCAL CHILDREN'S HOSPITAL AND THE BATTERIES IN OLLY CROMWELL'S NEW MODEL ARMY ARE FLAT AGAIN.

ROGER MELLIE

THE MAN ON THE TELLY

I'M SORRY ABOUT THIS, MR. BAZALBRUSH... IT'S NOT LIKE ROGER TO BE TWO HOURS LATE FOR A MEETING
HMMMM!
...IT'S USUALLY AN HOUR AND THREE QUARTERS AT THE MOST

YES, WELL, I'M ON A VERY TIGHT SCHEDULE, TOM... PERHAPS WE SHOULD TAKE A RAINCHECK ON THIS ONE AND RE-SCHEDULE...

MORNING, TOM... SORRY I'M A COUPLE OF MINUTES LATE.
A COUPLE OF **MINUTES!?** ROGER, IT'S HALF PAST...

BZZZ-ZAP!
HNNG!

J.. J... JESUS... WHAT THE HELL JUST HAPPENED?
STUN GUN, TOM... 240,000 VOLTS. GOOD, ISN'T IT?
JESUS
JUST DONE A CORPORATE VIDEO FOR THE COMPANY THAT MAKES THEM. AND THEY GAVE ME A FREEBIE.
THEY SELL THOUSANDS OF THESE FUCKERS TO THE COPPERS IN SOUTH AMERICA AND THE MIDDLE EAST

THOUGHT I COULD USE IT T'GET TO THE BAR WHEN THE BOOZER IS A BIT CROWDED, OR IF ANY AUTOGRAPH HUNTERS GET A BIT TOO CLOSE FOR COMFORT.
I... I'VE WET MYSELF, ROGER.
DON'T WORRY ABOUT IT TOM... THAT'S SUPPOSED TO HAPPEN...

240,000 BIG ONES AND YOUR MUSCLES ARE JUST JELLY. MOST PEOPLE SHIT THEMSELVES AN' ALL...
YOU'VE NOT SHIT YOURSELF HAVE YOU, TOM?
ER... NO...

SMASHING... ANYWAY, WHAT DID YOU WANT TO SEE ME ABOUT?

ROGER, THIS IS PETER BAZALBRUSH. HE'S THE EXECUTIVE PRODUCER OF TOP-RATED COOKERY CONTEST "THE GREAT BRITISH BAKE OFF"
PETE
HI, ROGER
WE'D LIKE YOU TO TAKE PART IN A CELEBRITY BAKE-OFF SPECIAL WE'RE FILMING TOMORROW

TOMORROW, EH?.. I WAS SUPPOSED TO BE OPENING A HOSPICE, BUT I COULD FUCK THEM OFF. WHAT'S THE FEE, PETE?
THERE ISN'T ONE, ROGER
SHUT THE DOOR ON YOUR WAY OUT
THERE'S EXPENSES, OF COURSE, BUT £5000 GOES TO A CHARITY OF THE WINNER'S CHOICE
£5000 EH?

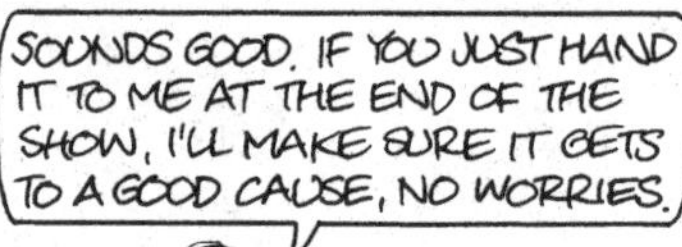
SOUNDS GOOD. IF YOU JUST HAND IT TO ME AT THE END OF THE SHOW, I'LL MAKE SURE IT GETS TO A GOOD CAUSE, NO WORRIES.

WELL, THAT'S ASSUMING YOU WIN, ROGER... ARE YOU GOOD AT BAKING?

NEVER REALLY TRIED IT TO TELL THE TRUTH... IT CAN'T BE THAT DIFFICULT, THOUGH... IT'S JUST FLOUR AND EGGS AND SHIT, ISN'T IT?
THERE'S A BIT MORE TO IT THAN **THAT** ROGER
ANYWAY, I ALWAYS COME TOP IN A VIEWER VOTE, PETE...
...THE GRANNIES WHO WATCH THIS SORT OF SHIT LOVE ME.
NO... IT'S NOT A PHONE VOTE, ROGER
WE GET EXPERT JUDGES TO TEST THE CAKES AND DECIDE WHICH ONE IS THE WINNER

EXPERT JUDGES?.. ...**WHO?**
WELL, THERE'S MARY BERRY
CAT WOMAN!? FUCK ME! FANTASTIC!
NO... **MARY** BERRY, ROGER

AND WE'VE GOT PAUL HOLLYWOOD.
EH?... THAT SHIRT LIFTER WHO DID "RELAX"?.. WHAT THE FUCK DOES **HE** KNOW ABOUT BAKING?

NO, ROGER... YOU'RE THINKING OF PAUL **RUTHERFORD** OUT OF FRANKIE GOES TO HOLLYWOOD.
THAT'S HIM, TOM
NO... NO... HE'S ONE OF BRITAIN'S FOREMOST PASTRY CHEFS.

EVERYBODY KNOWS THAT.. JUST GOT TO SEE HIM IN THE VIDEO PONCING ABOUT WITH HIS BIG MOUSTACHE AND LEATHER CAP... I MEAN, DON'T GET ME WRONG, PETE, I'VE GOT NOTHING AGAINST THEM...
JUST AS LONG AS HE DOESN'T TRY TO BUM ME WHEN I BEND OVER TO PUT SOMETHING IN THE OVEN

JESUS, ROGER... HERE'S THE DETAILS OF THE SHOOT... JUST BE ON SET BY 9.00AM TOMORROW
COUNT ON ME, TOM. I'LL BE THERE... I'M A PRO.

11.30 NEXT MORNING...
VROOM! SCREECH!
BBC
MORNING, TOM
CHRIST, ROGER, WHERE HAVE YOU BEEN? WE WERE JUST ABOUT TO PHONE PAUL ROSS

ANY CHANCE OF A CUPPA, TOM?
NO, ROGER, THERE ISN'T...
WE'RE WELL BEHIND SCHEDULE THANKS TO YOU... **AGAIN!**

ROGER, THIS IS MEL AND SUE WHO'LL BE PRESENTING THE SHOW
HELLO, ROGER
FUCKING HELL, TOM! IT'S THEM TWO OFF THE BREAD ADVERTS

HEY, YOU MUST'VE MADE A FUCKING **BOMB** OUT OF THEM... THEY WERE ON EVERY TWO MINUTES. HOW MUCH DID YOU GET, EH?..
CASH, WAS IT?
ERM... I.. DON'T...

ROGER, DON'T BE SO RUDE!.. COME ON... LET'S GET ON WITH IT... YOUR COMPETITOR HAS BEEN HERE FOR HOURS.
WHO AM I UP AGAINST, TOM?

IT'S RONNIE CORBETT, ROGER, AND HE WAS BROUGHT UP IN A BAKERY, SO HE'S GOING TO BE PRETTY STIFF COMPETITION
WELL THE LITTLE TWAT WILL HAVE TO COOK UP SOMETHING SPECIAL TO BEAT **THIS** FUCKER.

PIECE OF PISS WITH THIS, TOM... JUST ADD WATER AND BUNG IT IN AN OVEN FOR A BIT... BISH! BOSH!
Betty Crackers
CAKE MIX

THAT FIVE GRAND IS AS GOOD AS MINE, TOM...

...WELL, AS GOOD AS MY CHARITY'S, I SHOULD SAY
...THERE WE GO...

RIGHT! TIME TO HIT THE BAR, TOM...
KEEP YOUR EYE ON THAT, LOVE. GIVE US A SHOUT IF IT STARTS TO BURN.

2 HOURS LATER...
HEY, TELL YOU WHAT, TOM, THAT PETER BAZALBRUSH MIGHT BE A BIT OF A TWAT, BUT HE KNOWS HOW TO PUT ON HOSPITALITY FOR THE TALENT, I'LL GIVE HIM THAT!
BAAARP!
RIGHT! LET'S SEE IF THIS FUCKER'S DONE

OOH! THAT'S COME OUT A TREAT, THAT. FUCKING FANTASTIC, ISN'T IT?

WHAT D'Y' RECKON TO **THAT**, FANNY? IS THAT THE WINNER OR **WHAT**, EH?
IT LOOKS A LITTLE OVER DONE TO ME
CLUNK!

YES! DON'T COUNT YOUR CHICKENS YET, ROGER. I THINK RONNIE'S CAKE IS READY... LOOK!
GOSH! THAT LOOKS WONDERFUL

OH, HO! I THINK WE COULD HAVE A WINNER HERE, MARY
YES... HAVE YOU EVER SEEN ANYTHING SO...

BZZZ-ZAP!
NNNG!

WHAT A SHAME... THE POOR OLD TWAT'S GONE ARSE OVER TIT INTO HIS CAKE. MUST'VE STEPPED IN A LITTLE DIVOT IN THE GRASS OR SOMETHING... TSK!

ANYWAY, I SUPPOSE THAT MAKES ME THE WINNER... YOU COULDN'T GIVE ME CASH, COULD YOU?.. ONLY THE CHARITY I HAVE IN MIND DOESN'T DO CHEQUES
I THINK HE'S SHIT HIMSELF

LETTERBOCKS

letters@viz.co.uk

Viz Comic
PO Box 841
Whitley Bay
NE26 9EQ

NO WONDER the pandas at Edinburgh Zoo are having trouble getting pregnant, what with everyone watching them at it and all. What they need is an expert consultant, and I suggest the UK's finest cock-wangler Ben Dover. Not only would Mr Dover be able to give the pandas helpful tips about getting it up and performing while strangers are watching, but he'd also be able to help any resultant cubs find jobs in BBC sitcoms.

David Wharton, e-mail

MY GRANDSON played me a pop song on his computer the other day. It was called *Gangster Style*, I think. It was sung by a Chinaman and it was a very bouncy tune. There was a little film to go with it with all these Chinese pretending to be on horses. It was very good and I wondered if any of your other readers had seen it. I think it might get to number one in the hit parade one of these days.

Albert Tintis, Leeds

WHY DO people always get into fights over seemingly pointless things like their postcode or what football team they support? They never come to blows over grand philosophies or theories on dark matter. Come on, thugs. Start contextualising your dust-ups a bit better.

Prof Adam Hogarth, e-mail

I'VE JUST read my son a bedtime story by Hans Christian Andersen. Seriously, who writes this shit? I swear, you couldn't make it up.

Edward Teach, Bristol

IS IT any wonder that the citizens of Gotham City can never suss out Batman's real identity? First it was Adam West, then it was Michael Keaton, Val Kilmer, George Clooney and now it's Christian Bale. I'm sorry, but it's just taking the piss out of people in my book.

William Kidd, Cromer

HARRY Secombe sang 'If I ruled the world, every day would be the first day of spring.' Given that the vernal equinox this year was one of the coldest on record, I for one am glad that Sir Harry never achieved his megalomaniacal ambition.

Phil Godsel, e-mail

OUR SON made a real mess whilst painting model soldiers in his bedroom after specifically being told to paint them outside. "What part of 'Don't paint model soldiers in your bedroom' did you not understand?" my furious wife asked him. I had to laugh. It was obviously the *'don't'* part.

L. Logic, Frinton

I DON'T know why people use the saying "I would like to be a fly on the wall at that meeting." If they were, the first thing they would do is fly out the window and look for a dog shit to land on and start to eat the bastard. And that is so fucking disgusting it makes me want to vomit.

Derek Chunn, NSW

HOW COME foxes have always been deemed to be cunning? I saw one being caught in my neighbour's garden this morning and to say he looked embarrassed as he was being dragged into an RSPCA van would be an understatement to say the least.

T. Cake, London

IN THE film *Spartacus* starring Kirk Douglas, I reckon his followers might have avoided crucifixion had they not each claimed to be him when they were finally cornered. Pillaging, murder and rape are all very well but the Romans took identity theft extremely seriously.

Humphrey Cushion, Hickory

QUEEN guitarist Brian May earned a PhD in Astrophysics, Professor Brian Cox used to play synthesiser in D-Ream and stargazer Patrick Moore was a dab hand at the glockenspiel. Yet Stephen Hawking can't be arsed to learn so much as the mouth organ. Talented, but lazy.

H. Horatio, Pinner

I DON'T see why the Queen felt the need to take her recent bum-gravy-induced sabbatical. Her face always looks like she has just pappered herself whilst whenever a commoner is within 500 yards, Prince Phillip has a look that suggests someone is holding a freshly laid cable under his nose. The way I see it, they should have said nothing about their recent spot of royal pebbledashing and no-one would have been any the wiser.

Simon Hoffmann, e-mail

TOILET roll makes a very poor and highly flammable mummy costume.

Desulph Daz, Burns unit, Fulchester hospital

CONVINCE neighbours that your colours have run in the wash by soaking all of your pink clothing in a bucket of water and hanging it out on the line with a red sock.

Jimmy Boogaloo, e-mail

ENTREPRENEURS. Save money on alarm clocks by sleeping on the kitchen floor and setting the oven timer.

Sam Sherwood, e-mail

CONSERVATIONISTS. Assist the survival of Polar Bears by moving a quantity of them to Antarctica.

Adrian Pardue, e-mail

DECENT men. Avoid going mad over that woman you truly love, by keeping a few others on the go at the same time.

Angus Lambkin, e-mail

RECREATE the innocent wonder of your first day at school by clinging desperately to your mum's leg whilst screaming hysterically.

Fat Al White, Wrenthorpe

HUSBANDS. If your wife asks you if you have done the job she asked you to do yesterday, the chances are that she knows you have not and she is just being sarcastic.

K Turnip, e-mail

BARBED wire makes ideal ordinary wire for sado-masochists.

Billy Bloodorange, e-mail

MAKE your friends think you have a bowl of limes, by painting a bowl of lemons green.

Anthony Corten, California

NEVER get conned into calling premium-rate prize draw phone numbers, unless there's a really big prize such as £250,0000.

Martin Connelly, e-mail

MOTORISTS. Convince your neighbours that there has been a frost in the night by dusting their car windscreens with icing sugar. For added realism, draw a cock or pair of tits with your finger after the dusting.

Mr Turps-Substitute, e-mail

PUBLIC Toilet Users. Avoid having to wash your hands after going for a piss by washing your penis in the sink beforehand.

Kazimir Malevich, e-mail

WHILST watching the BBC news the other night, Fiona Bruce told me to look away from the TV as she was going to reveal the England result. I did so as I didn't want the highlights spoilt for me. But I was in bed and saw the score reflected in the wardrobe mirror doors. So I put my foot through the TV and sent the BBC the bill.

Mike Tatham, Dundee

WITH reference to Mr Tatham's letter *(above)*. I think he is completely in the right and I hope the BBC pays up for a new television. In future, newsreaders should advise people to "close their eyes" rather than look away, just in case there is a reflective surface nearby.

H Bendworthy, Stoke

WITH reference to Mr Tatham's letter *(two above)*, I think he acted rather rashly, since the advice given by Ms Bruce was both measured and sensible. If anything, it was the mirror that was at fault. After putting his foot through his television, surely it would have been more reasonable to send the bill to the manufacturer of the mirror, or failing that, to the company that installed his wardrobe.

Luton Van, Herts

I DON'T know what Mr Tatham is complaining about in his letter *(three above)*. The football result he saw reflected in his wardrobe mirror would surely be the reverse of the actual result. If England won the game, the reflection would say that they had lost, and vice versa. So it would have been a surprise watching the game anyway.

Frank Battenburg, Cromer

MR TATHAM's letter *(four above)* just doesn't ring true to me. This isn't the first letter he has written to your magazine where he ends up by putting his foot through his television. I think he has some kind of insurance scam going. Either that or else he owns a television repair shop and is just trying to drum up trade.

Orlando Fogg, Notts

HARDLY a day goes by without some sort of erroneous type of meat appearing in our food. Fortunately I have an O-level in biology and have developed a test which ensures that the subject has been consuming 100% bovine protein. So far my test is only suitable for female subjects but a simple, visual breast examination is all it takes to put your mind at rest. So think of the little ponies, ladies, and e-mail me your topless photographs for a confidential and scientific analysis today. It only works on under 30s I'm afraid.

Basil Chives, e-mail

I THINK boilermen get a pretty bad rap in the motion picture industry. Freddy Krueger was a boilerman, as was Michael Elphick in *The Elephant Man*. Why can't we have more films where the boilerman is actually the hero for a change and doesn't horribly mutilate teenagers or beat up people with Proteus syndrome?

Maurice Shoes, Luton

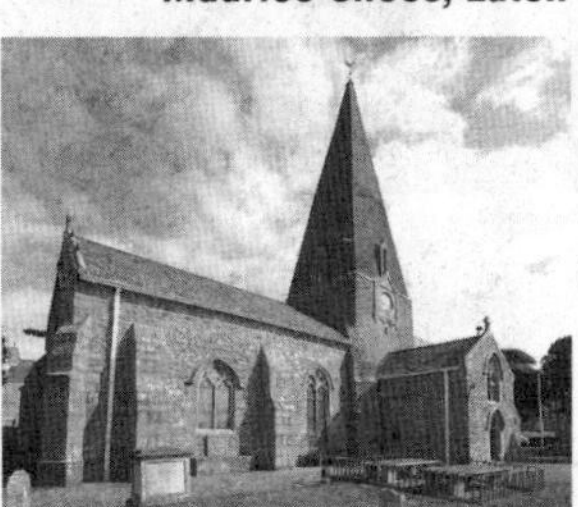

LIVING next door to a church is a nice thing. On Sunday mornings I am gently awoken by the choral strains of many a harmonious hymn. And the other day I was privileged to find a delightful-looking pale blue envelope tucked under my windscreen wipers with the words "God is Love" and "I Pray for Thee" written on the front. It was obviously some kind of a heartfelt gesture from the local vicar and his throng, I thought. Upon opening the envelope there was a similarly-shaded pale blue piece of paper. I unfolded it and I was warmed to receive the Holy Message as if from Jesus himself. It read "Stop parking in front of these gates." What a joy it is to be welcomed into the bosom of the Lord. As long as I get the fuck away from his gates.

John Mason, e-mail

HOW about a picture of a hot-air balloon with the design of a woman wearing stockings and a pair of arseless knickers on it? It'll cheer up my old grandad no end, particularly as he's been dead for nearly fifty years.

Bobby Bowels, e-mail

WHILE shifting in my seat to let out a particularly troublesome fart, I nearly rear-ended the car in front at a level-crossing. Luckily I managed to slam on the brakes, but followed through at the same time. Can any readers beat this lucky/unlucky escape?

Jim Evans, e-mail

FOR ALL we know, the Unknown Soldier could have been a deserter trying to make his way to Switzerland. Name and shame, I say. This has gone on long enough.

Roc Brazilliano, Portsmouth

WHY DO hospital staff insist on using a hand gel that only kills a mere 99.999 percent of germs when Toilet Duck kills a whopping 100 percent? This cavalier attitude to public safety is breathtaking.

Ross Caldwell, e-mail

FOOTBALL teams. Try and win more games at the beginning of the season so you don't feel as much pressure going in to the 6-pointers at the business end of the season.

Daniel Ben, e-mail

TRICK people into thinking you're a Londoner born and bred by wearing a Man Utd shirt.

Steve Stash, Townend

FORMULA One drivers. Put a "Baby On Board" sticker in your car and watch the drivers behind you slow right down, thereby allowing you to win every time.

TC, e-mail

RUGBY coaches. Improve your players' dodging and tackling skills, by employing *Big Issue* sellers to stand at strategic points on the pitch during training sessions.

Steve Jefferson, e-mail

SPECTATORS of US golf. Shouting "get in the hole", no matter what the volume or cadence of your utterance, rarely, if indeed ever, affects the trajectory or velocity of the ball.

Graeme Winning, e-mail

Had an accident with a sausage that wasn't your fault?

We're here to help. We are

Sausage Litigation Specialists

Sausage Lawyers 4-U are Britain's foremost Sausage Law Firm who work to get the compensation YOU deserve in a sausage related accident.

- ***Sausage skin split whilst cooking?***
- ***Been sold sausages past sell-by date?***
- ***Tripped over sausage in butcher's shop?***

Call SAUSAGE LAWYERS 4-U

018 800 8055

"A sausage spat hot fat at me whilst frying. Sausage Lawyers 4-U got me £4500 compensation" Mrs. B, Essex

"I was disappointed by the number of sausages in a tin of Heinz Bangers 'n' Beans. Sausage Lawyers 4-U got me £8750" Mrs. B, Essex

COCKNEY WANKER
Y'SEE, AR'VE GOT NAFFINK AGAINST BLACKS PERSONALLY, AR AIN'T. LIVE AN' LET LIVE AR SAY... JAST NOT NEXT DOOR T'ME...
COULD YOU WATCH THE ROAD, PLEASE?
AR MEAN, WE'RE A WHITE COUNTRY F' FAAHSANDS OF YEARS, AN' THEN THAT BOAT FROM JAMAICA TURNS AP AN WOLLOP!.. WE'RE IN A DABBLE DIP RECESSION...
THE ROAD...
WELL, YOU DON'T 'AVE T' BE EINSTEIN T' WORK THAT ONE AHT, DO YAH?.. JAST JOIN THE FACKIN' DOTS
PLEASE, WATCH WHERE YOU'RE GOING
NO OFFENCE, CHIEF... AR'M SURE YOU MIGHT BE A NARCE GEEZAH. AN' AWL THAT, BAT YOU'RE DIFFER-ENT FROM AS, AINCHA? AR' MEAN, JAST LOOK AT THEM CLOVES YOU'VE GOT ON
LARK AR SAY, AR'M NOT A RACIALIST... OH, NO, NO... NOT AT AWL.. IT'S JAST THAT IF AR 'AD MAR WAY, AR'D SEND...
LOOK OUT!!
CRUNCH
OH MAR GAWD! NO!
GAW!
SCREACH!!
OH, FACKIN' 'ELL! WOT 'AVE 'AR DAN!? IS SHE ORWIGHT!? GAWD! PLEASE TELL ME SHE'S ORWIGHT!
SHE'S ORWIGHT, WANKAH! CALM DAAAAHN!
GROAN!!
BUT, BARSTARD... AR HIT 'ER FULL ON... FULL ON!.. IS SHE ORWIGHT?.. GAWD! AR DAREN'T LOOK
LET'S AVE A BUTCHERS
GASP!!
SHE'S FINE, WANKAH!... SHE'S FINE!
OH, FANK GAWD.
SHE'S FINE...
...JAST A LITTLE SCAFF ON YER NEARSIDE WING... THAT'LL T-CAT AAHT, WANKAH
PHEW!
MAR FACKIN' HEART STOPPED FOR A MINUTE, AR TELL YER... SHE'S ONLY JAST CAM BACK FROM THE BODY SHOP ARFTER THAT BLEEDIN' PRAM RAN INTO ME ON A ZEBRA CROSSIN'
GROAN!
AR TELL YER WOT, THOUGH... YOU'VE GOT A LITTLE CWACK IN YER BACK BWAKE LART!
MY... MY... LEGS...
DO WOT?
YOS! IT MAST'VE BEEN THE IMPACT. IT SENT A VARBRATION FROO YER CHASSIS AN' CWACKED THE HOUSIN'.
FOWTY KNICKER A POP, THEM'S IS, WANKAH!
YER. AN' AR'LL NEED TWO, ELSE THEY'LL BE MISMATCHED... LOOK AWL CHEECH AN' CHONG THAT WOULD... AR'LL GO AN' GET THE MANNY OFF 'ER
'ERE... IS THAT BRAKE FLUID OR BLAD?
ER... BLAD!
FANK CHRIST FER THAT
'ERE, YOU MAPPET! YOU OWE ME EIGHTY FACKIN' QUID
I'VE CALLED AN AMBU...
CAM ON! CAM ON! DON'T JAST LIE THERE... COUGH AP, DARLIN
WHERE'S YER PURSE?..
IN... IN... MY... SADDLE... BAG

AR FINK IT'S ANDAH YER MOTAH, WANKAH
CAN Y' REACH IT, BARSTARD?
AR'LL 'AVE A GO

OLD AP... AR FINK AR'VE GOT IT
NO, THAT MAST'VE BEEN 'ER FOOT...
'ERE WE GO... BINGO!
AAARGH!
TAXI

LET'S 'AVE A LOOK... HMM. SHE'S ONLY GOT A CAPPLE OF DEEP SEA DIVERS
AS SHE GOT A CARD?
YUS
AR'LL GET YER MACHINE AAHT THE CAB
CREAK! CRUNCH!
AAARGH!
TAXI

RIGHT... EIGHTY QUID... PLAS... TWO PAAHND FIFTY CARD CHARGE... PLAS ME JOCKEY'S WHIP...
WE'LL CALL IT A RAAHND 'ANDRED

'ERE Y'GO... PUT YER PIN IN, GAL AN' PRESS ENT-AH'
I... I... CAN'T MOVE... MY... MY... ARMS
OH, FER CRYIN' AAHT FACKIN' LAAHD!

WOT'S YER NAMBAH!?
ERM... I... ER...
YER NAMBAH! AR 'AVEN'T GOT AWL FACKIN' DAY!
0... 1... 8... 1...

BIP! BIP! BIP! BIP!... BIP!
YER... THAT'S GOIN' FROO NOW, TREACLE...

SIGH!
TAXI

TAKE FER BLADDY EVAH, THESE FINGS, DUN'T THEY?
GAW!
YUS!

THERE Y'GO, GAL... IT'S GAWN FROO... I'LL PUT YER CARD IN YER TITFER, LAV... ORWIGHT?

ARE YOU GOIN' T' JAMP BACK IN, GUV? AN' WE'LL GET ON AR NART AN' DAY
WHAT!?.. NO! NO, I'M WAITING FOR THE AMBULANCE TO COME
SUIT YERSELF

...THAT'LL BE FIRTY-FREE PAAHND... PLAS ME TIP... ONLY 'AR'VE KEPT ME METER RANNIN' FROO THIS FACKIN' PANTOMARM

AR'LL WOTCH YOO AAHT, WANKAH.
YOU'RE A DIAMOND, BARSTARD
ENCAMBULAH
SCREECH!

AWL CLEAR! BACK Y'CAM, WANKAH! BACK Y'CAM...
VVVV
BACK Y'CAM... BACK Y'CAM...

VROOM!! BA-DUNK! CLUNK!
TAXI
WOT THE FACK!?

GAW! Y'VE LOST YER SILENCER, WANKAH... IT GOT CAUGHT ON THE PEDALS OF 'ER TROUT AN' PIKE
STROLL ON
ENCAMBULAH

IT AIN'T MAR FACKIN' DAY IS IT, BARSTARD?
IT AIN'T, WANKAH, MAR OLD SAN
GOIN' T' SET YOU BACK BEST PART OF A MANKEY, THAT IS

'ERE, OLD AP A SECOND, LADS...
...'AS SHE STILL GOT 'ER VISA CARD IN 'ER 'AT?
?

THERE Y'GO, GAL... TWO 'ANDRED AN' FIFTY... PLAS VAT... PLAS YER LAY-BAH!... LETS CALL IT FIVE 'ANDRED, EH?
PUT YER PIN IN AN PRESS ENT-AH!

"My psychic skills have cracked countless crime cases," says public-spirited medium Moreton

Forensic Seance!

Is there anybody there? ~ Clairvoyant medium Moreton Henmarsh consults the spirits to solve the crimes that leave West Midlands police baffled.

As told to ***Fanny Gaslight***

MODERN DETECTIVES have an impressive armoury of crime-solving techniques at their disposal. Psychological profiling, computer-enhanced forensic imaging and DNA fingerprinting make it harder than ever for miscreants to escape the long arm of the law.

But when even these high tech approaches don't lead cops to the criminals' doors, less conventional approaches can often pay dividends. And one man who has helped the police solve more cases than he cares to remember is West Midlands psychic ***MORETON HENMARSH***.

Those who have passed over to the other side are around us all the time," says the Digbeth-based medium. "They are silent witnesses to everything that goes on, but can only pass on the details of what they have seen to those of us who are blessed with the gift of clairvoyance."

"I've lost count of the number of criminal cases I've cracked with the help of the spirits, because what they tell me is the truth, the whole truth, and nothing but the truth."

Moreton says he will never forget the first time he was called in to help the police with their enquiries. It was 1976 and a man had been seen hiding in some bushes, jumping out and exposing himself to women. The local press was full of the story.

"I'd read in the paper all about this bloke who had been flashing round the back of the Typhoo tea factory. The cops had apparently drawn a blank, but they'd had a few phonecalls from people suggesting that I might be able throw some light on the case. A detective came round to see me at my flat, coincidentally just a stone's throw from where the crimes had taken place.

I told them I was more than happy to help, and began a seance there and then. It didn't take long for my Red Indian spirit guide Chief Billy Two Rivers to manifest himself in the room and start passing on information from the other side. And what he told me was dynamite.

Billy explained that the criminal didn't live anywhere near Digbeth, and was probably based somewhere really far away like Cornwall or Scotland. This surprised the police, who had expected the flasher to be a local man, but I pointed out that the spirits were never wrong.

The police made an arrest shortly after speaking to me. Nearly 40 years later, I can't quite remember exactly where the offender lived, but I do know that he accepted a police caution for Indecent Exposure. Of course, there wasn't the social stigma of having to go on the Sexual Offenders Register back in those days, so that came as great relief to the man in question. I should imagine."

"I can't quite remember exactly where the offender lived, but I do know that he accepted a police caution for Indecent Exposure"

Moreton was now known to West Midlands Police as the go to guy whenever they'd drawn a blank in an investigation. And it wasn't long before he found himself once again being called upon to bring his remarkable psychic skills to bear on another tricky case.

"A man had apparently interfered with himself at three women in the space of half an hour behind the Irish Centre.

Nobody had got a good look at him and there was no forensic evidence so the cops had really been left scratching their heads. This time they came round in a panda car and took me to the station. They really did seem determined to catch the culprit and bring him to book.

They sat me down in an interview room and turned on the tape recorder, eager not to miss the smallest scrap of information that Chief Billy Two Rivers could provide. And he didn't let them down.

Speaking through me, Billy gave the cops a top-to-toe description of the man they were looking for. He had ginger hair, an enormous scar on his right cheek and one leg. It was plenty for them to go on and they seemed confident they would soon have the offender in custody. And so it proved. Later that afternoon a man was picked out of an identity parade by a barmaid from the Irish Centre, who had seen the whole thing through a window. Caught bang to rights, the culprit quickly confessed to Lewd Conduct in a Public Place and Behaviour Likely to Cause a Breach of the Peace.

I can't recall now how closely he matched the description provided by my Red Indian spirit guide, but he was probably pretty similar. However, I do remember that he was sentenced to six months in prison, but the magistrates suspended the sentence for two years. As you can imagine, I was extremely relieved. That I had helped the police to bring this man to justice, that is. ”

"The police didn't even wait for me to open the door, they kicked it in. That's how keen they were to find out who had been stealing all these knickers and bras"

Line of Enquiry ~ Henmarsh had to call upon all his psychic skills to bring a local knicker snatcher to justice.

After aiding West Midlands Constabulary twice, with both cases leading to successful arrests and convictions, Moreton found his psychic services in increasing demand. And over the years his paranormal skills have proved invaluable in successfully resolving many more police inquiries. One such case occurred in 2006, when detectives came knocking once again following a spate of underwear thefts from washing lines on a nearby estate.

“It was the early hours of the morning when they turned up. They didn't even wait for me to open the door, they kicked it in. That's how keen they were to find out who had been stealing all these knickers and bras, and that's why they had come to me. Rubbing the sleep from my eyes, I got out my ouija board, preparing to part the veils and make contact with the ethereal realm.

The psychic forces were particularly powerful that night, as it was a full Moon, and I could barely keep a hold of the glass as it raced across the board, spelling out the information the police were after, letter by letter.

One thing that the spirits were certain of was that the spate of washing line thefts would end immediately, as it turned out that the criminal had fled abroad earlier that day. Chief Billy Two Rivers explained to the cops that it was just a few bras, pants and suspender belts anyway, and a couple of pairs of tights, so they could close the case there and then, safe in the knowledge that the miscreant was now hundreds, if not thousands, of miles away, and would definitely not be re-offending.

Peeping Tom ~ *Digbeth Leisure Centre (main image), and the police artist's sketch of the voyeur spotted peering through the women's changing room windows.*

But the police were determined to bring the thief to justice. In fact, they must have involved Interpol, because just a few minutes later a man was arrested and taken to Digbeth Police Station, where he admitted thirty counts of underwear theft. This time, they threw the book at him and he was sentenced to forty days in prison, although he was released after three weeks for good behaviour. ”

The changing room at a ladies only gym should be a place where women feel safe and secure. So when, early in 2011, a peeping Tom was spotted peering in through the windows at the back of Digbeth Leisure Centre, detectives went straight round to see Moreton.

“Twelve women had managed to get a good look at the suspect, allowing a police artist to make a detailed drawing of the person they wanted to bring in for questioning. He was described as a short, unshaven white man in his mid-to-late fifties, with thick glasses and a Bobby Charlton-style combover.

However, my spirit guide had some bad news for them. Speaking from the afterlife, Big Chief Billy Two Rivers explained that the man they were looking for was black, or possibly Chinese. Not only that, he was quite tall, well over six foot six, possibly even a basketball player. You see, when people are scared they can go into shock, and their eyes can play tricks on them, and that is what had happened in this case. Those twelve women in the changing room had experienced a sort of mass hysteria that had caused them to completely misidentify the peeping Tom.

The information the police had got from Billy must have helped, because they were able to make an arrest just moments later. Nearly two years down the line, it's difficult to remember offhand whether the sick voyeur they apprehended was black, Chinese or white. What I do know is, he confessed immediately and was charged under the Sexual Offences Act 2003. Unusually, the magistrates didn't order him to sign the Sex Offenders Register as I was he was already on it. ”

Next week...

Moreton's spirit guide Big Chief Billy Two Rivers helps police track down the notorious "No.6 Frotterer" - a middle-aged man in glasses who has been rubbing up against women on the Digbeth to Bordesley Circus bus for nearly three months.

Have Your Say

Q: Should we be forced to donate our organs?

THE GOVERNMENT recently announced plans to introduce an opt-out scheme for organ donations. If the state gets its way, docs will be able to help themselves to our body parts the moment we turn up our toes. And whilst that's clearly good news for those on the transplant list whose lives may well be saved thanks to the proposed legislation, it's not such a rosy prospect for the rest of us. After all, who wants to end up getting butchered simply for the benefit of boozers and fatties who can't be bothered to look after their own livers and hearts properly?

We went out onto the streets to gauge the opinion of YOU, the Great British public....

...They're not having any of my wife's parts when she passes on. I'm getting her cremated, and it costs a fortune, so I'm determined to get my money's worth.

Gerald Blackbeard, teacher

...Forcing people to donate their organs is a bad idea. Surely a heart given willingly would be less likely to reject its new owner than one that had been taken without permission. I've got no specialist medical background or knowledge, but I'd imagine this to be the case.

Frank Sensible, binman

...They can have every bit of me except my eyes, because I want to be able to see the angels when I get to heaven. Though I'll have to remember to take my glasses with me because I'm very shortsighted.

Justine Kirk, Insurance broker

...A friend of mine had a heart transplant and when he came round from the operation he had this mysterious craving for custard creams, and he'd never liked custard creams before. So I don't think scientists should be meddling with things they don't understand.

Ian Fantastic, dentist

...I wouldn't want any of my organs to be removed after my death, because doctors might give them to someone who I wouldn't want to receive them. Not a specific person necessarily, but perhaps a certain type of person. Let's just leave it at that.

Nick Griffin, MEP

...My wife was knocked over by a bus and the doctors asked me for permission to take her organs for transplants. I said they could have everything except her knockers. I'm not having another man feeling my wife's knockers. It happened in 1973 at Butlins in Filey and I was furious, and I'm buggered if I'm going to let it happen again."

Walter Toast, bus driver

...What's to stop the scientists taking these body parts and building themselves a Frankenstein that could go on a rampage, perhaps after being scared by some fire? I wouldn't like to think of any of my organs being involved in such an outrage.

Jim Andtenille, panel beater

...Once I'm gone I don't care what they do with my body. When my old mum died I just wrapped her up in a few bin bags and took her down the tip. These funeral directors must think we were born yesterday.

Reg Hurricane, plumber

...I saw a documentary where a man had a hand transplant and the hands had come from a strangler. When the man came out of hospital, he strangled his wife. So, whilst I think the proposed opt-out scheme is basically sound, I think people in prison for strangling should be exempt.

Mark Candlestickmaker, GP

...If I ever need a transplant, I hope and pray that Terry Wogan perishes in a road traffic accident so that I can have his heart. He does so much for Children in Need and plays so many golf matches to raise money for the Variety Club of Great Britain, that he must have a truly wonderful heart that I would be proud to call my own.

Janice Porridge, housewife

...I had a kidney transplant last year, and honestly the new ones they gave me are absolute rubbish, and I have to get up twice every night for a piss. I don't know who doned them to me, but quite frankly I wish they hadn't bothered.

Terry Alldaybreakfast, egg farmer

...Rather than making somebody sign something when they're alive, once they're dead they should just get Derek Acorah to have a quick seance in the operating theatre to see if it's alright to take their organs.

Pete Nuggets, miner

Johnny Fartpants Breaking Bad Guts
QUACK!

BREAK TIME...

HI READERS! I'M IN THE SCHOOL CHEMISTRY LAB. I'VE DRANK FOUR BOTTLES OF A LEADING COLD REMEDY I CAN'T NAME FOR LEGAL REASONS

NOW, WHEN I FART THROUGH THIS CONCOCTION OF CHEMICALS, IT'LL MAKE CRYSTAL METH...
I HOPE OLD NETTLESHIP DOESN'T CATCH ME - HERE GOES!

BRAAAAAAAP!!
BUBBLE BUBBLE BUBBLE!

WAHEY! IT WORKED! THERE MUST BE CRYSTAL METH WITH A STREET VALUE OF A THOUSAND POUNDS HERE!

BUT...
FARTPANTS! WHAT ARE YOU DOING IN HERE AT BREAK TIME? AND WHAT IS IN THAT BEAKER?
OH, ERM... IT'S JUST SOME GLACIER MINTS I'VE MADE, MR NETTLESHIP

GLACIER MINTS, EH? MY FAVOURITE! YOU WONT MIND IF I TRY ONE...
PLIK!

VWOOOOOSH!
KLANG!
WHOA! TIGHT!.. TIGHT!.. TIGHT!
CHRIST AND A BEAR, FARTPANTS. THEM MINTS ARE SOME GOOD SHIT!
...ALTHOUGH I DONT LIKE THE WAY THEY MAKE ME FEEL LIKE THERE ARE ANTS CRAWLING UNDER MY SKIN

WELL AT LEAST I KNOW THAT IT WORKS...
...NOW TO GET IT SOLD...
SCRATCH SCRATCH

SHORTLY...
THANKYOU, PLEASE COME AGAIN...
CRYSTAL METH £5 PER TOKE

YOIKS! THIS IS GREAT! I'M MAKING A RODDY FORTUNE!

BUT...
HO, MOTHERFUCKER! THIS IS OUR HOOD!
YEAH! NOBODY SELLS CRYSTAL METH ON THIS CORNER BUT US, THE SALAMANCA GANG
WHAT HAVE YOU GOT TO SAY FOR YOURSELF, FARTPANTS?
NOTHING...

I'M GOING TO LET MY BUM DO THE TALKING...

QUACK!!
SEW A BUTTON ON THAT!
GAG! CHOKE!
GAG! QUICK! DRIVE!

HEH. THAT'S THE LAST I'LL SEE OF THOSE MOTHERSHAGGERS
COUGH! WRETCH!

SHORTLY...
WELL, THAT'S THE LOT SOLD...
...AT THIS RATE I'LL SOON HAVE THE REPUTATION AS FULCHESTER'S NUMBER ONE COOK!

...AND SPEAKING OF COOK, I WONDER WHAT MUM HAS MADE FOR TEA...
...ALL THAT SELLING CRYSTAL METH HAS MADE ME HUNGRY!
RUMBLE!

BUT...
HELLO, WHAT'S GOING ON AT HOME?
POLICE
AMBULANCE

EVERYTHING ALRIGHT DAD?
NO. EVERYTHING IS NOT ALRIGHT, JOHNNY. FAR FROM IT, IN FACT

I WAS AT WORK THIS MORNING WHEN I GOT A PHONE CALL FROM YOUR SCHOOL ASKING ME TO GO ALONG AND SEE THE HEADMASTER
OOER!
OOER INDEED! THEY TOLD ME YOU HAD POISONED ONE OF YOUR TEACHERS WITH CRYSTAL METH
AND WHEN I GET HOME, I FIND YOUR MUM AND GRANDMA HAVE BEEN STABBED TO DEATH
...AND THIS NOTE LEFT ON THEIR BODIES...

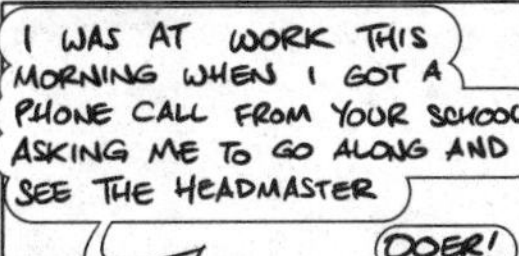

CRUMBS!
WHAT DO YOU HAVE TO SAY FOR YOURSELF YOUNG MAN?
SORRY DAD
We told you NOT to sell Crystal Meth on OUR PATCH FARTPANTS
SIGNED the Salamanca gang

WELL THAT'S NOT GOOD ENOUGH. IT'S THE SLIPPER FOR YOU, I'M AFRAID
ERK!
SWISH

SO...
OW!
OW!
OW!
WHACK WHACK WHACK!!
PSST! DONT WORRY READERS. JUST LIKE ALWAYS A PROLONGED, CONTROLLED ODOURLESS PUMP WILL GIVE MY BUTTOCKS A PROTECTIVE CUSHION - CHORTLE!
REMEMBER: ALWAYS FOLLOW THE RECOMMENDED DOSAGE WHEN DRINKING COLD REMEDY AND FARTING THROUGH CHEMICALS TO MAKE CRYSTAL METH

JASPER the CASPER
GISSA FAG!

KORF-KORF-KORF ... WHEEZE ...
KORF-KORF ... HACK-HACK ...
KORF-KORF-KORF-KORRF ...
Christmas Morn...
Mrs Gusset's Doss-AHSE fer DAHN an' AAHTS

... FUCK'S SAKE ... ONE O' THESE MORNIN'S AR'M GOIN' TER COUGH ME BLEEDIN' GUTS AHT ... AR NEEDS A BLOODY FAG ... KORF ...
WRACK! HOYLK!

... EH.?. EMPTY.?. THAT WERE A NEW PACKET O' TWENTY JUS' LAARST NIGHT, THAT WERE ... SOME BLEEDIN' TEA-LEAF'S SWIPED ME FUCKIN' FAGS .!.?.
GORN!
Premium CAPTAIN'S Extra Strong SNAAHT
SHAKE! SHAKE!

F-F-F-FFUCK!!

AR GOT TER AR'VE A FAG ... GA-A-AAASPP ... FANK FUCK FER COHEN'S 24 HOUR BACCY AN' SNUFF EMPORIUM ... PUFF ...
VOOM!

... EH.?. OH-NO ... N-N-NO-O-O-O!?
COH
Closed for the Twelve Days of Christmas... Season's Greetings!

NIST
Y-YE-E-ESS! LOOK AT THE SIZE O' THAT FUCKER!?

ONCE AR SPARK UP THIS BEAUTY, IT'LL KEEP ME PUFFIN' TILL TWELF FUCKIN' NIGHT ... HYEH-HEH ...

ORWIGHT, SQUIRE ... YOU GOT A FAG AR COULD BORRAH, 'AVE YER.?. AR WOULDN'T AARSK ... ONLY IT'S FER ME OL' MUM, INNIT ... POOR OL' MARE'S GOT THE CONSUMPTION AN' IT'S 'ER DYIN' WISH TER 'AVE A LAARST PUFF ...
... AN' SON, SHE SAYS ... YOU GO AHT AN' CADGE ME A FAG, 'COZ 'THO IT'S A CRUEL WORLD AN' NO MISTAKE ... THERE'S STILL SOME DECENT SORTS AHT THERE 'OO'D GIVE A POOR OL' WOMAN WOT'S SNUFFIN' IT THEIR LAARST FAG ...

... SO FANK YER MOST KINDLY, SQUIRE ... 'COZ YER A REAL GENT AN' A PROPAH DIAMOND GEEZAH ... AN' ME OL' MUM CAN GO TER THE AYVAH SIDE IN PEACE WIV 'ER FAG ... AN' GAWD BLESSYAH, SQUIRE ...
ZIP!

W-WOT THE F-FUCK 'APPENED THERE .!.?.
NYUK-NYUK!

FUCK.!. THE ARTFUL CADGER ... AR SHOULD 'AR'VE BLEEDIN' KNOWN ...
YOU 'AVE BEEN STITCHED AP BY THE ARTFUL CADGER

... WOT AN ARSE'OLE ... FANCY FALLIN' FER THAT OL' FLANNEL ... STILL ... IF 'E CAN BLAG A FAG LIKE THAT ... THEN SO CAN OL' JASPER ...
KORF-KORF ... 'SCUSE ME, GUV'NOR ... YER COULDN'T BE S' KIND AS TER LEND A POOR MISERABLE WRETCH A FAG, COULD YER, GUV'NOR.?. KORF-KORF ...
WHEEDLE! CRINGE!

IMPERTINENT RAPSCALLION!
OH, DO OBLIGE HIM, ALGERNON, DARLING ... 'TIS THE SEASON OF GOODWILL AFTER ALL ...
PLEAD!

YOU ARE A SILLY, SOFT-HEARTED OLD GOOSE, EMILY, DEAREST ... VERY WELL ... JUST FOR YOU ... HERE YOU ARE, MY GOOD MAN ... YOU MAY KEEP THE PACKET ...
TOSS

OH ... FANK YOU, SIR ... FANK YOU ... A SAINT IS WOT YOU IS, SIR ... A SAINT IN 'UMAN FORM, AN' NO MISTAKE ...
OH, RAGAMUFFIN FELLOW.?.
SOB!
SIMPER! GROVEL!
STROKE!

... HERE'S ANOTHER CHRISTMAS PRESENT FOR YOU ... NOW FUCK OFF!!!
GNNN!?
HOOF!

OH, ALGERNON... YOU REALLY ARE A CARD... GIGGLE... TITTER...
GNNNNUMPHHH! OOH... ME F-FUCKIN' COBBLERS!!
THWOB! THWOBB!
...PHEW... NEVAH MIND... THESE 'IGH CLAARSE POSH SMOKES WAS WELL WORF A BOOT UP THE ALBERTS... AR CAN TASTE 'EM ALREADY... DROOL...
AHH... SPLENDID... MANY THANKS, SIRRAH... A MOST GENEROUS DONATION...
!?!
W-WOT THE FUCK!?
GRAB!
...OUR BRAVE LADS OUT IN THE SUDAN WILL BE MOST GRATEFUL FOR THESE... JUST WHAT THEY NEED TO CALM THE NERVES BEFORE FACIN' THE FUZZY-WUZZIES... EH... WHAT.?.
B-B-B-BUT!?
FAGS FOR THE TROOPS APPEAL
...M-ME LUVVERLY F-F-FFUCKIN' F-FAGS... WHIMPER...
FAGS FOR THE TROOPS... DONATE YOUR FAGS...
...GOOD JOB AR TUCKED ONE AWAY BE'IND ME OL' EAR'OLE, EH... HUR-HUR...
WHISK!
THAT'S THE SPIRIT, MY GOOD MAN...
NYOINK!
ERK!?
...TOGETHER WE SHALL CONSIGN SATAN'S NOXIOUS FUME-STICKS TO THE DUSTBIN OF RIGHTEOUSNESS HALLELUJAH...
ME FAG... ME P-P-PRECIOUS F-F-FAG!?!
SOUR-FACED WOMEN AGAINST SMOKING
BAN THE EVIL WEED!
UGLY FRUSTRATED HARRIDANS AGAINST ALL FORMS OF MALE PLEASURE
BAN THE EVIL WEED!
PLIP!
THE BASTARDS... THE ROTTEN, EVIL UTTER FUCKIN' BASTARDS!!
BOOM-BOOM! BAN THE EVIL WEED... BAN THE EVIL WEED...
TOM PATERSON
AR'VE 'AD IT... SOB... LIFE AIN'T WORF LIVIN' WIVAHT A FAG... SOB...
TRUDGE!
...AR MIGHT AS WELL JUS' LIE DAHN 'ERE IN THE SNOW AN' FREEZE TER FUCKIN' DEATH... KORF...
SLUMP!
'PON MY SOUL... IF I'M NOT MISTAKEN... THIS POOR FELLOW'S SUFFERING FROM A CHRONIC CASE OF BRONCHITIS... DOUBLE PNEUMONIA... AND GALLOPING PLEURISY...
KORF-KORF... KORF-KORF... HACK-HACK... KORF-KORF... KORRF...
...THE PERFECT GUINEA PIG I NEED TO TRY OUT MY REVOLUTIONARY NEW CURE!!
KORF-KORF... EH... WOT THE F-F-FUCK... SANITORIUM...?
Dr. Scrote's SANITORIUM for the Treatment of PULMONARY, CONSUMPTIVE, and BRONCHIAL Maladies
...N-N-NO... AR AIN'T NEVAH GOIN' IN NO BLEEDIN' 'OSPITAL AR TELL YER... AR CAARN'T LIVE WIVAHT ME SNAAHT!!
BOOT!
LASH!
I MUST WARN YOU, SIR... THIS REGIMEN IS ONE OF SPARTAN RIGOUR AND IRON DISCIPLINE... YOU WILL FOLLOW MY INSTRUCTIONS TO THE LETTER... IS THAT UNDERSTOOD?
KORF-KORF... Y-YUS, GUV'NOR... G-GULP
YOU WILL BE CONFINED TO BED FOR SIX MONTHS...
KORF KORF
...AND YOU WILL BE REQUIRED... WITHOUT FAIL... TO SMOKE 100 OF MY NEW PATENTED, REMEDIAL TRIPLE-STRENGTH, HIGH TAR CIGARETTES EACH DAY...
Dr. Scrote's PATENTED REMEDIAL LUNG FAGS Efficacious MEDICINAL cigarettes
...THEY HAVE BEEN SPECIALLY FORMULATED TO CLEAR THE BRONCHIAL TUBES... LOOSEN PHLEGM... AND REINVIGORATE THE LUNGS!!
LUMME... AR'VE DIED... AR'VE DIED AN' GORN TER F-FUCKIN' FAG 'EAVEN!?!
DRIBBLE! SLAVER!
HO-HO... KORF-KORF MERRY CHRISTMAS READERS... PUFF... HACK-HACK...
PUFF! PUFF!
Dr. Scrote LUNG FAGS

NORBERT
COLON
THE MONEY-SAVING EXPERT
NORBERT IS DOING HIS END-OF-YEAR ACCOUNTS...
TSK-TSK. DEARIE ME...
THE COST OF LIVING HAS DOUBLED IN THE LAST TWELVE MONTHS... DOUBLED!

...THE FIGURES SPEAK FOR THEMSELVES. IT'S GOING TO BE ANOTHER AUSTERITY CHRISTMAS IN THE COLON HOUSEHOLD.
...JUST LIKE IT ALWAYS IS.
BALANCE SHEET
INCOME
EXPENDITURE
2012
£3728·40
1p
2013
£3728·40
2p

FRANKLY, IT'S A WONDER I MANAGE TO SCRAPE BY THE REST OF THE YEAR ON ME PITTANCE OF A JOBSEEKERS' ALLOWANCE.

I CAN'T WORK, SEE, ME. I'VE GOT A CONDITION - NUMISMATOID METACARPAL ARTHROGRYPOSIS.
CLENCH
THERE IT GOES AGAIN.

KNOCK-KNOCK!
EH!? WHO'S THAT?! SOME THIEVING GET WITH DESIGNS ON ME FINANCES, NO DOUBT.

WHAT DO YOU WANT..?
DIB-DIB-DIB! WOULD YOU LIKE ME TO CLEAR THE ICE OFF YOUR PATH, SIR?
CASH

YOU MUST THINK I FELL OFF A FUCKING CHRISTMAS TREE. YOU'D PAY GOOD MONEY FOR ICE LIKE THIS AT A SKATING RINK OR IN A FANCY COCKTAIL AT CLARIDGE'S, YOU KNOW.

SO I'LL BE BUGGERED IF I'M GOING TO FORK OUT MY HARD-SIGNED-ON SPONDS FOR THE PRIVILEGE OF ALLOWING YOU TO STEAL IT!
GO ON... DOB-DOB-DOB OFF!
WAH!

SHITE. IT'S THE POSTMAN! HE'LL BE AFTER HIS PRIVATISED CHRISTMAS BOX, NO DOUBT, AS BLOODY USUAL.
WELL HE'S NOT GETTING A BRASS FARTHING OFF ME.
CASH
...ALSO AS USUAL.

MORNING, MR COLON. GOT A NICE CARD HERE FOR YOU OFF YOUR GRANNY...
I'VE SEEN THROUGH THAT ONE. SHE'S AFTER ME LOOT.

...AND THIS SACK OF RETURNED BEGGING LETTERS YOU SENT TO EUROMILLIONS LOTTERY WINNERS BUT DIDN'T PUT ANY STAMPS ON.
THE STINGY BASTARDS.

WELL... MERRY CHRISTMAS TO YOU ANYWAY, MR. COLON.
DOFF!

...A-HEM... AND A HAPPY NEW YEAR TO YOU TOO... A VERY MERRY CHRISTMAS AND A HAPPY NEW YEAR TO YOU, MR. COLON.
A-HEM.
DOFF DOFF DOFF DOFF
A-HEM... A-HEM...

SIGH I'D BEST BE OFF THEN, I SUPPOSE. THESE CHRISTMAS CARDS WON'T DELIVER THEMSELVES.

RIGHT. THAT'S HIM FROZEN OUT. NOW TO GO IN AND COUNT THIS MONEY AGAIN WHILST LISTENING TO THE WEEK'S GOOD CAUSE ON ME CAT'S WHISKER...

WOOO-
-AAAH!
SLIP!

SMACK!
?
OW! ME HIP!

THANK-YOU KINDLY, MR. COLON... £3728·38 - THAT'S A MOST GENEROUS CHRISTMAS BOX, IS THAT!
RATS' COCKS.

20 MINUTES LATER...

HELLO? IS THAT THE AMBULANCE SERVICE? WOULD YOU ACCEPT A REVERSE CHARGES CALL FROM A MAN WITH A COMPOUND FRACTURE OF THE PELVIS?

Wife on MARS!

THE ANNALS of space travel read like a roll-call of the great heroes of our age. Rocket pioneers such as *Yuri Gagarin* - the first man in space, and Neil Armstrong - the first man on the Moon will go down in history.

And now another name is set to be added to that illustrious list of space firsts. For Leeds-born *Terry Bostick* now aims to be the first man to put his wife on Mars!

British man's Red Planet mission set to make history

The 58-year-old Hunslet lime kiln cleaner has set his sights on launching his wife to the Red Planet within the next three years. And he is now looking for backers to fund his ambitious project.

He told us: "Ever since I was a boy I've loved everything to do with space and the stars. Like every lad back in the sixties, I wanted to be an astronaut. But sadly, it was not to be as I was very never good at science and I was extremely short-sighted. That and the fact that I got expelled for burning down the school library in a foolish prank effectively put paid to my dreams of interplanetary exploration."

spaceflight

But Terry never gave up hope, and spent the intervening decades eagerly monitoring every development in spaceflight technology. "Sputnik, Skylab, Mir, the Space Shuttle... if it went into space, I couldn't get enough of it," he continued.

And the recent successful landing of NASA's Curiosity Rover on the Martian surface only served to further fire up his passion for space travel. "After seeing those amazing pictures of the Martian landscape, it was clear that it was now technically feasible to fly a human being to our nearest planetary neighbour," he said. "And I had the perfect candidate right in front of me - the wife."

cooped

NASA experts say that the journey to the Red Planet would mean spending up to eight months cooped up in a tiny space capsule, but Terry insists that this would suit his wife down to the ground. "She doesn't really go out much anyway," he told us. "As long as she's got a bit of knitting to do and a selection of Mills & Boons to read she'll be happy as a pig in shit."

hutched

"And when she finally gets there and discovers that Mars is covered in a thick layer of bright red dust, she'll think all her Christmases have come at once," he continued. "She loves dusting things, does the wife."

"She won't stop till the whole planet is nipping clean. Or until her food and oxygen supplies run out."

starskyed

Bostick admits that his excitement at being the first man to set his wife on Mars is tempered with the sad realisation that his ground-breaking 140-million-mile mission is to be a strictly one-way journey. "Unfortunately, although we have the technology to put her onto Martian soil, at present there is no way to bring the missus back," he told us.

"I will be losing a wife, but I can comfort myself with the knowledge that my name will go down in history as one of the great space pioneers."

"And I could also get myself a new wife. You can order them off the internet from Thailand or eastern Europe, and some of them are only nineteen years old," he added.

5...4...3...2...1...lift off: Bostick plans to boldly go where no man's wife has gone before.

STARS bound for MARS

ACCORDING to recent news reports, plans are underway to send a manned mission to Mars before the 2030s. And NASA are already looking for suitable candidates to man the pioneering mission to the Red Planet.

In the past, astronauts have typically been recruited from the ranks of test pilots, engineers and scientists. But in our modern, celebrity-obsessed age, is it time for our favourite STARS to take their turn and step up to the launchpad? We've drawn up a sparkling crew of showbiz A-listers to fly off into the unknown, scoring each for the unique qualities they would bring to the marathon mission. Here are our heroic seven...

Captain: John Terry.......

FOR THIS all-important role, it is important to pick someone who is capable of bringing the best performances possible out of his crew. Therefore, who better to take the helm of the mission than former Chelsea and England football captain JOHN TERRY? After representing his country 78 times in international competitions, it is now time for him to don the NASA armband and represent the whole planet.

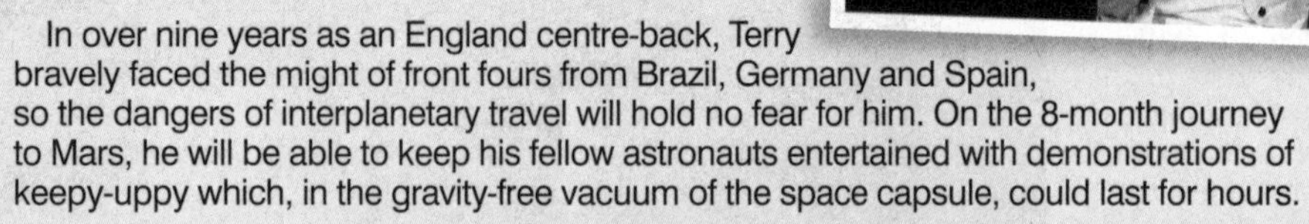

In over nine years as an England centre-back, Terry bravely faced the might of front fours from Brazil, Germany and Spain, so the dangers of interplanetary travel will hold no fear for him. On the 8-month journey to Mars, he will be able to keep his fellow astronauts entertained with demonstrations of keepy-uppy which, in the gravity-free vacuum of the space capsule, could last for hours.

However, Terry might prove a controversial choice if, as many astronomers believe, the mission discovers evidence of life on the Martian surface. If he were to organise an impromptu kickabout with the local aliens, an innocent remark referring to an opponent as a "fucking green cunt" may be misconstrued, leading to a "War of the Worlds"-style interplanetary conflict and the destruction of the Earth.

Chief Navigator: Michael Palin..................

MARS may be the Earth's closest neighbour in the solar system, but even so it's over 140 million miles away and finding the way there will be no easy task. Step forward celebrity navigator MICHAEL PALIN. The ex-*Monty Python* funnyman-turned-traveller has a proven track record, having single-handedly circumnavigated the globe several times. He also made short work of crossing the vast trackless waste of the Sahara desert, which is just like space only with sand instead of vacuums.

If he remembers to pack a dead parrot in his luggage, Palin will also be able to keep fellow crew members entertained during the journey with their favourite *Monty Python* sketch. With the sound of laughter ringing through the capsule every time he says: "This is an ex-parrot, it has ceased to be", the eight-month flight will simply fly by for the whole crew. Before they know it, they will find themselves stepping out onto the Martian soil.

But this may be where troubles begin for the zany, Sheffield-born globetrotter. An avid train enthusiast since his schooldays, Palin will be immediately struck by the lack of railway engines to spot on the Red Planet. In fact, there will be very little for him to spot at all, and he may find himself spotting red rocks, ticking them off in a little book in a desperate bid to keep insanity at bay.

Chief Medical Officer: Derek Thompson.............

IN THE CRAMPED confines of a space capsule, there are lots of opportunities to pick up bumps, bruises, cuts and scrapes. So as medical officer it makes sense to pick someone who has had a long career in a busy A&E department. And no celebrity has more experience of patching up the victims of minor accidents than actor DEREK THOMPSON who plays Charlie Fairhead in *Casualty*.

Thompson has now been pretending to be a nurse for 26 years, and it is inconceivable that over that time he won't have picked up a substantial amount of genuine medical expertise. So, if a crew member splits their head open on an oxygen duct 100 million miles from the nearest hospital, he will be able to bring all his acting experience to the fore and stitch it back together just as he would a prosthetic gash knocked up by the BBC make-up department.

But Thompson's no soft touch, having once played a bodyguard in 1970s gangster movie *The Long Good Friday.* So should the crew find themselves under attack from a warlike race of space aliens, such as Klingons, Cybermen or Daleks, he could prove handy in an intergalactic dust-up.

Security Officer: Pete Doherty........................

WHO KNOWS what dangers await any astronauts brave enough to blast off to Mars? In the mysterious void of the Cosmos, Aliens, Triffids and Predators could all be lurking, just waiting for an opportunity to attack the spaceship and take our celebrities prisoner. A security officer who can handle himself in a fight is a necessity to ensure the safety of the crew and Babyshambles frontman PETE DOHERTY is our surprising choice for the post.

Pop's bad boy is no stranger to fisticuffs, having been involved in countless dust-ups over the years with paparazzis on courtroom steps and outside nightclubs. Also, he's taken so many drugs in his time that any hideous lifeforms he finds himself squaring up to won't be half as frightening as some of the smack-induced hallucinations he has experienced whilst ripped to the tits on acid, horse and wobbly eggs.

However, NASA boffins may find it difficult to find a suitable launch opportunity for any mission with the former Libertines frontman as a crew member. There is a vanishingly-small period of time when Mars and Earth are suitably aligned to allow a successful launch trajectory to be achieved, and there is an even smaller period when Doherty will not be appearing in court on drugs, theft, assault or dangerous driving charges. Unfortunately, the chances of the two narrow windows coinciding are infinitessimally small.

Science Officer: Mary Berry.....

IN *STAR TREK*, Dr Spock was science officer of the Enterprise, but his Vulcan brand of emotionless logic and pointy ears would be little use on a real-life mission to boldly go where no man has gone before. Instead, in our dream team is filled by *Great British Bake Off* star MARY BERRY, who has perfected the art of baking into a pure science.

Here on earth where the force of gravity is 9.8kgm/s², Berry's cakes and pastries are deliciously light and fluffy. But on Mars, where the gravitational pull is a mere 3.724 kgNm/s², boffins believe they will be nearly two-and-a-half times more deliciously light and fluffy. By the same measure, you might expect any cakes she baked during the zero-gravity flight to the Red Planet to be infinitely light and fluffy, but you'd be wrong. That's because, in the absence of a gravitational field, the cake would have nothing to rise against the force of, ending up dense and unappetising.

The 78-year-old TV cook famously learnt her craft during the days of rationing, and as a result is able to whip up scrumptious desserts from very limited and unpromising ingredients. This is a skill that could well prove invaluable on a future Mars mission, where food scraps, urine and faeces will all have to be endlessly recycled to feed the crew.

Chief Engineer: Wilf Lunn........

"SHE CANNAE take any more, Captain!", "I'm givin' it all she's got!" and "I'll have to reverse the polarity of the dilithium crystals!" are just a few of the things that the chief engineer on an eight-month mission into farthest recesses of the galaxy might be expected to say. It's certainly a job for someone who can think on his feet and improvise solutions to unexpected problems using things that come to hand. And no-one fits this job description better than nutty *Vision On* inventor WILF LUNN.

With his unmatched ability to conjure up fantastic contraptions using nothing more complex than upturned bicycles, old coat hangers, spoons, string, umbrellas, collanders, candles and golf balls, the Yorkshire-born eccentric could leap into action the moment any part of the multi-billion dollar rocket's propulsion, navigation or life support systems failed. Apollo 13-style crises would be quickly averted thanks to Wilf's ingenuity and technical wizardry.

On the downside, however, his trademark straw hat wouldn't fit inside his astronaut's helmet, and were he to decide to wear it on top of his helmet, it could well float off. If one of the other astronaut's had inadvertently left a window open, the boater could drift off into space and be lost forever.

Entertainments Officer: Posh Spice................

OF COURSE, in an ideal world, all of the Spice Girls would be blasted off on a one-way 140-million-mile trip into space. Unfortunately, due to payload weight limitations, NASA scientists will only be able to include the lightest member of the nineties girlpower quintet on this mission - so POSH SPICE is commissioned as the Entertainments Officer. When she isn't mouthing along to a cassette of her hits, such as *Wannabe, Zig-a-Zig Eurgh, Tell Ya What I Want* and many others, she'll keep the crew entertained by pouting and posing in a wooden manner.

But once she gets her Jimmy Choo space boots onto Martian soil, she'll really make herself useful. For, although it's debatable whether or not she can actually sing, everyone agrees that Posh is good at having babies - four of them at the last count. And populating the virgin planet will be top of the to-do list for the star-studded seven.

However, Posh is well known for naming her children after where they were conceived, and it could prove to be a source of great confusion if a whole generation of her extraterrestrial offspring grew up answering to the name of "Mars."

20 Things you NEVER KNEW about... the RED PLANET

IF YOU DON'T count the Moon or Venus during certain phases of its orbit, it's our nearest neighbour in the solar system. For centuries, men have speculated whether there is life on it. There's even a bar of chocolate named after it that if you eat one a day of it helps you work, rest and play. It's the planet *Mars*, and it's been around since the Big Bang, so you might think we'd have its measure by now. But how much do we really know about this ball of rock that orbits the Earth in the weightless vacuum of space? Here's 20 little green facts you never knew about the Red Planet...

1 THE PLANET Mars is approximately half the size of the Earth. To put that into some sort of context, if the Earth was a football, Mars would be a football that was approximately half as big as the football that the Earth was.

2 AMAZINGLY, Mars has got not one, but two moons called Phobos and Demos, although they're not round like proper moons - they are shaped like jacket potatoes.

Galileo 1564~1642 yesterday

Phobos. Or Deimos, yesterday

3 TO COOK a potato the size of one of Mars's moons, you'd have to prick it with a fork as big as Wales before popping it in the oven for 20 million years. Or 2 million years in the microwave.

4 AND IF you wanted to fill Phobos and Demos with grated cheese, you would need an incredible 32 million billion tons of the stuff! That's enough Cheddar to fill 40 million Wembley Stadiums.

5 THE FIRST person to calculate the distance to Mars was 15th Century Italian astronomer Galileo Galilei, who announced that the Red Planet was approximately one-and-a-half billion miles away - ten times further away than the true figure. Scientists now believe that Galileo may have been looking at it through the wrong end of his telescope.

6 IN HG Wells's sci-fi classic *The War of the Worlds*, hostile Martians invaded the Earth, hellbent on the spectacular destruction of notable landmarks such as London Bridge, the Eiffel Tower and the Pyramids.

7 DAVID Bowie was inspired to name his band Ziggy Stardust and the Spiders from Mars after seeing glam rocker Alvin Stardust flicking a spider off a Mars bar before eating it backstage at *Top of the Pops*. Where the name Ziggy came from, nobody knows, and the Thin White Duke isn't saying!

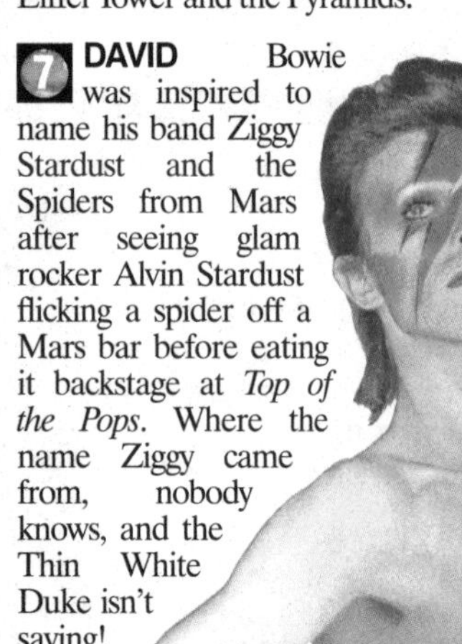

David 'Ziggy Stardust' Bowie and his Spiders from Mars (not shown)

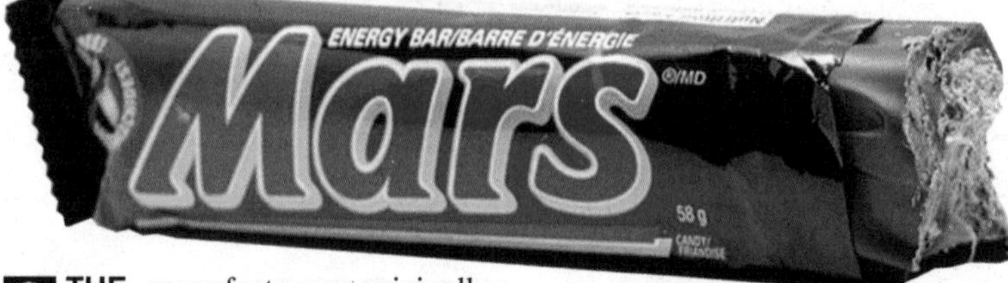

A Mars bar yesterday

8 THE manufacturers originally wanted to call the Mars Bar the "Uranus Bar", but changed their mind after focus groups felt that a turd-shaped, nobbly brown log with the word "anus" in its name had negative connotations in the snack confectionery marketplace.

9 FOR MANY years, astronomers wondered why the planet Mars looks red, but now the mystery is solved. "It's because it reflects light in the visible red part of the electromagnetic spectrum and absorbs all other wavelengths," explains D-Ream's Professor Brian Cox.

10 AFTER taking off from the Lunar surface and buoyed up by the success of their mission, Apollo 11 astronauts Neil Armstrong and Buzz Aldrin radioed back to Earth to ask if they should "press on" to Mars. But after a few hurried calculations, Mission Control in Houston decided against the suggestion, as they didn't think they'd got enough petrol.

11 ALTHOUGH Mars is the sixth biggest planet in the Solar System, it's the biggest one that begins with an 'M', beating Mercury and the Moon hands down.

12 JUST before he retired, astronomer William Herschel (1738-1822) announced his belief that Mars was coated with a thin layer of sugary almond paste. This substance, which he called "Marsipan" (literally "the bread of Mars"), is still known by that name to this very day.

13 IN HUNGARIAN composer Gustav Holst's *Planet Suite*, Mars is characterised as "the Bringer of War". It is the one that goes: *"Dur Dur Durr. Dur-dur. Dur-dur. Dah-Dah!"* whilst at the same time going *"Dom-diddly-on-dom, Dom-dom-dom-dom. Dom-diddly-on-dom. Dom-dom-dom-dom"* and ends *"Dur dur-dur-dur. Dur-dur-dur."*

14 WITH the Martian year lasting approximately twice as long as an earth year, the average human on Mars would only live to his mid-thirties before dying of old age. On the plus side, he would only have to tax and MOT his car half as often as his earthbound counterpart.

15 IN CONTRAST, a Martian day is just half an hour longer than an Earth day. As a result, were bid-up.tv to broadcast to a Martian audience, Peter Simon would be forced to prattle on about shite products for the equivalent of nine extra days per year.

16 OR EIGHTEEN days per Martian year.

17 THE MARTIAN atmosphere mainly consists of carbon dioxide, but includes 10 parts per billion of methane. This means that if you could breathe on the surface of the Red Planet, it would smell a bit like a lift where someone farted about five minutes ago.

A metha molec (shown larg than actual si

18 MARS is unique amongst all the planets in the Solar System because its rotation means that it bulges slightly around the equator, as do all the other planets.

19 NASA's latest Martian probe - the Curiosity Rover - was named after 80s synth-wave sophisti-pop band Curiosity Killed the Cat, which was the favourite group of Mission Control head Eugene Rosenkrantz. Lead singer Ben Volpolpierre-Pierrot broke off from writing songs for a comeback album to fly to Cape Canaveral, where he launched the multi-billion dollar rocket by breaking a bottle of champagne over its nosecone.

Volpolpierr Pierrot

20 IF IT wasn't so hard to get to, Mars would be the ideal holiday destination. The entire planet consists of golden, sandy beach, there's never a cloud in the sky and there's zero chance of rain. However, the lack of breathable oxygen in the Martian atmosphere could spoil an otherwise idyllic day of sunbathing.

FRY 'T.' BUNN
THE MASTER BAKER AND HIS GINGERBREAD SEX DOLLS

WHAT'S THIS..? A NOTE FROM THE MISSUS FOR ME..? I WONDER WHAT IT SAYS.

"DEAR FRUBERT, ME AND LITTLE CHELSEA HAVE GONE ON A SCHOOL TRIP TO LOURDES."

BINGO! I'VE GOT THE WHOLE DAY FREE TO SPEND HAVING GINGERBREAD CYBER-SEX ON THE INTERNET!

GAW! SHE LOOKS LIKE A DIRTY WHORE. I'LL STRIKE UP AN ONLINE CONVERSATION AND SEE WHERE IT LEADS!
BORED BILFS.COM

...NICE... MERINGUES... AND... GLACE ...CHERRY...NIPS... BUT... WHAT... ARE... YOU... WEARING... DOWN... THERE... YOU... FILTHY... SLUT?.. SMILEY FACE.
TAP TAP TAP TAP

VROOM!
BUNN

BUNN THE BAKER

TRAVEL TAVERN
FREE WI-FI!
RECEPT
BUNN THE BAKER

RECEPTION

1 2 3 4 5

416

TAP TAP
TAP TAP

RECE

VROOM!
BUNN THE BAKER

SHE'S REPLIED! "ICING STOCKINGS AND HUNDRED AND THOUSAND SUSPENDERS!" PHWOOAR! THE SEXY BITCH!

...WHAT... COLOUR... ARE... YOUR... KNICKERS?...

TAP TAP

LATER...
HELLO! FRUBERT! WE'RE BACK FROM LOURDES!
ZZ-ZZZ... WIFFLE... WAFFLE...

BIG VERN

citizens advice bureau
CAB

HI. CAN I HELP YOU?
I'M 'ERE TO SEE NORMAL, ERNEST C.
AH, YES. ERNIE. HIS DESK IS IN THE MAIN ROOM IF YOU'D LIKE TO GO THROUGH.
I OKAY. I KNOW THE DRILL.

ERM... IS EVERYTHING ALRIGHT, SIR?
JUST FACKING GET ON WITH IT. AND DON'T LINGER RAHND ME JUNK. I KNOW 'OW YOU SCREWS GET YER JOLLIES.

OH NO - I DON'T NEED TO SEARCH YOU. JUST GO RIGHT THROUGH.
OH..? RIGHT.
NOW, WHERE'S THAT FILE?

YOU CLEVER BARSTAD...
SLAM!
IT'S IN THE FACKING CAKE... AN' YOU KNOW IT!

YOU MAY AS WELL 'AVE THESE FACKERS AS WELL.

VERN! OVER HERE.

HELLO THERE, VERN. WHAT ARE YOU DOING HERE?
JUST COME VISITING, ERNIE. JUST COME TO KEEP YER SPIRITS UP... BRING YER THE NEWS FROM THE AHTSIDE.

WELL, IT'S NICE TO SEE YOU... BUT I AM VERY BUSY... LOTS OF BOUNDARY DISPUTES TO SORT OUT...
OH YEAH? D-WING TRYING TO MUSCLE IN ON YER SNOUT RACKET, EH? GETTING A BIT TASTY, ARE THEY?

IT'S MAINLY OVERHANGING BRANCHES AND FENCES AND SUCHLIKE...
FENCES? GREAT ON THE AHTSIDE, BUT A PAIN IN THE FACKIN' PROVERBIAL ON THE INSIDE, ERNIE.
CAN'T DO THE BIRD, SEE?

I SHARED A CELL WIV ONE IN WANDSWORF ONCE AND HE FLIPPED. WOKE UP ONE MORNING AN' HE WAS SAT ON 'IS BUNK EATIN' 'IS OWN FOULAGE, ERNIE.

YOU DON'T FORGET A THING LIKE THAT, ERNIE... IT STAYS WITH YER.
YES... I CAN WELL IMAGINE...

ANYWAY, VERN... I'M MEETING MY WIFE FOR LUNCH, SO I'VE REALLY GOT TO CRACK ON WITH THIS PAPERWORK...
WIFE?! YOU'VE TOOK A WIFE IN 'ERE, THEN, 'AVE YOU ERNIE?

IT AIN'T NAFFINK T'BE ASHAMED ABAHT, ERNIE. THE 'ARDEST MEN GO NICK-BENT ON A LONG STRETCH.
DONE IT MESELF... IN WANDSWORF.
JUST TAKE MY ADVICE...

...BE THE DRIVER, NOT THE FACKIN' PASSENGER. ONLY YER WANT YER 'ARIS TO WORK WHEN YER GET AHT.
ERM... RIGHT. OKAY...

TALKING OF WHICH, KEEP IT TO YERSELF, BUT I'VE SMUGGLED A LITTLE SAMFINK PAST THE SCREWS IN THE OLD SHIT-LOCKER...
...COULD 'ELP YER GET AHT OF 'ERE WITHOUT TOO MUCH...

AND YOUR SISTER SENDS HER LOVE, ERNIE. WANTS YOU TO KNOW YOUR NEPHEW IS DOING WELL AT SCHOOL. HE'S JOINED THE CHOIR AND...

IT'S A SHIV, ERNIE... A SHARPENED TOOFBRUSH... PLASTIC, SEE, SO IT WON'T SET THE BELLS OFF..!

OOH... 'OLD ON... AAGH... OW... OOPS... NEARLY THERE...
GODDIT!

THERE YOU GO, ERNIE. I SUGGEST YOU STASH IT IN THE BANK OF BOMB-BAY TILL IT'S NEEDED.

YOU LOOK STRESSED, ERNIE... 'ERE... 'AVE ONE OF ME SMOKES.

I'LL LEAVE YOU THE 'OLE PACKET WHEN I GO, NATCH.

COUGH! COUGH! COUGH! COUGH!
ERNIE! PUT THAT OUT AT ONCE. THIS IS A NO SMOKING OFFICE, AS YOU WELL KNOW!
...AND YOU DON'T SMOKE.

YOU LEAVE 'IM ALONE, D'YER 'EAR ME..?!
YOU FACKIN' SCREW CANT!

'OW DO YER LIKE THIS, EH? 'OO'S THE FACKIN' DADDY NOW, EH? EH?!
VERN! NO!
STAB! STAB! STAB!
GARGLE!

COME ON! LET'S FACKIN' TAKE THE PLACE!
OH JESUS! OH CHRIST! OH JESUS!

RIGHT! YOU WATCH THE WINDOWS... YOU WATCH THE ROOF... AND ERNIE... I WANT YOU TO WATCH THE DOOR!
BUT VERN...

...AND IF ANYONE STICKS THEIR NAPPER FROO THAT RORY, YOU BLOW THE FACKER OFF... NO QUESTIONS ASKED!
ORWIGHT!?

AN HOUR LATER...
...WE WANT A CHOPPER ON THE ROOF AND A PLANE AT THE AIRPORT WITH ENOUGH JUICE TO GET US TO MEXICO AND A MILLION QUEENHEADS IN A HOLDALL..!

TEA ANYONE..? BISCUITS..?
?

WHO FANCIES A NICE CUPPA?
GET DAHN, ERNIE! SHE'S PACKIN' A SHOOTAH!

BLAM!

WELL, ERNIE... IT'S GOODNIGHT FACKIN' VIENNA. NO WAY WE'RE WALKIN' OUT OF 'ERE NOW... NOT NOW WE'VE WASTED TWO SCREWS...
...ONLY WAY WE'RE LEAVIN' THIS DRUM IS IN A BODY-BAG, ERNIE.

WELL NO COPPER'S GOIN' TO TAKE US ALIVE...
...THERE'S ENOUGH SLUGS 'ERE FOR ONE EACH.
CLACK!

I'LL GO FIRST AN' SHOW THE REST OF YER HOW IT'S DONE.

BLAM!

EVERYTHING ALRIGHT IN HERE..? ONLY I HEARD A LOUD BANG...

You've Got FEMALE!

INTERNET DATING is big business. These days more than 1 in 5 relationships begin online, and it's a trend that's set to continue as more and more of us take to the web to find that special someone.

But it's not just singles, divorcees and the lovelorn who are turning to the net in search of romance. Place an ad on a lonely hearts site and you'd be surprised at the sort of people who reply. And one man who knows this only too well is serial online dater *Taplow Dung*.

SEXCLUSIVE!

King of the Internet Daters Reveals Secrets of Logging In!

Broadband connections: Derbyshire dad Taplow's a real-life online Romeo.

THE 58-YEAR-OLD unemployed Glossop father of fifteen has a wealth of first hand experience of the online matchmaking world. He told us: "If I told you some of the stuff that goes off on my blind dates, it would make your hair curl. Unless it was curly already, in which case it would make it go even curlier, like one of those Kevin Keegan bubble perms from the 1970s."

TAPLOW'S online blog - *dungfreeandsingle.blogs.freewebs.com* - in which he details his outrageous experiences at the singles game, has become an internet sensation, with over 200 hits since 2009. Now, in these exclusive extracts, he tells of some of the more eyeopening blind dates he's been on...

"I'd been happily married for more than twenty years and I'd never once strayed. Except for a few times when I was drunk. But when the twelfth sprog come along, I realised that the wife was starting to lose her allure a bit.

appetites

I've always been a man of natural appetites, with an eye for the ladies, so I decided to try internet dating to put a bit of the sparkle back into my love life. I typed my details into a lonely hearts site and sat back to see if any fish would take the bait.

"It was a night of passion I shall never forget. Our love-making literally re-wrote the Kama Sutra"

Within two hours I'd had a reply from a woman in her early twenties, asking to meet me. I couldn't believe my luck. There was no photograph, unfortunately, but I reasoned that she couldn't look any worse than the missus did. Having all them kids under her feet had really took it out of her. She was run down, with a nasty sty and impetigo round her nose, so I thought a break from having to look at her would do me a power of good.

I messaged my blind date and we agreed to meet that very night at a nearby Yates's Wine Lodge.

I'd certainly been round the block a few times in my younger days, but I must confess I felt a little bit anxious as I sat in the bar clutching a copy of the *Sun* and with a carnation in my button hole.

nerves

I was a few minutes early, and to steady my nerves, I started leafing through the paper. I was pleased to see that that day's Page 3 girl was Samantha Fox, one of my favourites. Her happy smile and 38DD charms never failed to brighten my mornings. I put on my glasses and leaned in close for a proper look.

topless

Suddenly, I heard a voice behind me. 'You must be Taplow Dung.' I shut the paper, embarrassed at having been caught checking out a topless stunna. But my embarrassment soon turned to shock, and then delight, as I turned to see my date.

bottomless

For it was none other than the very Page 3 bird whose 38DD assets I had just been ogling! 'Hi I'm Samantha Fox,' she said. 'But it looks like you already know that,' she giggled.

From the very start, we got on like a house on fire. I won't bore you with all the details of our date. Suffice to say, one thing led to another and we ended up back at her place. It was a night of passion I shall never forget. Our love-making literally re-wrote the Kama Sutra, and I woke spent but happy in the morning.

I asked if I could see her again, and she said yes... *for ever!*

Sam wanted me to divorce my wife and marry her instead. I felt dizzy. Things were moving too quickly and it was all getting out of hand. I explained there was no way I was going to leave my wife, as the Nash would take all my benefits off me, and the Child Allowance alone came to more than £300 a week.

unfathomable

I'd gone out looking for a a bit of fun and ended up shacked up with a bunny-boiler. I couldn't get out of Fox's swish penthouse flat fast enough, I can tell you. I made my excuses and left. And as I ran down the stairs I made myself a vow; From now on, each of my dates was going to be like a trip to Pizza Hut...

...one visit only to the gorilla salad bar."

Laptop to Big Top: Taplow's on line date turned out to be circus star who treated the Romeo to a three ring performance.

ALTHOUGH he was shaken by his experience with Samantha Fox, it wasn't long before Dung fancied dipping his toes back in the water again...

"My wife told she was expecting again and my heart sank. Being pregnant always made her impetigo worse, and this time it had spread to her ears and started weeping. I needed cheering up, so I logged onto an internet lonely hearts site to get myself a blind date. Just like before, it didn't take long for a reply to drop into my inbox.

• Pussy Galore:
32-year-old woman, slim, blonde, cat-lover would like to meet older gent for sexy fun :)

flirty

This one sounded perfect: *"Pussy Galore. 32-year-old woman, slim, blonde, cat-lover would like to meet older gent for sexy fun."* We exchanged a few flirty messages and arranged to meet that very night at a nearby Wetherspoons.

I couldn't believe my luck when I saw her. She told me she was called Katarania and she was absolutely gorgeous, wearing sexy thigh-length boots with high heels. We hit it off immediately. After a few drinks, I told her my wife was dead and she invited me back to her place.

dirty

I knew this was going to be no ordinary date when, instead of the flat I was expecting, we pulled up by a small caravan parked next to a giant red and white marquee in a field. 'I didn't tell you that I worked at the circus,' she laughed in her sexy East-European accent, opening the caravan door. 'Come inside and meet my cats.'

To cut a long story short, it turned out she was a circus lion tamer and her "cats" were five fully-grown Bengal tigers, who lived with her in the caravan. But I didn't let that put me off my stroke. We got straight down to business and I made passionate love to Katarania whilst she held the tigers at bay with a chair.

Let me tell you, if you've never had it off whilst locked in a two-berth Elddis with five angry Bengal Tigers slashing at your buttocks with their razor-sharp claws, you've literally never lived. There is something primeval and exciting about making love in the midst of a pack of man-eating wild animals The sex we had was mind-blowing, taking us both to heights of ecstasy we could only imagine.

In fact, the sex was so good that I decided to break my one-night-stand only rule, and the following evening I went back for another shot. But when I got to the field, the circus had packed up and moved on to another town. Of Katarania and her caravan full of tigers there was no sign. The lady who had tamed the restless beast within me could have been anywhere - Preston, Chorley ... even Standish.

I knew I would never see her, or her tigers again."

BEFORE long, Taplow was internet dating women every night, and the roll call of his online conquests soon ran into triple figures. But his romantic adventures didn't always work out as he expected...

"It was a crazy time. I quickly lost count of the number of one-night stands I had, but it was about 236. I had literally gone into overdrive, hooking up with lonely women on the web. I suppose it was just my way of trying to forget about my wife, who was now expecting number fourteen and had developed shingles to go with her impetigo.

"Perhaps I'd had my fill of having it off with an endless succession of pert-breasted 18-year-old airheads"

One day, I arranged a date with a woman I'd met on an online matchmaking site. Her ad read: *"Mature lady, homely. WLTM fun-loving, well-hung gent for one night stand. No strings."* I don't know why it appealed to me. Perhaps I'd had my fill of having it off with an endless succession of pert-breasted 18-year-old airheads. Maybe it was to have sex with a woman who knew how to pleasure a man. Who knows?

shirty

We agreed to meet in the cafe at Collectibles, and I couldn't believe my eyes when she walked in - she looked just like Dustin Hoffman in the film *Tootsie!* She told me her name was Dorothy and we got chatting. She explained that she wasn't married, but she had a voracious sexual appetite and longed for the touch of a man. I told her she'd come to the right man if she wanted a long touch.

We went back to her place for a stolen afternoon of passion. We were about to get down to it when Dorothy excused herself for a quick gypsy's kiss. I remember thinking it was odd that I could hear it splashing in the bowl, as when my missus goes I can never hear a thing. And I thought it was odder still when she came out of the bathroom doing up the zip on her trouser suit.

But I didn't put two and two together until she came over and kissed me and I felt the stubble on her chin. I immediately jumped up, and as I did so I knocked my date's wig off her head, revealing "her" true identity. I couldn't believe my eyes - it WAS Dustin Hoffman!

I got out of that flat pretty quick, I can tell you. I'd had a very close shave, which is more than I can say for Dustin. The whole experience left me determined to be more careful in future.

If he'd remembered to shave that morning, I could of ended up bumming him."

TAPLOW'S *Tootsie* episode shook him, and he didn't turn his computer on for a week, vowing to stay faithful to his wife, the mother of his fourteen children. But a few days later, Mrs Dung added a goitre to her catalogue of unsightly ailments, and the lure of internet dating once again proved too much for him...

"I posted my ad and waited for a reply to drop into my inbox. It didn't take long. From her description, the bird sounded just my type - a blonde, busty, full-lipped millionaire.

Imagine my delight when my date turned up at Glossop Town Hall steps and introduced herself. It was famous tit model and reality star Jordan! She told me she'd had a row with her boyfriend, and was looking to have a one night stand to teach him a lesson. I told her that was fine by me, and we went back to her place.

trousersome

Jordan and I went to bed together. She may be well known for her love of horses, but her passion was certainly unbridled that night, I can tell you. She rode me like a thoroughbred stallion, her mane of blonde hair blowing out behind her in the wind, having multiple orgasms left, right and centre, each one more earth-shattering than the last.

But then disaster struck. Her cagefighter boyfriend Alex Reid came back unexpectedly and caught us at it. He was driven mad with jealousy, just as Jordan wanted, and he literally got the red mist. He pulled me off his girlfriend and threw me against the bedroom wall.

coat-like

Now he may be one of the world's hardest cagefighters, but what Reid didn't know was that before my back went, I was in the SAS. Consequently, I'm pretty tasty in a dust up. By the time I'd finished with him, he was in the middle of next week, whimpering like a puppy. As it turned out, the sight of two grown men fighting over her affections had really turned Jordan on, and it was seconds out, round two!

This time our bout went the full distance, and my cock didn't throw in the towel until both of us were out for the count with pleasure."

Next week: *Dung's wife develops an anal fissure. And when Taplow's "Slim brunette, 25, non-smoker" blind date turns out to be Hollywood starlet Scarlett Johansson, the Girl with the Pearl Earring gets a pearl necklace to match.*

mr. LOGIC

HE'S AN ACUTE LOCALISED BODILY SMART IN THE RECTAL AREA.

hmm

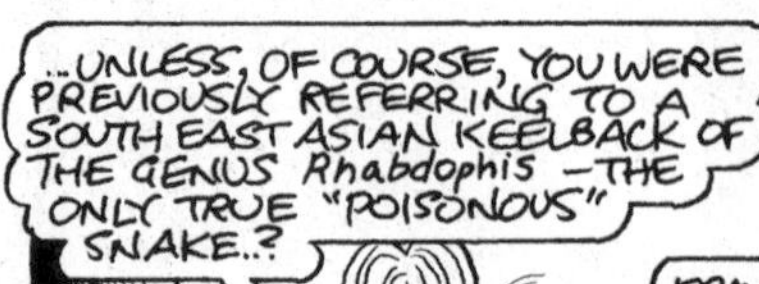

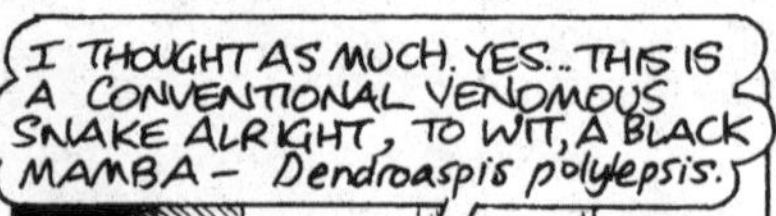

Get married at...

maplin

Because it's ***your*** big day too!

A big church wedding with all the frilly nonsense might be fine for her, but has she considered what you want?

At Maplin we can arrange your big day ***your*** way.

For many men, getting married can be confusing. But Maplin is a safe place, a comforting place, where things make sense... and where you can connect anything to anything!

So what better place to make a symbolic union between yourself (male connector) and your partner (female connector / male-to-male adaptor)?

That's why all our larger stores are now approved wedding venues, where you can be 'coupled' together by one of our Maplin Chaplains, and get 15% off cables, storage media and solder into the bargain!

here's what you get!

CCTV video of your special day & complimentary SCART cable

Choice of motion- or sound-activated 'mood' lighting

2 x USB-warmed Big Trak-compatible champagne cups

AA / AAA Batteries charged while you marry

Carabiner-fastened wind-up mini-Maglite, only £1

maplin

It's safe in here

NOTE: **We no longer marry customers to robots, either commercial or self-assembled.**

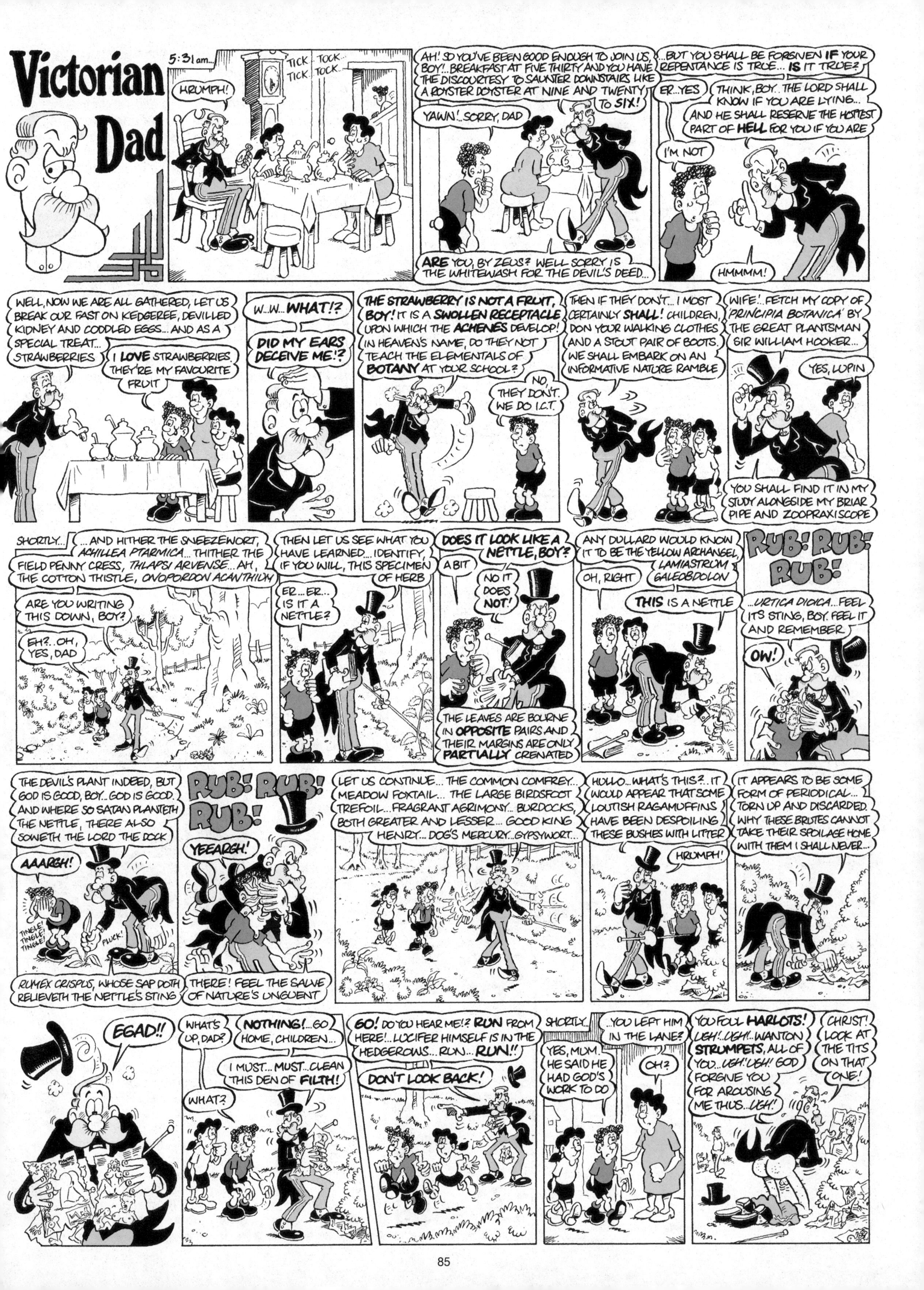

Victorian Dad
5:31 am...
TICK... TOCK... TICK... TOCK...
HRUMPH!
AH! SO YOU'VE BEEN GOOD ENOUGH TO JOIN US, BOY!.. BREAKFAST AT FIVE THIRTY AND YOU HAVE THE DISCOURTESY TO SAUNTER DOWNSTAIRS LIKE A ROYSTER DOYSTER AT NINE AND TWENTY TO SIX!
YAWN!.. SORRY, DAD
...BUT YOU SHALL BE FORGIVEN IF YOUR REPENTANCE IS TRUE... IS IT TRUE?
ER...YES
THINK, BOY.. THE LORD SHALL KNOW IF YOU ARE LYING... AND HE SHALL RESERVE THE HOTTEST PART OF HELL FOR YOU IF YOU ARE
I'M NOT
HMMMM!
ARE YOU, BY ZEUS? WELL SORRY IS THE WHITEWASH FOR THE DEVIL'S DEED...
WELL, NOW WE ARE ALL GATHERED, LET US BREAK OUR FAST ON KEDGEREE, DEVILLED KIDNEY AND CODDLED EGGS... AND AS A SPECIAL TREAT... STRAWBERRIES
I LOVE STRAWBERRIES. THEY'RE MY FAVOURITE FRUIT
W..W... WHAT!?
DID MY EARS DECEIVE ME!?
THE STRAWBERRY IS NOT A FRUIT, BOY! IT IS A SWOLLEN RECEPTACLE UPON WHICH THE ACHENES DEVELOP! IN HEAVEN'S NAME, DO THEY NOT TEACH THE ELEMENTALS OF BOTANY AT YOUR SCHOOL?
NO, THEY DON'T. WE DO I.C.T.
THEN IF THEY DON'T... I MOST CERTAINLY SHALL! CHILDREN, DON YOUR WALKING CLOTHES AND A STOUT PAIR OF BOOTS. WE SHALL EMBARK ON AN INFORMATIVE NATURE RAMBLE
WIFE!.. FETCH MY COPY OF 'PRINCIPIA BOTANICA' BY THE GREAT PLANTSMAN SIR WILLIAM HOOKER...
YES, LUPIN
YOU SHALL FIND IT IN MY STUDY ALONGSIDE MY BRIAR PIPE AND ZOOPRAXISCOPE
SHORTLY...
...AND HITHER THE SNEEZEWORT, ACHILLEA PTARMICA... THITHER THE FIELD PENNY CRESS, THLAPSI ARVENSE... AH, THE COTTON THISTLE, ONOPORDON ACANTHIUM
ARE YOU WRITING THIS DOWN, BOY?
EH?.. OH, YES, DAD
THEN LET US SEE WHAT YOU HAVE LEARNED... IDENTIFY, IF YOU WILL, THIS SPECIMEN OF HERB
ER... ER... IS IT A NETTLE?
DOES IT LOOK LIKE A NETTLE, BOY?
A BIT
NO IT DOES NOT!
THE LEAVES ARE BOURNE IN OPPOSITE PAIRS AND THEIR MARGINS ARE ONLY PARTIALLY CRENATED
ANY DULLARD WOULD KNOW IT TO BE THE YELLOW ARCHANGEL, LAMIASTRUM GALEOBDOLON
OH, RIGHT
THIS IS A NETTLE
RUB! RUB! RUB!
...URTICA DIOICA... FEEL ITS STING, BOY. FEEL IT AND REMEMBER
OW!
THE DEVIL'S PLANT INDEED, BUT GOD IS GOOD, BOY... GOD IS GOOD. AND WHERE SO SATAN PLANTETH THE NETTLE, THERE ALSO SOWETH THE LORD THE DOCK
AAARGH!
TINGLE! TINGLE! TINGLE!
PLUCK!
RUMEX CRISPUS, WHOSE SAP DOTH RELIEVETH THE NETTLE'S STING
RUB! RUB! RUB!
YEEARGH!
THERE! FEEL THE SALVE OF NATURE'S UNGUENT
LET US CONTINUE... THE COMMON COMFREY... MEADOW FOXTAIL... THE LARGE BIRDSFOOT TREFOIL... FRAGRANT AGRIMONY... BURDOCKS, BOTH GREATER AND LESSER... GOOD KING HENRY... DOG'S MERCURY... GYPSYWORT...
HULLO... WHAT'S THIS?.. IT WOULD APPEAR THAT SOME LOUTISH RAGAMUFFINS HAVE BEEN DESPOILING THESE BUSHES WITH LITTER
HRUMPH!
IT APPEARS TO BE SOME FORM OF PERIODICAL... TORN UP AND DISCARDED. WHY THESE BRUTES CANNOT TAKE THEIR SPOILAGE HOME WITH THEM I SHALL NEVER...
EGAD!!
WHAT'S UP, DAD?
NOTHING!... GO HOME, CHILDREN...
WHAT?
I MUST... MUST... CLEAN THIS DEN OF FILTH!
GO! DO YOU HEAR ME!? RUN FROM HERE!.. LUCIFER HIMSELF IS IN THE HEDGEROWS... RUN... RUN!!
DON'T LOOK BACK!
SHORTLY...
...YOU LEFT HIM IN THE LANE?
YES, MUM. HE SAID HE HAD GOD'S WORK TO DO
OH?
YOU FOUL HARLOTS! UGH!.. UGH!.. WANTON STRUMPETS, ALL OF YOU... UGH! UGH! GOD FORGIVE YOU FOR AROUSING ME THUS... UGH!
CHRIST! LOOK AT THE TITS ON THAT ONE!

FLASK ASPEL

Britain's Bubbliest Flask Forum

"Hi, Michael Aspel here. You probably recognise me off the telly. But when I'm not watching Oliver Reed doing a dance with his shirt hanging out on my chat show or presenting the Antiques Roadshow and Miss World 1973, I'm absolutely mad about flasks! I can't get enough of these thermally insulated, usually tartan, liquid storage vessels. Anyway, that's enough about me, it's time to park up at the seafront and pour out a piping hot cupful of this week's best flask letters!" *Mike*

I MADE a flask of coffee in 1975 and it's still hot today. I'd like to see a modern flask keep something hot for the best part of forty years. And I think they're letting too many immigrants in.

Jemima Ukips, Rotherham

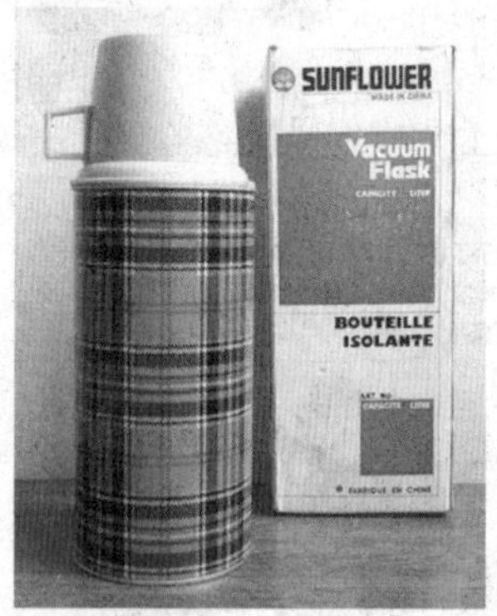

MY WIFE and I fancied having some hot soup on a picnic and we went to buy a flask. We told the shopkeeper what we wanted it for and he assured us that the one he was selling us would be perfect for our needs. However, when we got to the picnic site and opened it, imagine our disappointment to discover that the flask he'd sold us was completely empty. Likewise, there was no food in the picnic hamper we'd bought from the same shop.

Geoff Clitoris, Esher

FLASKS are a complete rip-off. A normal cup will keep coffee at a constant room temperature indefinitely. If you like your coffee hot and want it to stay that way, just increase the temperature of the room. Flask manufacturers must think we were born yesterday.

Sarson Feltch, Goole

I BOUGHT a flask once and the first time I used it was on a picnic. I didn't reckon much to it, as my coffee was luke warm and full of bits of broken glass. I've been using it for ten years now, and although the amount of glass in the coffee has significantly reduced over the years, it still doesn't keep a drink warm for more than ten minutes.

Hector Vinaigrette, Salad

MY HUSBAND and I have two flasks which we take on picnics, a blue one and a red one for hot coffee and cold lemonade. You would think that we'd put the cold drinks in the blue one and the hot drinks in the red one. But we actually do it the other way round in the hope that, if our flasks get stolen, the thieves will burn their bloody lips on the hot coffee, thinking it's lemonade.

Ada Mingepiece, Labia-on-Sea

MRS MINGEPIECE *(previous letter)* should be careful. If thieves did steal her flask and burnt their lips, they'd probably sue her, claiming negligence for putting hot drinks in a blue flask. And they'd probably win, and she and her husband would end up in prison, and have to pay the thieves compensation when they got out. You couldn't make it up. It's political correctness gone mad. We're going to hell in a handcart.

Richard Littlejohn, London

I'VE PUT a notice on the side of my flask that reads "No soup is left in this flask overnight" to prevent a hungry person breaking into it and stealing the contents when I'm not there.

Charlie Prepuce, Scrotum-under-Lyme

MY WIFE bought me an unbreakable flask for my birthday. However, after

Roy Plomley's Desert Island Flasks

Each week, a celebrity guest chooses eight flasks to take away to a desert island.

Today's castaway:
Clare Balding

1. *Tea with milk and two sugars.*
2. *Black coffee.*
3. *Tomato soup.*
4. *Bovril.*
5. *Iced tea.*
6. *Lemonade.*
7. *Hot chocolate.*
8. *Cocoa.*

Luxury item: *A spare flask cup.*

Book (as well as the Bible and the Observer's Book of Flasks): *King of the Jungle by Joe Swash.*

1 VACUUM flasks can keep anything hot, from tea and coffee to tomato soup and Bovril. Well, *almost* anything. Because, believe it or not, they can't keep Cream of Mushroom soup hot... and scientists don't know why. *"It's probably something to do with the fact that mushrooms are a sort of cross between animals and vegetables,"* says TV physicist **Dr Brian Cox**. "There's a lot more research needs doing before we can explain this bizarre phenomenom, and that's for sure."

2 THE WORD Flask comes from the Old Norse word *Fløsk*, which means Flask in Swedish.

3 WE OWE the invention of the vacuum flask to an accident. In 1868, whilst carrying out a series of experiments on evacuated glass tubes, kinetic physicist **William Kelvin** inadvertently knocked one of them off his laboratory bench and into a metal tube with a tartan pattern printed on it. As he turned to survey the damage, Kelvin brushed a plastic cup off his bench which landed upside down on the tube. And the rest is history!

4 WHEN archaeologist **Howard Carter** broke into Tutankhamun's tomb in 1922, he found alabaster flasks which had been filled with tomato soup for the boy king to eat on his journey into the afterlife. When they were open, the mummified soup was still piping hot!

5 LUMPY-faced Motorhead frontman **Lemmy** - real name Leamington Sparsworth - owns the world's largest collection of Nazi and Third Reich flasks. Amongst his estimated 10,000 pieces are Joseph Goebbels's wide-necked soup flask from the Nuremberg Rally, an insulated travel cup used by Rudolph setting about it with a sledgehammer for five minutes it was as flat as a pancake and could not hold any liquids. In my book that constitutes being broken. I showed it to my wife and told her she had been ripped off.

Hector Plywood
Hove

IN MY opinion, these 'unbreakable' flasks take all the fun out of picnicking. When I was a child, half the fun of a picnic was the excitement of wondering if the flask had broke. If it hadn't, the tea tasted all the better. If it had, we made the best of things and carried on.

Rampton Mingle
Chesterfield

I'M NOT prejudiced, but I don't think gay people should be allowed to have flasks. I dread to think what they might put in them and then a kiddy could open it. It beggars belief.

Mary Sourkraut,
Cheltenham

DON'T FLASH ME....

With flask expert Dr Magnus Pyke

● **IF THE VACUUM** in a flask is what keeps the contents warm, then how come astronauts in the vacuum of space have to wear thick space suits and gloves to prevent themselves getting cold?

B Miller, Cambridge

** There are many reasons why this is so. Firstly, the vacuum in a flask is tiny - only an eighth of an inch across - whereas the vacuum of space is millions of light years across. This means that whilst it could keep a cup of coffee the size of a galaxy nice and hot, it has little effect on something as little as an astronaut. Secondly, heat rises, and since there is no gravity in space it rises very quickly out of an astronaut. Thirdly, astronauts are much colder than coffee, on average about a third as warm, so they are nearer being cold to start off with. Finally, it is always night time in space, so there is no sunshine that tends to warm things up.*

● **IS THE VACUUM** in a flask the same kind of vacuum you get in a vacuum cleaner?

B Cox, Cern

** These two vacuums are very similar, but not identical. The vacuum in a flask has absolutely nonthing in it, not even a single atom, whereas the vacuum in a vacuum cleaner will contain fluff, dog hair and little bits of Lego.*

Send your flask science queries to Dr Magnus Pyke (deceased), c/o Yorkshire Television, Leeds, 1975.

...FLASK the FAMILY...

with the corpse of *Robert Robinson*

For mothers and eldest child only: Here is a picture of part of a flask photographed from an unusual angle. All you have to do is identify which particular part of a flask it is. Send your entries to: ***Robert Robinson, Ealing Cemetery, London.***

You Never Knew About...

FLASKS

Hess in Spandau Prison and a 0.5litre stainless steel thermos from which Hitler drank his last cup of tea before shooting himself in the head and setting fire to his own body.

6 **IN 1956**, to commemorate a state visit to Gabarone, **Queen Elizabeth the Queen Mother** was presented with a magnificent thermos flask by the King of Botswana. With a vacuum vessel hewn from a single Koh-i-Noor blood diamond, and an exterior fashioned from solid rolled white gold enamelled with a Balmoral tartan design, the flask was topped with a 24-carat plastic cup. The Queen Mum's butler Back Door Billy later recalled: *"Sadly, her majesty dropped the flask on a picnic, and because her coffee was all full of bits of broken diamond, she had me lob it in the bin for her."*

7 **THE TINIEST** ever flask was specially manufactured by the Thermos Corporation for the world's smallest man **Calvin Phillips**. Made by placing the glass from a Christmas tree fairy light bulb inside an empty .22 bullet case, the miniature vessel was painted tartan and topped off with a plastic cup fashioned from the end off an Argos biro. Phillips kept his flask in a hamper made from a Shredded Wheat, but sadly he never got to find out if it worked as, the first time he took it on a picnic into the countryside, he was carried off and eaten by a vole.

8 **ACCORDING** to pop chartologist **Paul Gambaccini**, the subject of flasks has never featured in a Top 40 single. *"It nearly happened in 1979, when Fiddler's Dram's one-hit-wonder Day Trip To Bangor reached No.4,"* says the former Radio 1 DJ. *"Sadly, however, in spite of the fact that the song was about a picnic, there was no mention of flasks, although it is safe to assume that someone on the charabanc probably had one with them."*

9 **DESPITE** being the star of several Hollywood blockbusters, including *Smokey and the Bandit*, *Boogie Nights* and *Cannonball Run*, movie star **Burt Reynolds** has never owned a flask. Except for a short period in the 1980s when he owned two.

10 **SCIENTISTS** have calculated that all the tomato soup in the world would fit in a flask the size of the Leaning Tower of Pisa. However, if the flask was tilted at the same angle as the famous tower, boffins fear some of the soup might spill out the top.

MAJOR MISUNDERSTANDING

Raffles The Gentleman Thug

ROGER MELLIE
THE MAN ON THE TELLY
IN THE STUDIO...
ROGER... WHAT'S GOING ON?
JUST GETTING STUFF READY FOR THE SHOW, TOM. ROGER'S SCIENCE KITCHEN
BUT WHY THE MICROWAVE?
ROGER'S SCIENCE KITCHEN

I THOUGHT THAT THE FIRST EXPERIMENT WAS STICKING A BALLOON TO THE WALL USING STATIC ELECTRICITY
FUCK THAT
I'M MAKING IT MORE EXCITING, TOM... I'VE DONE ANOTHER SCRIPT

'PETROL AND MATCHES WRAPPED IN TINFOIL IN THE MICROWAVE'?
YEAH! MAKES A FUCKING FANTASTIC BANG, THAT
BUT, ROGER...
YOU'VE GOT TO HAVE A FEW EXPLOSIONS TO KEEP THE X-BOX GENERATION WATCHING.
BUT IT'S DANGEROUS
DON'T WORRY, TOM... I'LL HAVE SAFETY GOGGLES ON.
AND WHAT'S THIS?... 'FUN WITH FIREWORKS'...
...'HOW TO MAKE A BANGER-POWERED NAIL GUN'... JESUS!

'WHAT HAPPENS WHEN YOU TIE TWO ROCKETS TOGETHER'...
THAT'S A GOOD 'UN, TOM. DEMONSTRATES ISAAC FUCKIN' NEWTON'S LAW OF SOMETHING OR OTHER
CHRIST!
IT'S A FUCK OF A BANG, ANYWAY. HAVE YOU SEEN IT DONE, TOM?
NO!... AND I'M NOT GOING TO, ROGER... IT'S TOO DANGEROUS.
A BIT OF DANGER'S FUN, TOM. RICHARD HAMMOND STUCK BANGERS UP CAT'S ARSES AND STUFF ALL THE TIME ON BRAINIAC

AND THIS... 'HOW TO RECREATE THE HINDENBURG DISASTER USING TWO BIN BAGS AND THE GAS COOKER...' THIS IS KIDS TV, ROGER
BEFORE YOU SAY ANY MORE, WE TELL 'EM TO RUN A HOSE PIPE OUT AND DO IT IN THE GARDEN

'MAKE YOUR OWN LIGHTNING'?
THAT'S A GOOD 'UN, TOM. YOU WRAP A ROLLING PIN IN TIN FOIL AND WIRE IT UP TO THE MAINS...
THEN YOU WAVE IT NEAR SOME EARTHED METAL, LIKE A GAS PIPE OR RADIATOR AND YOU GET A CHRIST ALMIGHTY SPARK
AND THAT'S SAFE FOR KIDS TO DO, IS IT?
WELL, WE TELL 'EM TO WEAR A RUBBER GLOVE ON ONE HAND AND KEEP THE OTHER IN THEIR POCKET.
OH, GOOD. WELL THAT'S CERTAINLY PUT MY MIND AT REST, ROGER

ON AIR IN TEN, ROGER...
BETTER SCRUFF THE HAIR UP A BIT... GIVE IT THE OLD NUTTY PROFESSOR BOLLOCKS
5... 4... 3... 2... 1... ACTION!
RUFFLE! RUFFLE! RUFFLE!
ROGER'S SCIENCE KITCHEN

HI, KIDS... WELCOME TO ROGER'S SCIENCE KITCHEN... AND HAVE I GOT SOME EXCITING EXPERIMENTS FOR YOU TODAY...
LATER, I'M GOING TO SHOW YOU HOW TO BUILD A WORKING CHAINSAW...

BUT FIRST, WE'RE GOING TO MAKE SOME NYLON... RIGHT HERE IN THE SCIENCE KITCHEN...
SUGAR
ALL YOU NEED IS SOME TURPS FROM YOUR DAD'S SHED, SOME BLEACH, AND A BAG OF SUGAR.

NOW, THE FIRST THING YOU DO IS PUT THE TURPS IN A SAUCEPAN AND HEAT IT UP ON THE COOKER UNTIL IT STARTS TO BUBBLE...
IF IT BURSTS INTO FLAMES, GET A GROWN UP TO PUT IT OUT...
...SAFETY FIRST, REMEMBER

NEXT DAY...
YES, DIRECTOR GENERAL... YES... YES YOU'RE RIGHT... YES... NO... YES... YES... YES... THE PRIME MINISTER SAID THAT, DID HE?... OH... THE UNITED NATIONS!?... IT'S GONE THAT FAR?...
YES... I WILL... GOODBYE.

LOOK AT THIS, TOM... IT'S IN ALL THE PAPERS... FOUR SPREADS IN THE SUN...
...YOU CAN'T BUY PUBLICITY LIKE THAT!
YOU KNOW, ROGER, YOU'RE RIGHT... YOU CAN'T...
RECORD COMPLAINTS AFTER SICK TV SHOW
FOR ONCE I AGREE WITH YOU

I'VE GOT SOME GREAT STUFF LINED UP FOR THE NEXT SHOW, TOM... HOW TO UNBLOCK A SINK USING A BAG OF FERTILISER, A SPARK PLUG AND A PP3 BATTERY... WHAT DO YOU RECKON?
HMM...
I'M SURE IT WOULD'VE BEEN SPECTACULAR, ROGER, BUT THERE ISN'T GOING TO BE A NEXT SHOW

ROGER'S SCIENCE KITCHEN HAS BEEN CANCELLED
CANCELLED?
WHAT THE FUCK FOR, TOM?

BEATS ME, ROGER... PERHAPS THE DG'S DECISION HAS SOMETHING TO DO WITH 70 HOUSES BEING BURNT TO THE GROUND AND 200 CARS BEING BLOWN UP LAST NIGHT
FUCKING CHICKENS! ANYTHING A BIT EDGY AND THE BBC SHIT THEIR PANTS. I SHOULD'VE TAKEN IT TO CHANNEL 5

I DON'T THINK THEY WOULD HAVE DONE ANY DIFFERENT, ROGER... SIX THOUSAND CHILDREN ADMITTED TO CASUALTY UP AND DOWN THE COUNTRY WITHIN AN HOUR OF THE SHOW GOING OUT...
SIX THOUSAND?
SIX THOUSAND, ROGER...

...ACCORDING TO THE PAPERS, BRITAIN'S A & E UNITS HAVE NEVER BEEN SO OVERSTRETCHED AS THEY WERE LAST NIGHT.
REALLY? FUCKING HELL...
...I'VE JUST HAD A FUCKING GREAT IDEA FOR A SHOW, TOM

HELLO, AND WELCOME TO FULCHESTER INFIRMARY FOR 'ROGER'S KIDDIE A & E LIVE!'... AND IT'S BEEN AN EXTREMELY BUSY NIGHT FOR ALL THE STAFF...
X-Ray
...BUT LET'S HAVE A WORD WITH SOME OF THE PATIENTS...

...SO WHAT HAPPENED TO YOU YOUNG MAN?
I WAS BOILING SOME TURPS ON THE COOKER
YOU WERE BOILING TURPS ON THE COOKER?...
...TUT! TUT! TUT!... WELL THAT WAS A SILLY THING TO DO, WASN'T IT, EH?

Lett's Takes a look at... The British Seasi

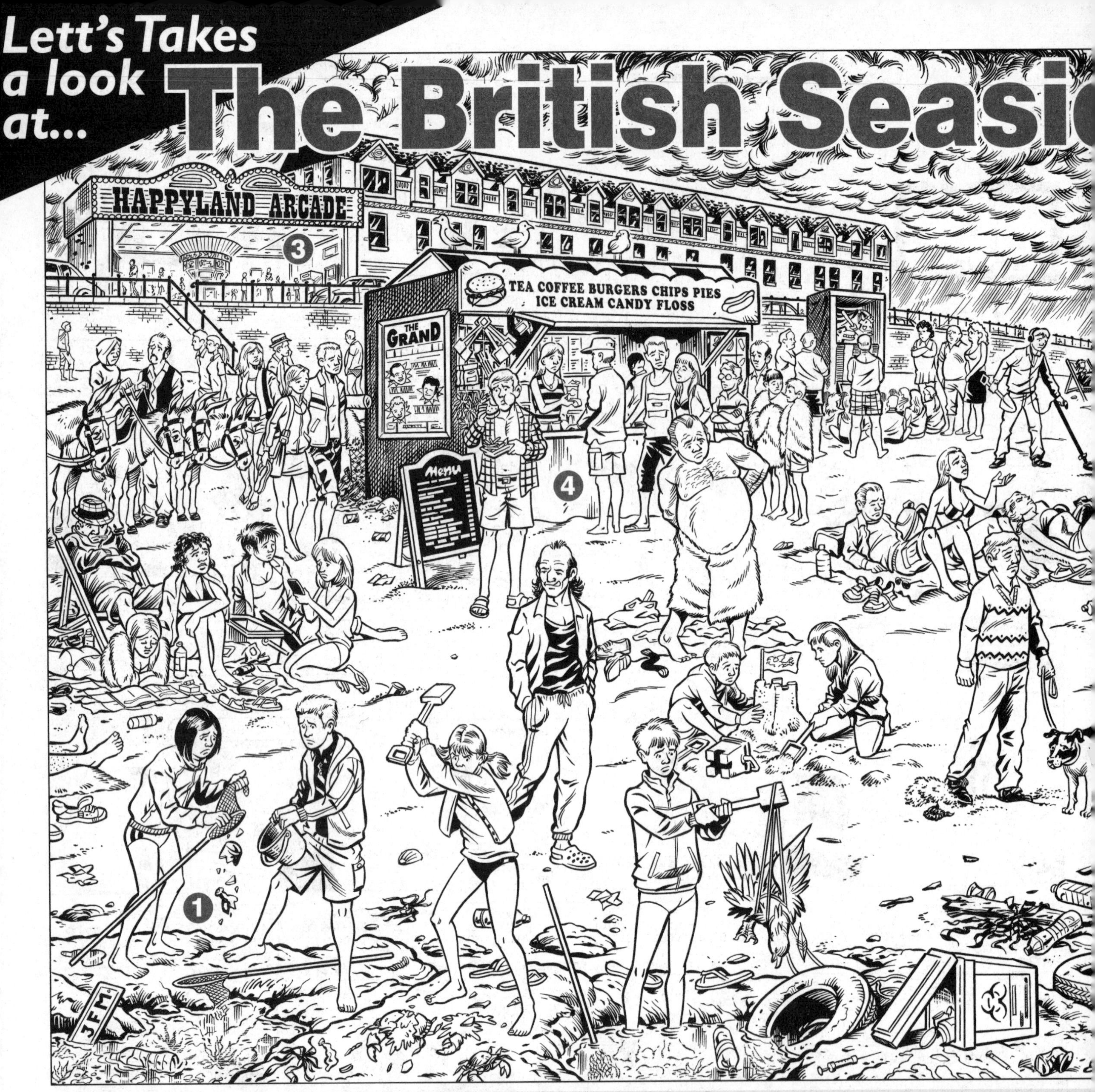

1 The Rock Pool

MANY HAPPY hours can be spent fishing about in rock pools, searching for the fascinating treasures mother nature has left behind when the tide goes out. Seahorses, shrimps, colourful anemones and eels all make their homes in the tidal rock pool. Although probably not in this country. Here, your net is more likely to ensnare a broken beer bottle, a dead crab or the remains of a seagull caught in orange fishing line. But wait, is that a strange species of jellyfish bobbing about in the pool waiting for the next tide to take it back out to sea? No, it's a used rubber johnny with a knot tied in the end.

2 The Pier

NO BRITISH seaside town is complete without a pier. These Victorian monuments to the golden age of leisure are the jewels in the crown of our coastal resorts. Their mile-long fingers stretching out to sea are almost a town in themselves with their elegant boardwalks, shops, cafes, theatres and amusement arcades. But after a hundred years of sitting in salt water, braving all the elements nature can throw at them, many are sadly in desperate need of expensive repair. Unfortunately this one caught fire in the early hours of the morning. Luckily the owner took out a generous insurance policy on it just the day before.

3 The Amusement Arcade

WITH THEIR flashing lights, ringing bells and chances of hitting the jackpot, who can resist the allure of the amusement arcade? Each one of these pleasure palaces has all the glamour and excitement of a mini Las Vegas, right here on our doorstep. And where else could a family of five shelter from the rain for an hour and keep themselves amused for less than £80 per head? But what to do? There is something to keep the most demanding holidaymaker happy. Mum may want to try the crane grab, with its grip just too feeble to lift that packet of 20 Consulate with the 1970s £5 note elastic banded to it. The kids will make for the tuppenny waterfalls, with their heap of permanently glued coins hanging tantalisingly over the edge of the sweeper. Nan will surely settle at the bingo counter in the hope of getting a fu house and winning a toilet roll cosy which would have cost her 50p at the indoor market. Whilst dad will happily feed a week's wages into the fruities, using all his skill and judgement in an attempt to win the jackpot on a machine that is programmed to pay out 74.8p for every pound put in.

4 The Beach Shop

THE BEACH shop is the hub around which any day at the beach revolves. As long as it's open, which it won't be for a goo ten months of the year. Or on Sundays or Bank Holidays. And some other times. Here is where the fun really starts. Forget rollercoasters, log flumes and big budget thrill-rides, for holiday memories they'll never forget, kids only need a simple bucket and spade and a few paper flags with Welsh dragons on them. And when they've had enough of building sandcastles, after about three or four minutes tops, they can use their spade to smash crabs. If the wind gets up, why not splash out on a super stunt kite for half an hour's fun running up and down the beach e

ASK ANY CHILD where they want to go on their summer holiday and they won't tell you Benidorm, Florida or Disneyland. They'll say Blackpool, Filey or Skegness. Because we Brits do like to be beside the seaside, oh we do like to be beside the sea. Nowhere on earth can match this country's beaches for fun, frolics and entertainment. There's always something to keep us amused from from sun up till sun down, whether we're 9 or 90. A fortnight is never long enough to fit in every attraction the British seaside has to offer. So let's take a stroll along the prom, prom, prom and take a closer look at a typical British seaside resort...

ragging it along the sand before tossing its broken, tangled emains aside?

5 In the Sea

STEP INTO the invitingly warm waters of the Aediterranean or the Aegean, and you risk being stung to death y jellyfish, bitten in two by a shark, or even worse, having tropical stickleback swim up your jap's eye. It's simply too angerous to take the risk. But there are no such fears when you enture into the bracing waters of the British seaside. Even at the eight of the summer the water remains refreshingly marrow-hilling, too cold for any exotic predator, or indeed bather, to urvive for more than a few minutes. Other than hypothermia, he only risk a British swimmer runs is the ingestion of a floating urd or sanitary towel. For, although the waters around our island re some of the cleanest in the world, the tide can bring back all orts of unwanted flotsam from the untreated sewage discharge ipes which dot our coastline, placed the legal minimum distance ut to sea.

DID YOU SPOT...?

- *A couple being mobbed, pecked and shat on by angry seagulls whilst trying to share a cone of chips*
- *A poster for the local theatre advertising a show featuring three people now being questioned as part of Operation Yewtree*
- *An irresponsible dog owner making a "barker's Scotch egg" by nonchalantly kicking sand over his pet's recently-deposited feeshus*
- *A metal detector enthusiast sweeping the sand for lost valuables which he can then hand in at the police station*
- *A deluded surfer in a wetsuit*
- *A herd of exhausted donkeys spending their last days at work before a well-earned retirement at a glue factory*
- *A man whose children buried him in sand earlier in the day, getting crosser and crosser as he vainly searches for his car keys*
- *A family huddled together for warmth behind a windbreak, desperately trying to stave off the onset of frostbite*
- *A young woman desperately searching for somewhere to have a piss in the dunes, because the sea's too cold and public toilets are a mile-and-a-half away. And closed.*
- *A couple of bored children poking a dead jellyfish with sticks*
- *A 56-year-old, 20-stone man modestly struggling to get changed inside a beach towel, as if everyone is desperate to catch a glimpse of him naked*
- *A local man who lives with his mum, who spends the whole of May to August walking up and down the beach, smiling at children and licking his lips*
- *A Liberian registered container ship flushing out its diesel tanks with seawater*

TOP TIPS

A STAG makes an excellent place to hang your coat in a forest.
Stratford Bellend, Cromer

BAGGAGE handlers at airports. Why not put massive blocks of sushi on the conveyor belt? Or sushi restaurants could put little suitcases on their conveyor belts so as hamsters could pretend that they're at the airport or something. I have to admit, I haven't really thought this one through properly.
Marvin Chickweed, Bolton

COMMUTERS. Get more value for money by sitting on top of the bus. Considering the circumference of the earth, you will travel 0.0000000013% further than your fellow passengers downstairs who have paid the same fare.
H Broomhandle, Wales

SCRABBLE players. Before each game ensure you engage in a little smalltalk with your competitors, saying what a ziquyiv day it's been, and how you're feeling extremely voxy, kiq and jjxkeee.
Brandreth Piles, Crawley

MOURNERS. Comfort grieving relatives at funerals by telling them what a massive bell-end the deceased was so that they don't feel so bad that they have gone.
Milford Boots, Bucks

DOG owners. Walk your pooch from the comfort of your home by tying the flex from your hoover to his collar and sending him out on his own. When its time for him to return, simply press the cord rewind button and he'll come whizzing back.
Stan Blowfly, Standish

QUAVERS make ideal saddles for seahorses. Except that they float and tend to disintegrate in the water.
Ada Scroffula, Preston

LOST your coat in a forest after hanging it on a stag? Simply make a noise like a female red deer in heat and at some point your coat will be delivered back to you.
Stratford Bellend, Cromer

LETTERBOCKS

Viz Comic P.O. Box 841
Whitley Bay NE26 9EQ
letters@viz.co.uk

I THINK sex offenders should be remedially forced to watch posh, middle class people like David Mitchell and Victoria Coren having sex. Rather than watching common German couples thrashing about, shouting "Oooh ja, das is gut," it would considerably cool their ardour to see couples paying obsessive attention to the rounding of vowels and the correct pronunciation of expletives. In my opinion, seeing the celebrity pair working on a post-coital *Times* Crossword rather than the usual money-shot facial might well do the trick and cure them of their aberrant behaviour.
Bartram Ohms, Surrey

WHY are blokes called Jerry always synonymous with conflict? There's Jeremy Kyle, Jerry Springer, Jeremy Paxman and Jerry out of *Tom and Jerry* - and let's not even mention the war. Come on Jerrys of the world, a bit of civility costs nothing.
Bartholamew Roberts, Hull

BEING a staunch royalist, I think the Queen does a marvellous job. But on the other hand if she were to pass on I would get a day off work. An alive monarch or a long lie-in followed by a case of beer and a full day of internet porn? Its a tough one, but I think the alcohol and wanking just shades it. Sorry, ma'am.
Tam Dale, e-mail

STAR LETTER

LAST week I arrived at a motorway petrol station and squeezed off thirty quid's worth of unleaded. Imagine my embarrassment when I went in to pay and realised that I had forgotten my wallet. Things quickly went from bad to worse when the irate petrol station manager pointed out that I had also forgotten my car.
Hector Ampere, Notts

WITH reference to David Wharton's letter *(page 64)*, what is it with pandas? I've just read that a lady panda was inseminated because it failed to mate. Apparently they have a mating window of just a few hours each year during a two week period in April/May. They only eat one food, they are generally lazy, they can't be arsed, and they are way too fussy. Let them go extinct, I say. I saw the pandas at Edinburgh zoo and they were rubbish. Nearly every other animal there was better and more interesting. Fuck them, they've had their chance. There are still plenty of other bears doing just fine for us to enjoy, such as black, koala, grizzly, teddy, polar etc.
Bertram Twatflap, e-mail

I THINK all these Christians who are against gay marriage are probably all closet homosexuals themselves, and are just trying to create a smokescreen to prevent themselves being outed. The phrase 'the lady doth protest too much' springs to mind, and I think they are right.
Morten Breadboard, Leeds

WHEN my girlfriend tells me she's "got the painters in," I understand the euphemism and I know that sex is off the menu for a few days. So imagine my surprise when after telling me just that last night, I called round to her flat for a simple game of Scrabble and discovered her with two blokes in bib & brace overalls. And they were giving her a double penetration over a pasting table.
Trevor Cardboard, Hull

BEING a teacher is low-paid, hard and stressful work. But one perk it has is that I can fart all day and blame it on the kids.
Agnes Celcius, Truro

NOW that most kids write in 'text speak', shouldn't Heinz be removing a few superfluous letters from their Alphabetti Spaghetti and reducing the price?
Ann Bonny, Southampton

THERE'S a chef on telly who, in my opinion, looks like the kind of man who hits his wife. Obviously I can't say name him for legal reasons, but I suspect he knows who he is.
Ada Velocity, Cardiff

I RECENTLY got kicked out and barred from a branch of Timpsons shoe shop. Have any other of your readers been barred from such a crap place?
Dibs, e-mail

I LOOKED in the mirror while I was shaving this morning and noticed that I am actually left-handed. You live and learn, don't you?
Bob Millar, e-mail

THEY say that you are significantly more likely to die in hospital on a Friday than you are on a Monday. Well obviously, you are five days older on a Friday. What do these statisticians get paid for?
John Gillard, e-mail

WHILST at work, I picked up a packet of 3 bourbons, but to my amazement there were only 2 bourbons in the packet, which was sealed. Have any of your readers had an exciting biscuit-related event at work?
Richard Tea, e-mail

HISTORIANS are always banging on about the military genius of Alexander the Great and Julius Caesar. But can they be sure they were really that good? There were no alarm clocks in those days, so it could just be that the other side had overslept. Watches hadn't been invented either, so they couldn't even stop someone to ask what time the battle kicked off.
Rosemary Becquerel, Luton

JAMES Bond seems to have sex with every woman that he comes in contact with. I wonder if he gave the Queen a quickie when he appeared with her in that film before the opening ceremony of the Olympics.

Hampton Charlesworth, Tooting

TO add a little spice to our love life, I like to pretend my wife is a robot when we have sex. I wrap her in tin foil, put a couple of metal lemon squeezers on her breasts, a colander on her head, a spring in each ear and off we go.

Bramley Apples, Herts

WITH reference to Mr Apples' letter *(above)* about pretending his wife is a sex robot, how do we know these things don't actually exist? Can we be absolutely sure that scientists haven't invented a realistic sex robot and they aren't just keeping it 'for testing' for themselves? Is anyone actually looking into this?

Umberto Kelvin, Glasgow

** Well, readers, do YOU think scientists have invented a sex robot and are trying to keep it for themselves? Maybe you work in a lab where one of your colleagues is very secretive about what he does. Perhaps you've spotted a scientist rushing furtively into a laboratory undoing his trousers. Or maybe you've seen a scientist drop his briefcase on a bus and all robot women's tits and fannies fell out and rolled down the aisle. Write to the usual address and mark your envelope or e-mail "I think scientists have invented a sex robot."*

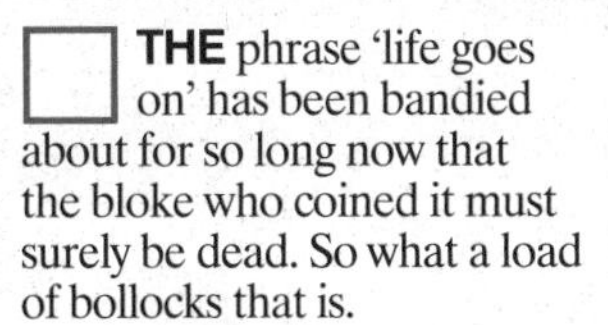

THE phrase 'life goes on' has been bandied about for so long now that the bloke who coined it must surely be dead. So what a load of bollocks that is.

Gary B, Southampton

SO, politicians and local councillors want us to vote with our feet, do they? Well I tried it earlier this month at the council elections but the little pencil was too thin for my toes to grip and I made a right fuck up of the polling card and they wouldn't let me have another go. Happy now?

Stanley Coulomb, Dudley

WILDLIFE film makers are constantly banging on about how rare it is to see a snow leopard. Might I suggest that they try looking for one somewhere where it doesn't snow, then they'll be somewhat easier to spot?

Hector Joule, Leeds

HIS Holiness the Pope recently performed an exorcism on a disabled man in St Peter's Square. The man shuddered slightly and slumped a bit in his wheelchair, and that was it. I was most disappointed at this poor performance. When Max Von Sydow exorcised that girl on the telly, she floated up to the ceiling, her head spun round and gallons of green vomit spewed all over the room. I had hoped for much more from his Holiness and now regret voting for him.

Cardinal Seamus O'Nonce, Vatican

WHY don't people in soaps ever close the fridge door slowly to see if the light goes out? We've all done it so why don't they? Come on, soap writers, a little realism, please.

Ross Kennett, e-mail

I AGREE with Mr Kennett *(above)* about the lack of realism in soaps. When characters have a shave, they just do it all in one go. They never leave themselves a little Hitler moustache like everybody does, just to see what it looks like, before completing the job.

Frank Sievert, Wapping

THE previous two correspondents have hit the nail on the head, realism in soap operas has hit an all-time low. I can't remember the last time I saw a character in the toilet of the Queen Vic or Rover's Return seeing how far back he could stand from the urinal, or pinching his foreskin to make it all balloon up whilst having a piss.

Renton Hertz, Cheam

I JUST found a chicken nugget shaped exactly like the former president of The United States of America Bill Clinton, but ate it before I took a photo. I don't care if you don't believe me.

Rossco Peako, e-mail

I WISH these fundamentalist terrorists wouldn't keep pointing their fingers at the camera when making their threats on the telly, it's a very impolite thing to do. I've got nothing against them making their hate-filled diatribes towards the west, but there's no need to be rude about it.

Dolly Newtons, Tring

Looking for an Exciting challenge in your Gap Year? Why not become a PIRATE!

The **British University Pirate Sabbatical Association** have 1000 places for pre-university students to experience life on the sea as a feared swashbuckler. With over 250 ships flying the BUPSA skull and crossbones plying the trade routes off the coast of west Africa, it's a great chance to have fun, meet people and make money.

Just look at these advantages:

- ***Fully inclusive accommodation including hammock, grog and ship's biscuits.***
- ***Earn up to 500 pieces of eight TAX FREE every week.***
- ***Plenty of spare time to play the concertina.***
- ***Bulks out your UCAS personal statement.***

Places on this exciting project are limited so apply now. If you are starting university this year, your place may be deferred.

"I joined the crew of The Devil's Mermaid after my A levels. After just 10 months I'd made enough to pay my first year's tuition fees and half the cost of my first year's accommodation in halls of residence."

J.D., Bioarchaeolgy, York

"I thought there'd be a lot of clambering about the rigging and walking the plank. But we were armed with machine guns and mainly attacked oil tankers and container ships. It was great fun."

J.A., Maths, Durham

"I made loads of new mates aboard The Black Barnacle. I learned lots of new skills and even got to kill someone on my first day. It was great preparation for my degree in Medieval History at Exeter Uni."

R.L., Med. History, Exeter

Please send me details of the British Universities Pirate Sabbatical Scheme.

Name............................ Address ....

....Post Code ....

Beard colour..................Expected A Level Grades......................

I am interested in: ☐ travel ☐ knots ☐ maps ☐ burying things ☐ doubloons ☐ running people through

BUPSA welcomes applications from disabled students, particularly those with one leg or one eye. Or a hook for a hand.

BUPSU, The Dockyard, Bristol

WHENEVER I walk past a pot or a lamp I always give it a rub in case a genie pops out and grants me three wishes. It hasn't happened yet, but you never know.

Edna Cheese, Dorking

HOW come Stephenson's Rocket was named after a type of spaceship that hadn't been invented at the time? Come to think of it, why did spaceship inventors name their rockets after a shit old train?

James Brown, Edinburgh

IF scientists want to know how to solve global warming, why don't they just go on Wikipedia like the rest of us? It would save a fortune in all this research money. And while they were at it, they could check what the name of that actor is in that film. The one with the hair who does that thing with his mouth.

B Microcurie, Hull

TOP

PASTY British tourists. Save time achieving that authentic sunburnt look by aggressively rubbing your body with sandpaper before you go on holiday. Complete the effect by applying some deep heat rub.

Simon Hoffman, e-mail

ARCHAEOLOGISTS. Double the amount of artefacts you find by using a spade twice as big.

Hector Littleparts, Dudley

CONVINCE people down at your local that you're an extra on *Emmerdale* by standing by the dartboard in a woolly hat, nodding and chatting to nobody in particular all night.

Talbot Rothamstead, Surrey

TOURETTES sufferers. When you suddenly shout a profanity during a conversation, immediately follow it up with "I forgot to switch off the gas."

D Williams, Donegal

POUR sand into your shower gel bottle and Hey Presto! 'Exfoliating wash'.

Richard Karslake, e-mail

TOUPÉE owners. Keep warm during the winter months by turning your wig inside-out before affixing it to your pate.

Gerry Paton, e-mail

PORK medallions make ideal prizes for any butcher competitions.

Alan, e-mail

A CORKSCREW makes a perfect prosthetic tail for a pig. And it means that it can open bottles with its arse, which is a better trick than my mate Dave can do.

Mickey Spikeytop, Chorley

HOUSEWIVES. Make dusting in hard-to-reach places a doddle by sellotaping a pigeon to the end of a bamboo cane. Hey presto! An automatic duster.

Lambton Worm, Durham

GILBERT
RATCHET
EASTER EGG
FINDER-
O-MATIC
DJ '13

SLURPAROONIE! WE'RE ABOUT TO HAVE OUR TRADITIONAL FAMILY EASTER SUNDAY DINNER...
...A GIANT CHOCOLATE EGG STUFFED WITH MORE CHOCOLATE EGGS, AND SERVED ON A BED OF CHOCOLATE EGGS!

NO CHOCOLATE EGG FOR YOU, DAD — JUST THIS TINY FRAGMENT OF LETTUCE
WHA-?! WHAT'S THIS?

STAY AWAY FROM THE CAKE! REPEAT: STAY AWAY FROM THE CAKE!
STOP EATING YOU FAT FUCKS
HAVEN'T YOU HEARD? WE ARE IN THE MIDST OF AN OBESITY CRISIS!
IF BRITISH MEN DON'T LOSE SOME WEIGHT, THE WHOLE COUNTRY IS GOING TO COLLAPSE!

BAH! IT'S NOT FAIR! I WANT TO EAT CHOCCY EGGS!
CHOMP SCOFF!
SURELY THERE'S A WAY OF LOSING WEIGHT THAT DOESN'T INVOLVE HEALTHY EATING AND EXERCISE

LOOK DAD — ALL THE DAFT CELEBRITIES USE COLONIC IRRIGATION TO SHED A FEW POUNDS
OK! MY ENEMA JOY
APPARENTLY IT FLUSHES ALL THOSE INCREDIBLY HEAVY BITS OF WASTE MATTER RIGHT OUT OF YOUR BODY!

WELL IT SOUNDS PREFERABLE TO LETTUCE; BUT IT DOES APPEAR TO BE RATHER EXPENSIVE.
LUXURY HEALTH SPA
DON'T WORRY DAD — I'LL KNOCK YOU UP A HOME-MADE COLONIC IRRIGATOR FOR FREE!

IN THE BACK YARD
I'VE ATTACHED A STIRRUP PUMP TO OUR OLD WATER TANK, AND STUCK THE HOSE UP DAD'S BUM.
ARE YOU READY TO HAVE THE WATER PUMPED INTO YOUR BOWELS, DAD?
AS I'LL EVER BE, GILBERT.

PUMP! PUMP! PUMP!
HANG ON A MINUTE, SON...
...SURELY THATS OUR OLD WATER TANK, OVER THERE.

HOY! WHAT ARE YOU DOING WITH OUR LARGE TANK OF BITUMEN?!
PUMP! PUMP! PUMP! PUMP!
EH?
WE NEED THAT TO RESURFACE THE ROAD!

YOU IDIOT, GILBERT! YOU'VE PUMPED FIFTY GALLONS OF ASPHALT INTO MY GUTS!
IF ANYTHING, IT HAS MADE ME HEAVIER THAN EVER!

HM! MAYBE IT'S NOT YOU THAT IS TOO HEAVY, DAD — MAYBE IT'S THE PLANET EARTH!
HUNH? WHAT DO YOU MEAN?

WELL, YOUR WEIGHT IS A MEASURE OF THE EARTH'S GRAVITATIONAL PULL ON YOUR BODY. A LARGE PLANET HAS MORE GRAVITY.
ω=mxg
DAD
GRAVITY
EARTH
IF THE EARTH WAS SMALLER, ITS GRAVITY WOULD BE REDUCED AND CONSEQUENTLY YOU WOULD WEIGH LESS!

I'LL CONSTRUCT A PLANETARY LIPOSUCTION DEVICE, WHICH WILL SUCK OUT SOME OF THE EARTH'S EXCESS "FLAB" AND DECREASE ITS GRAVITATIONAL FORCE
SUPER POWER VAC
GREAT! I'LL LOSE WEIGHT IN NO TIME!

THE EARTH IS A FAT BASTARD WEIGHING OVER SIX SEXTILLION TONS, DAD.
SHLURP! SHLURP!
SUPER POWER VAC
IT MAY TAKE A WHILE TO SLIM IT DOWN.
RIGHT. I'LL SIT ON THIS OLD BIT OF PIPING AND WAIT.

WE'LL SOON HAVE THIS "GLOBAL OBESITY" PROBLEM SOLVED, DAD!
SUPER POWER VAC
SHLURP! SHLURP!
OLD 'L'-SHAPED PIPE
GOOD WORK, SON!

GAH! ALL MY INNARDS ARE BEING HOOVERED OUT OF MY ARSE!
OO-ER!
SUPER POWER VAC
SHLURP SHLURP!
THIS WASN'T MEANT TO HAPPEN!

WHEE-OOO
EMERGENCY AMBULANCE
AMBULANCE
WHEE-OOO

AT HOSPITAL
GULP! APPARENTLY MY CONTRAPTION LEFT DAD COMPLETELY GUTTED AND FILLETED!
POWERFUL VACUUM CLEANER MISHAP WARD
VISITORS
I'LL BE IN BIG TROUBLE NOW!

BUT IN FACT
WELL DONE GILBERT! BY SUCKING OUT ALL DAD'S BONES AND INTERNAL ORGANS, YOU'VE HELPED HIM LOSE LOADS OF WEIGHT!
-gasp!-
SO I'M ALLOWING HIM TO INTRAVENOUSLY INGEST THESE CHOCOLATE EGGS, AS A TREAT.
Cheers son!

BO AND LUKE BRUMMELL THE REGENCY DUKES OF HAZZARD

BOYS! LOOK HERE IN THE TRUNK!
A TRUNK YOU SAY! DOES IT BELONG TO THE ELEPHANT THAT WIPED ITS POSTERIOR ON THE RAGS YOU'RE WEARING?
CHORTLE!
THIS AIN'T MOONSHINE - IT'S THE MONEY FROM THE BANK THAT JUST GOT ROBBED IN TOWN!

WHY, I BET BOSS HOGG HIRED THOSE ROBBERS TO PLANT THE MONEY IN THE GENERAL LEE AND FRAME YOU BOYS!
BOSS HOGG?
I HEARD HIM TALKING AT THE BOAR'S NEST ABOUT A GOVERNMENT TRUCK PASSING THROUGH HAZZARD TODAY CARRYING $100 BILL PRINTING PLATES!

Finbarr Saunders & his Double Entendres

Peeping Tam

OH, LORDY! IT'S... THE FAT SLAGS

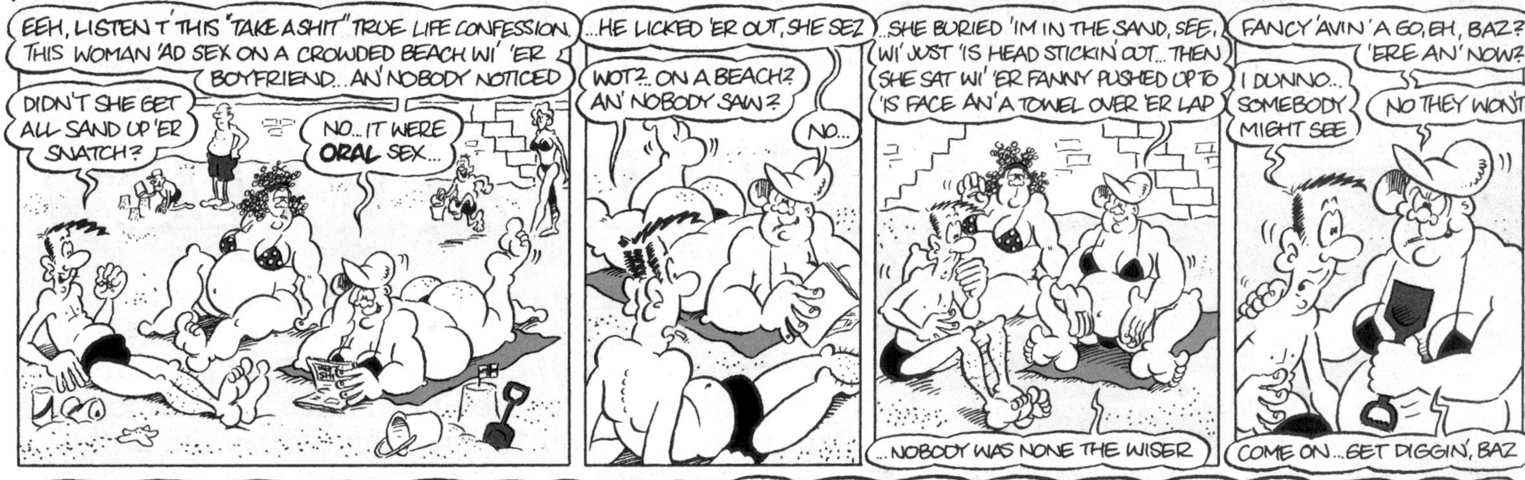

Happy Mondays Star Bez To Become Spaniel

~Reuters

THE WORLD OF POP was rocked today by the shock announcement that Happy Mondays not-quite-frontman Bez is to become a dog. The maraca-bothering freaky dancer declared his intention to become canine at a press conference in Cheadle this morning.

"I'm really up for it," the ecstasy-addled pop-muppet told reporters. "I'm definitely gonna do it, just as soon as I can afford it, like. I think I'll be a spaniel, 'cause they've got like the nicest ears and stuff. Dead good ears, spaniels."

Madchester

Bez (real name Barry Bezington), 62, found fame as a dancer/free-loader in the late-1980s on stage with his friend Shaun Ryder's band. The Happy Mondays accidentally became successful on the 'Madchester' scene, selling over 10 million albums worldwide. But now he's set his sights on a loftier ambition.

"I can't wait to become a dog," he says. "It's gonna be brilliant. I've always liked dogs, me, and as I've got a bit older and maybe a bit wiser

EXCLUSIVE!

I've thought a lot more about being one. I've always liked scratching and chasing stuff. Know what I mean?"

The former shape puller told reporters that his life on the road had taken its toll, and that being a dog would be good for his health.

Insanewhipsnade

"When I was young I was just really up for it, y'know. I wanted to be on one, doing one, 365 all the time, you know what I mean? But now I'm getting on a bit I feel like I want to take things slower," he said.

"You don't see dogs staying up for days, pilling their nuts off and gurning like twats. Dogs never sell their clothes to buy crack . They're all like

running about the park all day, come home, lie around, have a bit of a scratch and that," he added.

"Dogs have got it sorted. I want some of that."

Bez believes that scientific advances can make his canine dream a reality. "Apparently they can do all this dead clever stuff with science an' that now. You just have an operation where they give you like a tail an' floppy ears and you're set. It's proper boss."

"Some people might say 'don't be

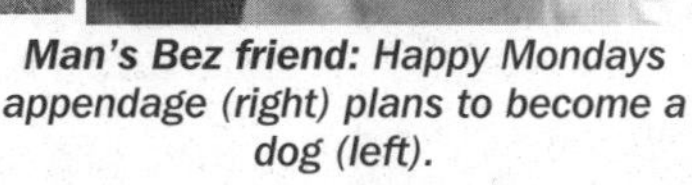

***Man's Bez friend:** Happy Mondays appendage (right) plans to become a dog (left).*

daft Bez, you can't be a dog', but if there's one thing that not really being in a band has taught me it's that you've got to follow your dreams. It's a shame Tony Wilson's not with us any more. He would have paid for me to become a dog. He was a top bloke, Tony."

When asked whether Bez's doggy dreams could become a reality, a scientist told us, "No, I very much doubt it."

Forget global warming, Arab springs and double dip

Gagarin

Who's the B

WE'VE ALL got our own ideas about who is th greatest Uri G. Whether we plump for Russk Cosmonaut *Gagarin*, whose 1961 flight in Vostok 1 fire the starting gun for the Space Race, or whether we sid with Israeli bender *Geller*, who baffles the boffins wit

Round 1: *Time spent in space*

Gagarin...

YOU MIGHT expect this round to be a pushover for the Rocket Man of Red Square, but despite being the first man to fly above the stars Gagarin made only one trip to space during which he spent a measly one hour 48 minutes floating about in the weightless vacuum of the Cosmos - that's not even enough time to watch *We're the Millers* starring Jason Sudekis and Jennifer Aniston. So, surprisingly, it's a disappointingly low-scoring round for the Russian contender.

4/10

Geller...

URI WAS famously gifted his miraculous spoon-bending powers by space aliens, who travelled for light years from a distant galaxy to endow the young Israeli with the ability to spoil the contents of his mam's kitchen drawer. According to his authorised biography *Uri* by Andrija Puharich, Geller was taken aboard a UFO as a child, so chances are he has spent much more than Gagarin's tally of an hour and three quarters in space.

8/10

Round 2: *Friendship with Jacko*

Gagarin...

IT IS UNLIKELY that the Soviet rocket hero ever got the chance to pal up with the moonwalking King of Pop. The Jackson 5's first hit *Big Boy* was released on January 31st 1968, a mere 54 days before Gagarin's untimely death in an experimental plane crash. The space pioneer had less than eight weeks available to him to hear of the band and become such a fan that he travelled to their hometown of Gary, Indiana to meet and befriend 10-year-old lead singer Michael. Whilst it's a scenario that cannot be completely excluded, the chances that it actually happened are vanishingly small.

5/10

Geller...

THANKS TO his lifelong fascination with parapsychology and telekinesis, Wacko Jacko was irresistibly drawn to paranormal mentalist Geller like a bluebottle to a dog turd. Meeting backstage at a glittering showbiz bash, the two megastars quickly became firm friends; so much so that the chimp-bothering baby-dangler agreed to be best man whe Geller and his wife Mrs Geller renewed their marriage vows in 2001. Later, as a thank-you, U invited the *Thriller* star to join him for a slap-up finger buffet in the directors' box at Exeter FC' St James Park ground. One of the firmest friendships in showbiz had been cemented.

10/1

Round 5: *Horrible QVC jewellery range*

Gagarin...

YOU MIGHT suppose that Gagarin's death a full 25 years before QVC began broadcasting would have prevented him hawking a range of horrible jewellery on the popular TV shopping channel. But death has not proved an obstacle for other bling-flogging celebs such as Jackie Kennedy, whose stylish collection of ear rings, necklaces and bracelets are eternally popular with discerning viewers despite her having been dead since 1994. However, jewellery was not allowed on Soviet era space missions, and as a result Gagarin never developed a taste for it. Indeed, if he had lent his name to a QVC product it would in all likelihood have been a technological one, such as a car tyre inflator, a pressure washer or a revolutionary home painting system which cut decorating times in half, and was not available in the shops. Not only that, if you ordered it today you'd get a set of interchangeable accessories absolutely free.

5/10

Geller...

MIND-BENDING spoon-boggler Uri is QVC's undisputed King of Bling. His best-selling range of mystical 9ct gold natural crystal jewellery, inspired by "important aspects of Uri's life, such as spheres, movement and Egyptian themes", is guaranteed to send the channel's sales switchboard into meltdown every time it is featured, so you might expect this to be a high scoring round for Geller. But wait! The theme of this round is "horrible" jewellery collections, and that is certainly not a word that anyone could use to describe the Israeli paranormalist's sublime creations. And neither are "tacky", '"tasteless", or "second-rate". The 9ct Gold Rock Crystal Pyramids of Wisdom Ring, the 9ct Gold Rock Crystal Lunar Transition Charm Necklace and the 9ct Gold Rock Crystal Planetary Orbit Ring are guaranteed to become the priceless heirlooms of the future, taking their place alongside Crown Jewels, treasures of Tutankarmoon and Fabergé eggs.

0/10

Round 6: *Maximum G-force experienced*

Gagarin...

AS HIS 200ft Vostok rocket blasted off from th Baikonur Technical Range on April 12th 1961, U Gagarin experienced a sustained acceleration c 5G for more than 2 minutes. Earlier, during the lon period of training for his mission, he had successfull withstood prolonged acceleration forces of up t 10G in a centrifuge without blacking out, so it's high-scoring round for the late Russian who, had h not died at the age of 34, would have celebrated hi 79th birthday in March.

10/1

Geller...

GELLER HAS lived his whole life at 1G - nominall accelerating towards the earth's core at 9.81ms^{-2} just like everyone else on the planet. Despite bein gifted by space aliens with spoon-buggering powe that are beyond ordinary mortals' comprehensio he doesn't know what it's like to suddenly feel te times heavier due to a massive rate of increase velocity. With 1 point available per G, it's a very po round for Geller who, had he died at the same age a his cosmonaut rival, would have departed this ve in 1981.

1/1

- **Close, but there's cosmo-nought for coming second. Despite a promising blast-off, it was a weightless performance from the Russian, who clearly lacked the (Y)Uri G-force needed to secure victory. At the end of the competition, it's an ignominious splash down to second space in the Geller-Gagarin race for the dead Red.**

ions. There's only ONE question gripping the nation...

vs Geller: st (Y)Uri G?

is amazing ability to distort spoons using only the power f his mind and hands, everyone's got a favourite. But in he end there can only be one best Uri G, and now it's time or Gagarin and Geller to finally go head to head in a bid to lecide once and for all which one is the greatest.

Round 3: *Charlatanism*

iagarin...

S EVERYONE knows, conspiracy theorists the world ver are convinced that astronauts never went to the loon. And once we accept that the Apollo programme as nothing more than a crude hoax cooked up on a ollywood sound stage, it's a short step to speculating at, like Armstrong and Aldrin's faked trip to the lunar urface, Gagarin's 1961 flight was nothing more than a remlin-inspired confidence trick - a cynical *Capricorn ne*-style propaganda exercise, with so-called national ero Gagarin as the hapless stooge.

9/10

ieller...

ESPITE numerous attempts over the years to prove that Geller's paranormal abilities e nothing more than simply party tricks that can be duplicated in every detail by any emi-competent birthday party conjuror, no-one has come close to explaining the Tel viv-born mystic's powers. Whether it's bending spoons, identifying which one of ur film canisters has got some water in it or reproducing a drawing of a cat that's a sealed envelope, Geller has consistently left boffins and debunkers baffled by his agical illusions. No charlatan he, Geller is the real deal.

0/10

Round 4: *Suing after accusations of charlatanism*

Gagarin...

IN THE seven years that elapsed between the flight of Vostok 1 and his death at the controls of a Mig-15 training jet, the pioneering cosmonaut was far too busy accepting honours, travelling the world and enjoying his new-found A-list status to sue anyone for accusing him of being a hoaxer. Indeed, if any allegations of flimflammery were made at the time, they must have been brushed under the carpet or settled out of court, as there are no records of any legal action being taken by Gagarin.

3/10

Geller...

GELLER QUITE rightly defends his reputation vigorously in court against his many detractors, debunkers and mudslingers. Indeed, critics would do well to think twice before accusing the Berkshire-dwelling fork-knobbler of merely dressing up magic set parlour tricks as the effects of psychokinesis and telepathy. Not surprisingly, with the truth firmly on his side, Uri sometimes even wins, forcing his accusers to eat their words... with a bent spoon! And pay him substantial damages.

9/10

Round 7: *Amount of bent spoons stuck to car*

iagarin...

S A middle-ranking Air Force major, Gagarin was well-off by Russian standards, riving a brand new 1967 Moskvitch. But the risks he ran as a test pilot flying xperimental aircraft at supersonic speeds were controlled and measured. Fixing storted items of cutlery onto the body panels of his car may well have seemed to m like an unnecessary risk. So, whilst we can't completely rule out the possibility at Gagarin's car was festooned with bent spoons, it is nevertheless extremely nlikely, and his score in this round reflects that uncertainty.

5/10

ieller...

I THE GARAGE of Geller's swish Sonning-on-Thames mansion sits a 1974 Cadillac nousine with over 5,000 bent spoons welded to the bodywork. According to the *uinness Book of Records*, the car is the most bent-spoon-covered vehicle in the orld, boasting over 1,000 bent spoons on the bonnet alone, and thousands more on the roof, doors and wings. And boot lid. 200 twisted soup ladles, a dozen mangled toasting forks and a psychically misshapen fish slice also adjoin this amazing vehicular work of art. Only the lack of spoons on the windscreen prevents Uri scoring a perfect 10 in this round.

9/10

Round 8: *Helping football teams win crucial matches*

Gagarin...

THROUGHOUT his career as a cosmonaut, Gagarin was more concerned with blast-offs than kick-offs. In fact it is not thought he ever played in, refereed or even watched a football match during his 34-year life. But bizarrely, he may have inadvertently influenced the outcome of the greatest match in history - the 1966 World Cup final. For, when the Russian linesman controversially declared that Geoff Hurst's shot had crossed the line, it may have been because he was distracted, thinking about Gagarin's flight in Vostok 1 five years earlier. Having said that, the linesman could also have been thinking about Laika the dog, Ham the chimpanzee or any of the dozens of fruit flies that made it into orbit during the early years of the Space Race.

3/10

Geller...

AT THE END of the 1996/97 football season, Exeter City FC were facing relegation from Division 3 of the Football League. On the eve of a crunch match against Chester City, Geller placed "energy-infused crystals" behind the goals at the team's St James Park ground which he said would help the home team to secure victory. During the game the crystals worked perfectly. However, due to a series of poor refereeing decisions, unlucky bounces and gaffes from the Exeter goalkeeper, the visitors won 5-1. However, without the benign mystic influence of Geller's magical crystals, Exeter's defeat would have been much, much worse, so as a result it's a high-scoring round for the paranormal fork-twister.

10/10

HEY DO? 47

• Although he bends spoons for a living, Geller didn't need to bend the figures to prove he is the king of the (Y)Uri Gs, and It's a straight triumph for him as a result. The boffin-bamboozler delivers a psy-kick in the teeth to his opponent with a resounding victory which is as utterly inexplicable as one of his conjuring tricks.

STEP-POPE AND SON

PLAYTIME FONTAYNE

NOW HAVE A NICE DAY AT THE BANK, WON'T YOU PLAYTIME.
AW BUT MUM- CAN'T I HAVE TODAY OFF? THE AREA MANAGER IS IN AND I HAVEN'T DONE MY QUARTERLY AUDIT RETURNS.

WELL YOU SHOULD HAVE THOUGHT OF THAT EARLIER. YOU'VE HAD ALL WEEKEND TO DO THEM.
COULD YOU WRITE A NOTE TO SAY I'VE GOT A TUMMY ACHE..?
NO I CAN'T.
AW... BUT MU-UM! I'LL GET DONE.

WELL IT'S YOUR OWN FAULT. HOW MANY TIMES HAVE I TOLD YOU TO GET YOUR QUARTERLY AUDIT RETURNS DONE ON A FRIDAY NIGHT WHEN YOU GET IN? NOW GET IN THAT BANK. I'LL PICK YOU UP AT FOUR.
BANK

?
PHWOOAR! LOOK AT THAT LADY'S MUDDLES!
CRUMBS! YOU CAN SEE HER SLOT AND EVERYTHING!

HEY! WHAT ARE YOU ALL LOOKING AT?
BARLOW FOUND A NUDIE BOOK IN A HEDGE THIS MORNING.
YOU CAN SEE EVERYTHING... TITS, BUM, FANNY... THE LOT!
WHERE? LET'S SEE!
TEN PENCE A LOOK, FONTAYNE.

LOOK OUT! IT'S PODMORE THE AREA MANAGER!
HIDE IT!

QUICK..! HE'S COMING OVER...!

WHAT'S GOING ON HERE? WHY AREN'T YOU IN YOUR OFFICE, FONTAYNE?
ERM... I DON'T KNOW SIR.

AND WHAT'S THAT UP YOUR JUMPER?
ERM...
IS IT THOSE QUARTERLY AUDIT RETURNS I ASKED YOU TO PREPARE?
ERM...

I'LL TAKE THOSE.
GULP!

I'VE GOT A MEETING WITH THE CHAIRMAN OF THE BANK THIS MORNING... I'LL GO OVER YOUR FIGURES WITH HIM.
GULP!

OI, FONTAYNE! GIZ ME NUDIE BOOK BACK, THEN.
I HAVEN'T GOT IT. PODMORE TOOK IT. HE THOUGHT IT WAS THE QUARTERLY AUDIT RETURNS!
WELL YOU'D BETTER GET IT BACK.

HOW!?
I DON'T CARE. JUST DO IT, RIGHT... OR I'LL GET LYNCHIE FROM THE INVESTMENT ARM TO KICK YOU IN.
GULP!

BUT...
...PLEASE SIR, IT'S NOT MINE! I GOT IT OFF FONTAYNE...!
DON'T TELL TALES, PODMORE. I'M CONFISCATING THIS FILTH AND REPORTING YOU TO THE BANKING OMBUDSMAN.

RIGHT! YOU'RE GETTING ME ANOTHER SKIN-MAG, FONTAYNE, OR YOU'RE DEAD. GO DOWN TO THE NEWSAGENT NOW!
B-BUT...

NOW!!

SO...
...48 ARE YOU..? WHEN WERE YOU BORN..?
ERM... 1974... NO... 1975...
1965!
OOH, LOOK, ISN'T THAT MRS. FONTAYNE'S LITTLE LAD..? THE ONE FROM THE BANK?
EEH, THE SHAME.
KNAVE

"What you like in your EASTER EGG says a lot about the type of DRIVER you are. And what sort of SEX you enjoy," says TV shrink Dr. Raj Persaud.

EASTER EGG ~SPOSED!

EVERYONE LOVES EASTER, except Jesus, for whom it perhaps brings back unpleasant memories of being nailed to a cross. But for the rest of us it's a happy time of Bank Holidays, fluffy bunnies and, of course, Easter eggs. At this time every year Britons smash their way through an estimated *120 million* of the delicious chocolate ovums to get at the tempting, sweet treats hidden within.

Smarties, Rolos, Maltesers, Cadbury's Buttons... there's an enormous number of varieties available, and we all have our favourites. *But what does our Easter morning egg choice say about us?* More than you might think, according to formerly discredited and now possibly recredited media psychiatrist ***Dr Raj Persaud***. For the platitude-spouting ex-*This Morning* sofa favourite believes that our simnel choccy preference can reveal the innermost secrets of our driving habits and sex lives! He told us: "Recent research suggests that what we like in our Easter eggs and how we behave when we're behind the wheel or in bed are triple facets of our personality that are inextricably linked."

So what does YOUR favourite egg brand reveal about your driving style and performance between the sheets? It's time to crack open your Easter ego and lift the lids on your driving and sexual ids!

1. Rolos

In the car...

"Do you love anyone enough to give them your last Rolo" was the old advertising slogan for these temptingly chewy treats. And it's a scientific fact that those who like them are very selfish drivers. Hogging the middle lane of the motorway, refusing to let other cars out of side roads and pulling into disabled bays outside the supermarket are just a few of the antisocial habits exhibited by Rolo-chewing motorists.

In the bedroom...

The picture doesn't get any better in the bedroom. Rolo-eaters are also selfish and uncaring lovers, slaking their own base urges without any regard for their partner's pleasure. Like their favourite toffee-centred chocolates, they are also "soft in the centre" and suffer from chronic impotence - an ability to achieve or maintain an erection. This often puts a strain on their relationships, and Rolo-eaters should watch out for their dissatisfied partners seeking out their sexual kicks elsewhere.

Typical car: *Rover 75 Connoisseur*

Celebrity examples: *Phil Collins, Gazza, Alan Titchmarsh, Dappy out of N'Dubz*

2. Smarties

In the car...

Smarties are candy-coated, making them streamlined, aerodynamic and fast to eat. And those who eat them drive in the same way, with a heavy right foot pressing the pedal to the metal whenever they climb behind the wheel. With a record of speeding offences as long as their arm, Smartie-eaters are just a Gatso flash away from a 12-month ban. But many simply get their wives to take the points instead, enabling them to keep their licences and live to burn rubber another day.

In the bedroom...

Grab a Smartie tube and give it a squeeze and a flick - the lid pops off in the blink of an eye. And sadly it's the same fast'n'furious story for Smartie-eaters in the bedroom. Two-push Charlies to a man, they suffer from extreme premature ejaculation, and although they may get hubbie's penalty points on their licences, their wives certainly won't receive anything in the way of sexual satisfaction from them. The frustrated partners of Smartie-eaters are left with no option but to seek out lovers with a bit more staying power in order to get their orgasmic thrills.

Typical car: *Subaru Impreza WRX*

Celebrity examples: *Chris Huhne, Jeremy Clarkson, Jenson Button, Ken Barlow*

3. Liqueurs

In the car...

You might suppose that a person who craved the breakfast-time buzz of alcoholic chocolates on Easter Sunday might be prone to driving whilst under the influence. But you'd be wrong, for in fact there's no-one less likely to find themselves on the wrong end of a breathalyser than a liqueur-eater, as they are amongst the most cautious and timid drivers on our roads. These people's idea of excitement and rebellion is a couple of sherry-filed chocolates once a year, and once they're behind the wheel you will only ever see them hugging the kerb at 20mph or endlessly circling a roundabout trying to pluck up enough courage to indicate left and head for the exit.

In the bedroom...

And liqueur-eaters are just as unadventurous when it comes to lovemaking. Sex - on the rare occasions it happens, such as birthdays, anniversaries, royal jubilees etc - takes place in the dark, in the bed, and in silence. The *Kama Sutra* remains a closed book to people like this, who will never know the kinky joys of sharing a soixante-neuf, a Cleveland Steamer or a sticky belly flapcock with their wife.

Typical car: *DAF Variomatic*

Celebrity examples: *Ronnie Corbett, Eddie Mair, Bamber Gascoigne, Vin Diesel*

4. Flake

In the car...

As it says on the adverts, this is the crumbliest, flakiest chocolate in the world, and as a result those who eat it invariably end up in a bit of a mess. So you won't be surprised to learn that drivers who opt for a Cadbury's Flake Easter egg become mobile disaster zones once they get on the road. In fact these drivers probably spend more time at the body shop, getting their various scrapes, dings and bumps straightened out, than they do on the highway. Chances are, if someone reverses into you in the supermarket car park, they'll be tucking into a flake egg come easter Sunday.

In the bedroom...

These people are no less disaster-prone in the sack as on the tarmac. No romantic evening is complete unless it culminates, not in multiple simultaneous orgasms, but in a high speed ambulance dash to the nearest Accident and Emergency department. Torsion injuries to the meatus and glans, bruising of the testes and snapped banjo strings are just a few of the results of a typical night of love-making for a Cadbury's Flake-eater. If they've got medical insurance, chances are their no-claims-bonus went years ago.

Typical car: *Volvo XC90*

Celebrity examples:
Richard Branson, George Osborne, Jamie Oliver, Professor Brian Cox

5. Toblerone

In the car...

Toblerone is the only triangular chocolate known to mankind, and each segment is bunched up close to its neighbours. Indeed, when you break one off, it's impossible to avoid it knocking into the one in front. And it's the same for Toblerone drivers, who are guilty of one of the worst driving sins - tailgating. As far as they're concerned, the two-second rule in the Highway Code is for other people, not them. Look in your rear-view mirror next time you head out on the road, and if there's someone sitting inches behind your bumper, it's odds-on he's a Toblerone-eater.

In the bedroom...

"Up close and personal" is the Toblerone-eater's mantra, so it's no surprise they like to pull up to the bumper in the boudoir too. Just as they live for the illicit thrill of tailgating on the road, the forbidden pleasure of taking someone from the rear is what keeps their motor running in the bedroom. Anal-sex-crazed fans of the honey- and almond-studded bars are never happier than when they're kicking the wife's back doors in. Whether they're at the wheel or in the fart-sack, there's nothing to match the rush they get from hanging out of an exhaust pipe.

Typical car: *Audi A6*

Celebrity examples:
David Baddiel, Tim Lovejoy, Chris Packham, Kofi Annan

6. Revels

In the car...

Revels are made for sharing, and this public-spirited ethos is reflected in the driving style of those who eat them. Signalling in good time, never cutting other motorists up and flashing their headlights to warn other drivers of a speed trap are some of the traits exhibited by Revel-eaters once they get behind the wheel. Also, because they're used to surprises whilst eating their favourite chocolates, Revel-eaters are always prepared for any eventuality on the road. You'll never see one lost on a ring road or pulled up on the hard shoulder with an empty fuel tank or a flat spare tyre.

In the bedroom...

Variety is the spice of life for Revel-eaters, both in their choice of chocolates and in their sex life. A single flavour of Revel would soon bore them, and it's exactly the same story when they get between the sheets. They are inveterate swingers, indulging in wild sex with multiple partners at orgies and gang-bangs every night of the week. Nothing thrills a Revel-eater more than slaking his lust on a dozen different women before lying back and watching as his wife is taken by as many men - their sweating bodies becoming a confused of writhing limbs as she is mercilessly pounded by their engorged members.

Typical car: *FSO Polonez*

Celebrity examples:
Joe Pasquale, Bill Turnbull, Lord Sugar, Mo Farah MBE

NEXT ISSUE: What the kind of Mothering Sunday card you send says about how tidy you are around the house and the girth of your penile shaft.

An Englishman in New York

Sting set to up sticks to Big Apple after being stung by criticism

NEWCASTLE-BORN pop star Sting has decided to leave the country after tiring of the British public's negative attitude towards him. Now the five times Grammy Award winner has set up home in New York where, he says, people are not jealous of his many achievements.

"In Britain, success has become a dirty word," he told Fox TV host French Letterman. "The public resent the fact that I have sold millions of records, starred in a succession of blockbuster films and can play the lute," he continued.

"For example, the other day I parked one of my Ferraris across a zebra crossing while I nipped into Fortnum & Masons for some quail eggs," said the 62-year-old former Police frontman. "I'd only been gone an hour or two and when I got back to my car a traffic warden had put a ticket on it."

"I couldn't believe my eyes. The man was clearly driven by nothing but small-minded bitterness and jealousy. There was no other explanation."

exhibits

On another occasion, Sting's PA asked the British Museum to close its doors to the public for a day so that the singer could look at the exhibits in peace. "They flatly refused," he told Letterman. "I was just amazed by their petty, small-minded way of thinking. It was a perfectly simple request and there was absolutely no reason for them to turn it down."

"I can only think that whoever decided not to close the museum so I could look around was simply envious that their little house would probably fit inside one of my bathrooms," he continued.

"But the loss was theirs, as I would have spent at least ten million pounds on pencils, rubbers and colouring books in the gift shop."

tim westwoods

"Me and Trudie have had enough of Britain's spiteful, vindictive mindset," continued the *Dune* star. "The US has a different attitude towards extremely successful celebrities. We're treated with respect."

hugh dennises

The *Walking on the Moon* singer went on to list a catalogue of incidents from the British public's long-running vendetta against him and his wife Trudie Styler, including:

- *The National Hot Air Balloon Society's refusal to cancel their annual festival in case one floated over his house in Wiltshire.*
- *The London Symphony Orchestra's insistence on concluding The Last Night of the Proms with Elgar's Land of Hope and Glory instead of De Doo Doo Doo de Dah Dah Dah.*
- *The Royal Mint's rejection of his suggestion that he should appear on the reverse of all UK banknotes playing the lute. And on the front wearing a crown.*

Sting continued: "I've had fifty hit singles in the UK, yet I'm still expected to give way to ordinary people on roundabouts and even stop at red lights."

steve punts

"The other day I even got a letter from the authorities asking me why I hadn't got a television licence. That simply wouldn't happen in the USA. It's simply because just jealous of my houses, cars, helicopters and lute playing."

The Stings will be flying out to begin their new Big Apple life in the new year.

"Thank God we'll be flying in our private jet and not out of Heathrow Airport," he told Letterman. "Or I dare say they'd be expecting us to sit in the First Class Departure Lounge like cattle and put our Louis Vuitton luggage through the same X-Ray machines as everybody else," he added.

How I Met the Missus

...I'm a dentist and I met my wife when she came in for a check-up one day. I told her she needed a filling and once under the gas I interfered with her sexually and it was wonderful. I put her knickers back on her and when she came round I asked her out on a date. We've been married six years now and she still doesn't know what I did in my surgery.

Mervyn Fassbender, Lincoln

...My wife is French and we are both cross-Channel swimmers. I met her when I was swimming from Dover to Calais and she was coming the other way. We hit it off immediately and trod water, chatting for hours. We arranged to meet mid-Channel the following week and that's when I took the plunge and proposed to her. We had our wedding 11 miles out to sea, with the vicar, best man, bridesmaids and all our friends and family bobbing about in the water, smeared in goose fat. Although 23 people drowned during the service and reception, it was a very special day that we will always remember.

Bartram Webster, Folkestone

...I'm a lady judge and I met my husband when he was up before me on a charge of aggravated burglary and grievous bodily harm. He gave me a cheeky wink as he pleaded not guilty and I fell for him there and then. He had clearly done it, but I found him not guilty anyway. I can't give our names as I clearly perverted the course of justice, but we've now been happily married for fifteen years.

Name and address supplied

...When I was 6 I fell in love with a girl in my class called Polly. We were inseparable, spending all our playtimes together and sitting next to each other in lessons. We were both heartbroken when her parents announced they were moving away from the area. Polly and I vowed that we would find each other and get married when we were grown up. But we never did because I got some girl from the estate pregnant when I was 17 and I had to marry her instead.

Mark Onions, Droitwich

...I met my wife Ekatriana when I replied to an internet pop-up advert offering Russian brides. When she turned up, I was disappointed that she wasn't the exact one off the photograph, but we got married anyway. My friends said it would never work, but we proved them wrong. We were happily married for two wonderful weeks before she disappeared with my wallet, passport and car keys.

Emerson Wakeman, Kenilworth

...They say you never know when you might run into the love of your life. Well I did - quite literally - when I had a head-on collision with another car. It was quite a bump, and I and the lady driver of the other vehicle got out to exchange insurance details and inspect the damage. Looking at the crumpled bodywork of our cars, we realised we had both been lucky to get out unscathed. We got talking, I asked her out to dinner that very night and to cut a long story short I proposed to her on our first date and she accepted. We had both been married before, but as it happened my wife and her husband had both been killed instantly in the crash that brought us together.

Adrian Solder, Cardiff

...I've got a very unusual story about how I met my wife. I first saw her at a disco and went over and offered to buy her a drink. We seemed to get on quite well, had a couple of dances and I asked her if she fancied going out the following Friday. Over the next couple of years we had hundreds of dates, mainly in pubs, restaurants and the pictures. We eventually got married in the local registry office. Few people believe me when I tell them, but it's absolutely true!

Paul Usual, Normanton

...I'm an airline pilot and I fell in love with the lovely voice of a lady air traffic controller at Heathrow. Every time I flew my Boeing 747 into London I would look forward to chatting with her, and although we had never met I became quite smitten. Eventually I plucked up the courage to ask her out and she agreed. However, when I arrived at the rendezvous we'd arranged, I discovered that "she" was actually a man with a high-pitched, effeminate voice. We went on the date anyway and hit it off. To cut a long story short, we had a civil ceremony and have now been married for 5 wonderful, happy years. I'm not even gay, so it just goes to show that true love can overcome all obstacles.

Clinton Cardshop, Windsor

...I am a Mormon and I've got eight wives who I met when their minibus had a puncture on the way to a Take That concert. I happened to be passing and I stopped to change the wheel for them and got chatting to them. I asked them all out for a drink, and then took them all to the pictures - I can't remember what the film was as I was too busy snogging them all on the back row to pay any attention to what was happening on the screen! After going out with them all for a few months I was sure that they were the ones for me and I decided to propose to them. To my delight, they all said yes. We've been happily married for five years now and have 46 children.

Merrill Young, Utah

How did YOU meet YOUR wife? Write and let us know at the usual address. There's an all-expenses-paid first class cruise to renew your wedding vows in the Bahamas with all your family and friends* for every one we print.

*Up to a maximum of 200 family and friends with £1000 spending money each.

DONALD TRUMP'S WORLD OF PUMPS

Flatulence news from around the globe with bottom-burp-named Billionaire Donald Trump

Buenes Aires, Argentina...

• **CROWDS** watching a Premira División football match between River Plate and Independiente were amazed when referee Mr ***Boco Perez*** showed home team defender ***Umberto Gonzalez*** the red card ... *for dropping his guts inside his own penalty box!* The 45-year-old referee said that the air biscuit stank so bad that its release constituted dangerous play, and he awarded a penalty to the visiting side. However FIFA president ***Sep Blatter*** later criticised the controversial sending-off decision, saying that under current rules, the offensive chuff should have been punished with a yellow card and indirect free kick. *"Gonzalez should only have been dismissed if the stench was so bad that it denied a goal-scoring opportunity,"* said Blatter.

Memphis, Tennessee...

• **A SULPHUROUS** fart dropped by ***Elvis Presley*** just before his death in 1977 is set to be inducted into the Rock & Roll Hall of Fame at a star-studded ceremony next month. The King's final release, a dense, eggy whiff which lingered in the lavatory at his Graceland mansion, has survived 35 years of windows being opened, doors being flapped and matches being struck. *"Just like Elvis sang at the end of American Trilogy, this fart goes marching on,"* said *Rolling Stone* editor ***Hymen Prepuce***. Over 500,000 people each year are expected to come and pay tribute to the legendary trouser cough at its new home in Cleveland, Ohio.

Beijing, China...

• **AT THE** 59th Congress of the People's Republic of China, President ***Xi Jin Ping*** announced a draconian new law restricting married couples from farting more than once a day. The new diktat has been introduced in an attempt to limit bum gas pollution from the country's 1.3 billon population. Couples will be permitted to release any one cheek sneaks they are currently brewing until the anal clampdown comes into effect next week. *"From September 1st, any couple farting more than once in any 24 hour period will be deemed to be enemies of the state,"* Ji Ping told delegates. Couples who do not fart at all will be held up as model citizens and rewarded with book tokens and Boots gift vouchers.

Tate Modern, London...

• **A MAN** sat farting into a metal bucket containing a dozen ping pong balls is the bookies' favourite to take the 2013 Turner Prize for Modern Art. The controversial installation - entitled Languor and Lassitude - is the work of conceptual artist ***Stringfellow Mockney***, and features a naked man sitting on a metal bucket whilst eating Chicken Tonight from a jar with a spoon. Mockney told Radio 4's *Front Row* programme: *"As he breaks wind, the ping pong balls rattle about in the bucket, and this raises questions about the nature of movement and sound. And the eggy smell challenges our preconceptions about mortality, birth, death and the futility of being. The whole piece is an allegory in the tradition of Raphael, Rembrandt and Peter Breughel the elder."* The National Gallery recently paid £30million pounds for another of Mockney's works - Ennui and Torpidity - which consists of a naked man eating pickled onion Monster Munch and farting into a Tupperware box full of Maltesers.

"More News of the Brews next week, fart fans!" *Donald*

That's Death

FORMER THAT'S Life presenter ***ESTHER RANTZEN*** **wept last night as she told of her horror at discovering that dinosaurs had gone extinct. And the tearful ex *Hearts of Gold* host said that society must take its share of the blame for the mass annihilation of the race of giant reptiles which stalked the earth millions of years ago.**

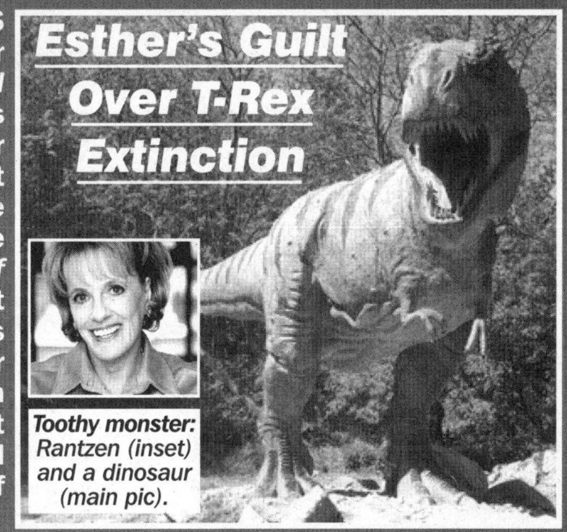

Toothy monster: *Rantzen (inset) and a dinosaur (main pic).*

The dinosaurs were wiped out during the Cretaceous-Paleogene extinction event, when a giant meteorite cooled the earth, spelling death for the huge, cold-blooded lizards. And Rantzen, 72, says it will take her a long time to forgive herself for sitting back and doing nothing.

heart

She told the *Daily Mail*: "It breaks my heart that we all stood by and allowed these innocent creatures to be destroyed and made into fossils. And now it is too late to put right the enormous wrong that has been perpetrated."

Rantzen said that lessons must be learned from the mistakes of the past, and dinosaurs must never be allowed to go extinct again. "If only we knew then what we know now, we could have averted this terrible tragedy," she said.

"I blame myself, but I blame everybody else on earth even more," she added.

TOP TIPS

WANT to sneak out of a room without being noticed? Simply moonwalk out, and people will think you are walking in.

Arthur Pewty, Brighton

CONVINCE your child he lives in an opera by singing everything you say, accompanied by the harpsichord.

D Cooper, e-mail

AVOID toast landing butter-side down if you're prone to dropping it on the floor by simply buttering it thinly on both sides. When dropped, it will land on its edge, making it easier to pick up.

Dave Strickland, e-mail

MAKE your neighbours think that Rod Hull lives next door by jumping off your roof with your arm stuffed up an ostrich's arse.

Tam Dale, e-mail

MAKE your goldfish look like an authentic Beefeater by shoving half a black olive on top of its head. This will also add a touch of regal class to the little plastic underwater castle.

Randy O'Toole, e-mail

TESCO economy baking foil makes ideal toilet paper for thrifty Cybermen.

Dave Anon, e-mail

ATTRACTIVE ladies. Before going to the dentist, ensure you put your knickers on the wrong way round. This will ensure that they will be correct when you wake up from your 'check up.'

Ian U, e-mail

CAT owners. Make sure your cat understands that the working week has begun by releasing mice around the house every Monday morning.

Jimmy Boogaloo, e-mail

TRENDY vicars. Get 'down with the kids' by having your Christian rock band smash up all the stage equipment after their gig. You can always have a baked goods sale in the church hall later to pay for the damage, and lace all the cakes with ketamine just to prove that you're the real deal.

Bramley Stoker, e-mail

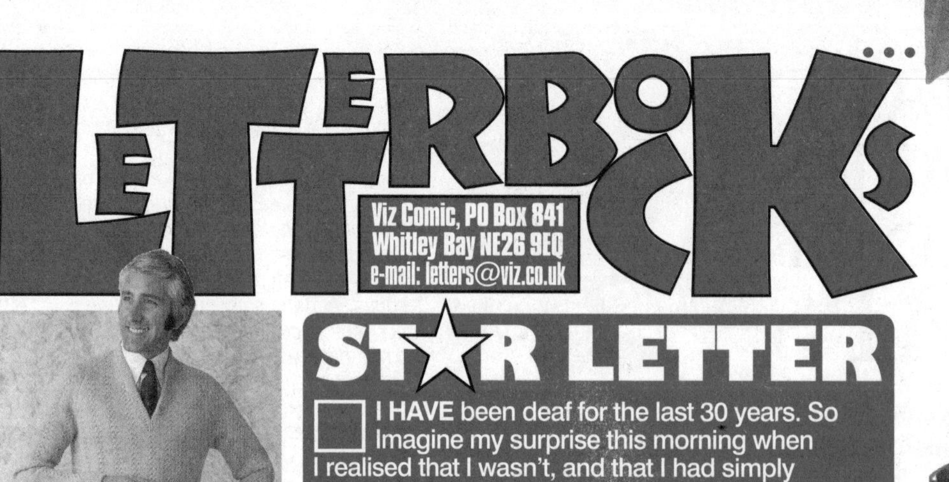

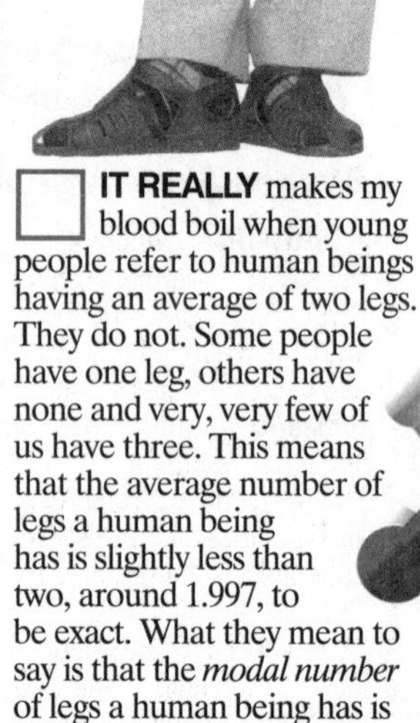

STAR LETTER

I HAVE been deaf for the last 30 years. So Imagine my surprise this morning when I realised that I wasn't, and that I had simply forgotten to take off my earmuffs when I came home one day in 1986.

Arthur Weber, Chesterfield

V-NECK jumpers are all well and good, but why not V-neck trousers? They'd look wonderful with a tasteful pair of shirt-collar underpants and bow tie. Or perhaps a pair of cravat boxer shorts for a less formal occasion.

Martin Farad, London

SURELY lesbians who want sex toys should be buying those rubber vaginas. If they're out getting big plastic replica cocks then it's the sheer hypocrisy of it that potentially bothers me.

Ron Maynard, Ilford

WHILST travelling down the M6 en route to a fortnight's holiday in Cornwall, my family and I stopped off for a sandwich at Forton Services. We were so enchanted by this undiscovered gem of a place that we immediately abandoned our holiday plans and spent a delightful two weeks there instead. I'm reluctant to draw too much attention to what must surely be Britain's best-kept secret, but I simply can't recommend this idyllic spot enough. We've already booked for two weeks next summer, plus a weekend break in November and another one the following February.

S Calder, Grasmere

I WAS using my computer the other day when my cat jumped up on my lap and walked across the keyboard. Afterwards, I was amazed to see that whilst doing so he had typed 'aqa2q2qq'. I believe that this is some sort of message or warning for me, something about my health or perhaps that my holiday flight is going to crash. Can anybody tell me what it means?

Dr M Butcher, Tintwhistle

WHY is it that people like birdsong so much? It's just a noise. If you were sitting peacefully in your garden trying to have a nap and the neighbours kids were playing the same five note tune on a tin whistle over and over again you'd poke your head over the hedge and tell them to shut the fuck up.

Herbert Pocket, Yorkshire

WHILST on holiday in Spain this year, my wife and I went to visit a monastery. There was a Spanish copper standing by the main gate telling tourists that they couldn't enter wearing shorts. This was fair enough, but I was alarmed to see that he was all tooled up with a baton and a pistol. Surely this is a little over the top. Unless of course they've had trouble with armed gangs wanting to enter the monastery in shorts.

Les Bloomer, Hull

WHY don't people who get tattooed choose a simple arial font instead of all this fancy calligraphy? I always struggle a bit to read their child's name or favorite quote down their neck or around their wrist.

Anne Claire, Leeds

MY GARDEN wall fell down a while ago, so I asked a local builder to come round and repair it. Last week he turned up in a van with some tools and set about putting it right, and I have to say he did a very good job. This morning I was staggered to find that he'd sent me a bill through the post! When ever happened to community spirit where people help each other out for the pleasure that being neighbourly brings?

Hampton Chopper, Crewe

IT REALLY makes my blood boil when young people refer to human beings having an average of two legs. They do not. Some people have one leg, others have none and very, very few of us have three. This means that the average number of legs a human being has is slightly less than two, around 1.997, to be exact. What they mean to say is that the *modal number* of legs a human being has is two. Do they teach children nothing in schools these days? The same goes for arms.

Digory Glovebox, Truro

A Different Sort of King for a Day

King Albert II of Belgium

"I'D BE **MARK KING** out of Level 42. I enjoy his band's trademark brand of rhythm-driven lightweight funk and I've always wanted to be able to play slap bass. However, as a reigning monarch of a major European nation, it would be considered undignified for me to play in a pop group, especially if I had my guitar on such a ludicrously short strap."

King Hans-Adam II of Liechtenstein

"DON'T tell my wife, Countess Marie Aglae Kinsky von Wchinitz und Tettau, but I've always fancied myself as a bit of a ladies' man, so I'd like to spend a day as 1970s heart-throb **JASON KING**. Each week on *Department S*, dandy dilettante King made thousands of women go weak at the knees. Not to mention one man in the lavatories at Gloucester Bus Station in 1975 as well."

King Juan Carlos I of Spain

"I LOVE animals, and in my capacity as honorary head of the Spanish branch of the WWF I've been privileged to travel around the world and shoot dead thousands of different exotic species. That's why I'd like the chance to spend a day as *Springwatch* presenter **SIMON KING**. His encyclopaedic knowledge of British wildlife would prove invaluable, letting me know if there were any endangered species worth shooting on my next trip to the UK."

King Bhumibol Adulyadej of Thailand

"I'VE been Thailand's head of state since June 1946, and believe you me after 67 years it's really starting to get on my tits. If I were New Orleans bluesman **BB KING** for 24 hours, I'd have a musical outlet for these negative emotions, and I'd do a song called "(I've got them) King of Thailand Blues." I've already written the first couple of lines, which

I LOVE the film *King Kong*, but I always felt sorry for the big monkey at the end. They didn't have to kill the poor thing for heaven's sake. They could have coaxed him down from the building with an enormous banana, or perhaps a monster truck tyre dangling from a helicopter.
Franklyn Siemens, London

IF absolutely everything is made from atoms, then why does toffee fudge ice cream taste wonderful and dog shite taste awful? Come on, Einstein, explain that one. Not that I've ever eaten dog shite, you understand.
Stuart Achilles, e-mail

I RECENTLY went to a pop concert to see an Al Qaida tribute band called Bomb Jovi. When they played *Living on a Prayer* the audience exploded. Have any other readers got any jokes that clearly have potential but still need a bit of work doing on them?
Alan Heath, e-mail

RECENTLY I witnessed three charming men in a white van compliment a young lady in the street on her pleasing décolletage. It's nice to know that in this day and age chivalry is not dead.
Lambert Sinmel, Coventry

EVERY KING dreams about what it would be like to be another sort of King for a day. But if they had the chance, which alternative King's identity would the male royals choose to take on for 24 hours? We asked a selection of reigning monarchs which other King's shoes they would like to step into for the duration of a single rotation of the earth on its axis.

go: "I done woke up this morning, and I got them King of Thailand Blues." I would probably repeat this refrain once more before moving onto the IV chord for a line about how my woman - Queen Sirikit of the House of Kitiyakara - done me wrong."

King Harald V of Norway

"EVER since I can remember I've been a huge fan of acapella singing, so if I got the chance I'd love to be **THE KING'S SINGERS** - all six of them. I love their close harmony vocals, except the lanky twat with the high pitched voice who looks like he probably couldn't grow a beard. Actually, now I come to think of it, I'm probably getting them mixed up with the Swingle Singers. Could you call me back when you're doing a space-filler called 'Young, Free and Swingle'?"

King Carl XVI Gustaf of Sweden

"AS A king, I have to look smart at all times. For appearing on stamps, coins and banknotes, I have to keep my hair cut short, groomed and combed, and frankly it's a bit of a drag. That's why it would be wonderful to try being boxing promoter **DON KING** and let my barnet go batcrap crazy for twenty-four hours. I wouldn't have any stamps or anything printed that day, and once I was back to my boring old self nobody would be any the wiser."

King Mswati III of Swaziland

"ACCORDING to Wikipedia, I've got fourteen wives and as you can imagine I'm bored shitless by normal sex with all my missuses. That's why I'd like to spend a day as ex-tennis champ **BILLIE JEAN KING**. I reckon twenty-four hours of hot girl-on-girl action in the Wimbledon changing rooms would be a great way of spicing up my jaded love life."

NEXT WEEK - We ask the Kings of Leon what they would do if they were assassinated civil rights leader Martin Luther King for a day.

IS THERE any point in eating breakfast? You're still going to have lunch later, and supper for that matter. Sounds to me like political correctness gone mad.
D Cooper, e-mail

WHILE playing football with the children I teach in primary school, I dribbled past the entire team, then dribbled back to the halfway line where I unleashed a shot so powerful that it hit a girl goalie in the chest, forcing her and the ball into the net. Have any of your readers ever scored such a marvellous goal?
David Katal, Lancs

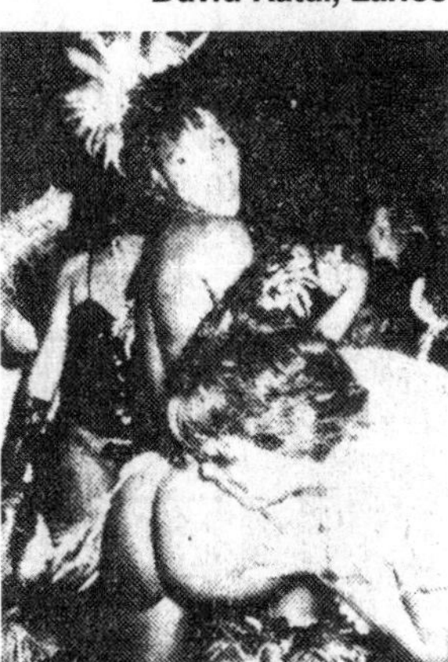

MY issue with that picture of that bloke kissing that bird's arse is not that it features a bloke inexplicably kissing a bird's bare backside, as that is normal and acceptable in any workplace. It is that he has also seen fit to place one hand on her bottom, a gross invasion of her privacy which she should immediately report to her line manager or supervisor. He should then be made to issue a public apology for turning an innocent, fun gesture into something altogether sordid.
Pete Cashmore, London

WHY don't female tennis players change their names to porn ones like Heavenly Sets or Felicity Forehand. With their skimpy outfits and rhythmic grunting surely that's the missing ingredient?
Vosene Shafferknackers, e-mail

I HAVE always been intrigued by dogs' behaviour where they sniff each other's bottoms. So when I was in the park last week, I crept up behind a dog and gave its anus a good sniff to see what it's all about. I must admit, I don't get what they see in it at all. I certainly won't be doing it again.
Hampton Steradian, Peebles

THE next Doctor Who? I reckon it should be ex-Leeds United frontman Arthur Graham. Either him or ex-Nottingham Forest legend Peter Grummit. I've got no idea why, though. And their assistant should have really big tits, and the character should in fact be called 'Big-Tits' so that the Dr could keep shouting "Come on Big-Tits" all the way through every episode.
Bobby Bowels, e-mail

ZOOS really are missing a trick. They should get the gorillas wearing little tutus instead of just lounging about, barely visible, in a bush at the back of the enclosure. Get the pigs wearing little wellie boots and while you're at it, give the tigers a giant ball of wool to play with. Come on, this is basic stuff.
George Pascal, Hove

THE news that the actor Clive Mantle had half his ear bitten off in a Travelodge came as no surprise to me. The last time I stayed in one I wasn't given any complimentary biscuits and the vending machine was broken. It was only a matter of time before someone turned to cannibalism.
Simon Hoffman, e-mail

FATTIES. A chocolate finger makes an ideal solider for a creme egg.
Phil Lawson, e-mail

PHISHING scammers. Putting three exclamation marks at the end of the subject of an e-mail makes me less inclined to believe it's actually from Barclay's Bank.
Alez Corrigan, e-mail

SINGLES. Don't waste money on using expensive dating sites to find your best matches. Simply tell the office gossip that you're shagging someone from work, but that they need to guess who it is. They will begin by listing the people whom they think it might be, starting with the one they consider most likely to shag you first and working down from there.
Barclay Fieldmouse, e-mail

TIME-strapped gym members. A chicken breast super-glued to each arm is a quick way to develop biceps.
Arnie Hauser, Birmingham

RECREATE a Welsh holiday by sitting under the shower whilst wandering around Blaenau Ffestiniog on Google Maps. And get all the family to pretend they don't speak English.
Rob Cottam, e-mail

A BARBIE doll cut in two and stuffed into half a fish makes an ideal 'Little Mermaid' for a girl's Christmas or birthday present.
Edna Boils, Loughborough

SAVE money on expensive nicotine gum by chewing regular gum every time you smoke a fag.
Andy Keen, e-mail

MAKE choosing lottery numbers fun for the whole family. Write the numbers 1 to 49 on sweet corn, eat them with your tea and see which six come out first. Don't forget to underline 6 and 9 (and use indelible ink).
James Brown, Edinburgh

BRASSO makes an ideal moisturiser for robots.
Fat Al White, Wrenthorpe

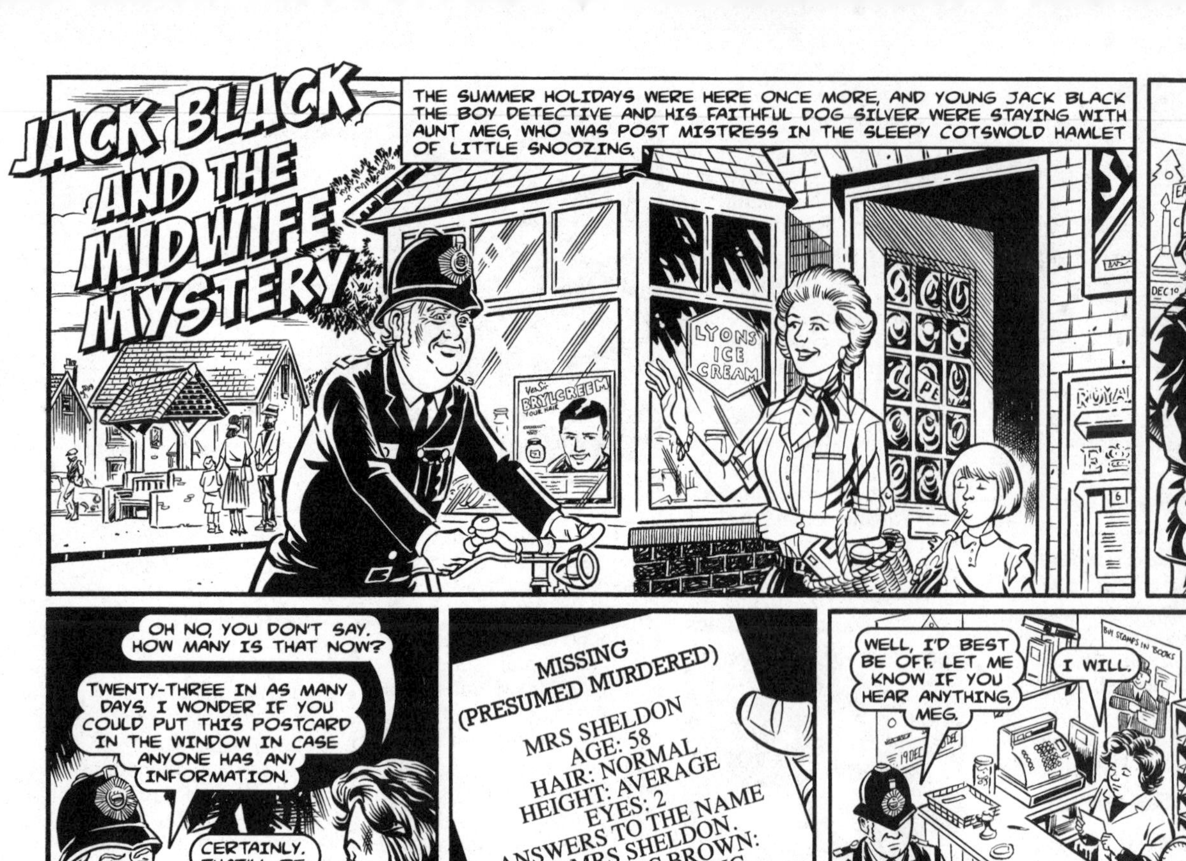
JACK BLACK AND THE MIDWIFE MYSTERY
THE SUMMER HOLIDAYS WERE HERE ONCE MORE, AND YOUNG JACK BLACK THE BOY DETECTIVE AND HIS FAITHFUL DOG SILVER WERE STAYING WITH AUNT MEG, WHO WAS POST MISTRESS IN THE SLEEPY COTSWOLD HAMLET OF LITTLE SNOOZING.
LYONS ICE CREAM
BRYLCREEM

GOOD MORNING, PC BROWN. AND HOW ARE THINGS TODAY?
NOT SO CHIPPER, I'M AFRAID, AUNT MEG.
ANOTHER VILLAGER HAS GONE MISSING. COMPLETELY VANISHED OFF THE FACE OF THE EARTH.
WARLORD
ATTACK AT DAWN

OH NO, YOU DON'T SAY. HOW MANY IS THAT NOW?
TWENTY-THREE IN AS MANY DAYS. I WONDER IF YOU COULD PUT THIS POSTCARD IN THE WINDOW IN CASE ANYONE HAS ANY INFORMATION.
CERTAINLY. THAT'LL BE TWENTY PEE PER FORTNIGHT.

MISSING
(PRESUMED MURDERED)
MRS SHELDON
AGE: 58
HAIR: NORMAL
HEIGHT: AVERAGE
EYES: 2
ANSWERS TO THE NAME OF MRS SHELDON.
CONTACT PC BROWN:
LITTLE SNOOZING
1212
GOODNESS, IT'S MRS SHELDON, THE GREENGROCER'S WIFE. WHY, I SAW HER ONLY YESTERDAY. SHE WAS DELIVERING SOME CARROTS TO MR HACKSTON'S HOUSE.

WELL, I'D BEST BE OFF. LET ME KNOW IF YOU HEAR ANYTHING, MEG.
I WILL.

HELLO, MISS KIPLING.
HELLO, MEG DEAR. I'VE JUST POPPED IN TO GET MY PENSION.
OF COURSE.
WARLORD
ATTACK AT DAWN!

AND WHO'S THIS HANDSOME YOUNG GENTLEMEN?
THIS IS MY NEPHEW, JACK, AND HIS CANINE SIDEKICK, SILVER.
WELL I NEVER. HASN'T HE GROWN?

YOU MIGHT NOT REMEMBER MISS KIPLING, JACK. BUT SHE WAS THE LOCAL MIDWIFE FOR OVER SIXTY YEARS.
YES. I THINK I MUST HAVE DELIVERED EVERYONE IN LITTLE SNOOZING, YOU KNOW. I EVEN DELIVERED YOU, JACK.

HAVE YOU HEARD ABOUT ALL THESE PEOPLE GOING MISSING IN THE VILLAGE?
I HAVE, BUT I'VE GOT MY OWN TROUBLES TO WORRY ABOUT AT THE MOMENT.
REALLY? WHAT'S THE MATTER?

IT'S MR HACKSTON, WHO LIVES NEXT DOOR. HE'S KEEPING ME AWAKE ALL NIGHT WITH HIS CHAINSAW.
A CHAINSAW? AT NIGHT? WHAT'S HE DOING?
I'VE NO IDEA...
...BUT YOU WOULDN'T BELIEVE THE SCREAMS THAT COME FROM HIS CELLAR IN THE EARLY HOURS. AND AS FOR THE STENCH FROM HIS DRAINS...WELL!

AND THAT'S NOT ALL. WHEN HE'S NOT CHAINSAWING, HE'S DIGGING HIS GARDEN AND LAYING PATIOS AT ALL HOURS.
OH, I SAY.

TWENTY-THREE PATIOS, HE'S GOT NOW, MR HACKSTON HAS. HE WAS PUTTING DOWN ANOTHER ONE AT THREE O'CLOCK THIS MORNING.
I TELL YOU, I HAVEN'T HAD A DECENT NIGHT'S SLEEP IN WEEKS
WELL, TRY NOT TO WORRY ABOUT IT, MISS KIPLING.

I'LL TRY. SEE YOU NEXT WEEK.
OKAY. BYE NOW.

AH, GOOD MORNING, MR HACKSTON. WHAT CAN I DO FOR YOU?
I'D LIKE A MACHETE, A HACKSAW AND TWENTY GALLONS OF HYDROCHLORIC ACID, PLEASE.
MORE THRILL

I'M SORRY. I'M AFRAID WE DON'T STOCK ANYTHING LIKE THAT.
OH DEAR. HOW VERY UNFORTUNATE.
I COULD ORDER THEM IN FOR YOU, IF YOU LIKE
THAT WOULD BE MOST KIND, THANK YOU.

I'LL GIVE YOU A RING WHEN THEY COME IN, SO YOU CAN POP ALONG AND COLLECT THEM.
YES. OR PERHAPS YOU COULD SEND YOUNG JACK ROUND WITH THEM.
OF COURSE.
HE WILL BE MOST WELCOME. GOODBYE TO YOU.

DID YOU SEE THAT, AUNT MEG
WHAT? YOU MEAN ALL THE BLOOD ON HIS APRON?

EH? NO, NOT MR HACKSTON. HE PROBABLY JUST CUT HIMSELF SHAVING. I WAS TALKING ABOUT MISS KIPLING.
DIDN'T HER BEHAVIOUR STRIKE YOU AS ODD AT ALL?
ODD? HOW DO YOU MEAN?

WHEN SHE COLLECTED HER PENSION, SHE FAILED TO PRODUCE ANY FORM OF PHOTOGRAPHIC IDENTIFICATION, SUCH AS A VALID ELECTORAL IDENTITY CARD, DRIVING LICENCE OR CURRENT UK PASSPORT.
BUT SHE DOESN'T NEED TO. SHE'S LIVED IN ROSE COTTAGE ALL HER LIFE. EVERYONE IN LITTLE SNOOZING KNOWS WHO SHE IS.

THAT'S NOT THE POINT. UNDER THE TERMS OF THE UK BENEFIT PAYMENTS ACT 2007 (AS AMENDED) SHE IS REQUIRED BY LAW TO PRODUCE HER CREDENTIALS BEFORE CLAIMING HER PENSIONS. MISS KIPLING IS CONCEALING HER IDENTITY...SHE'S HIDING SOMETHING.

AND SILVER AND I ARE GOING TO FIND OUT WHAT IT IS.

THAT NIGHT, JACK AND SILVER TOOK UP STATION BEHIND A BUSH IN MISS KIPLING'S GARDEN.
SHH! I THINK SOMETHING IS HAPPENING, SILVER!

HERE SHE IS. LET'S WATCH.

AH, SO THAT'S HER LITTLE GAME! COME ON, BOY. THERE'S NO TIME TO LOSE.

5:30, NEXT MORNING.
BANG! BANG!
OPEN UP, KIPLING! WE KNOW YOU'RE IN THERE!

OH IT'S YOU PC BROWN. I'LL BE DOWN IN A MOMENT.
QUICK! SHE'S GOING TO MAKE A RUN FOR IT OUT THE BACK!
BREAK THE DOOR DOWN! NOW!
YES, JACK!

GOOD GRACIOUS. WHAT'S GOING ON?
SMASH!

COUNCIL BYLAWS SAY THAT BINS MUST BE PUT OUT ONLY ON THE DAY OF COLLECTION, MISS KIPLING.
BUT I DID PUT IT OUT, JACK...
YES...AT THREE MINUTES BEFORE MIDNIGHT YESTERDAY!

OH, I'M MOST TERRIBLY SORRY...YOU SEE, I HAVEN'T BEEN SLEEPING VERY WELL AND I...
SAVE IT FOR THE JUDGE, KIPLING.
WELL DONE, JACK. THAT'S ANOTHER MISCREANT BROUGHT TO JUSTICE.

MORNING, MR HACKSTON. PUTTING IN A NEW PATIO?
YES, THAT'S RIGHT. YOU CAN NEVER HAVE TOO MANY PATIOS, I ALWAYS SAY, PC BROWN.

THE END

GARY NUMAN'S SCARS

Tell Me Doo

You Organ-related quieries answered by Loughborough University's Reader in Organ Studies **Dr Dougal Doo**

YOU see a lot of "organic" fruit and vegetables these days, and it got me wondering whether they have anything to do with my favourite musical instrument - the organ.

Mrs Audrey Leadbelly, Surbiton

• *IT WOULD be nice to think that organic vegetables were serenaded with sweet organ music whilst being grown, but sadly this is not the case. In agriculture, the word organic simply means undersized, unwashed and overpriced.*

WE are constantly reminded about the shortage of human organs for transplants, and it got me wondering whether hearts, kidneys and livers from our closest animal relatives - such as gorillas - could be used in place of human organs.

Jerry Leadbelly, Surbiton

• *IT'S A VERY interesting suggestion but unfortunately there are a number of obstacles to overcome before a successful human/gorilla organ transplant could take place. There are only 6,000 gorillas left in the wild and they tend not to get involved in road traffic accidents, and on the rare occasions when they do, they tend not to be carrying donor cards as they don't have wallets. Or pockets.*

Have you got any organ-related questions? Send them to:
Dr Dougal Doo, Room 3163, Organ Department, University of Loughborough.

Enjoy a soothing session of ancient Chinese muscle relaxation therapy with Zen Master...

Tommy Titsqueeze

Tommy is licensed to squeeze the following makes of tits: Swedish, Italian & Spanish. No French Please.

Tariff.
Normal Tits: £2.99
Not Normal Tits: £5

Barry Norman's

What they used for Snow in the Movies 2013

OVER THE YEARS, movie makers have used many different substances to simulate snow. And why not. Here's a list of five of the most unusual and imaginative snow substitutes used in films. And why not.

❄ *The Shining (1980)*

Whilst shooting the final scenes of his version of the Stephen King horror story, ***Stanley Kubrick*** used 25,000 boxes of Ariel soap powder to recreate the effect of a snowdrift in the hotel maze. Fortunately, the Spar round the corner from the Elstree lot had a 3-for-2 offer on 5kg boxes that week, so Kubrick managed to shave a cool £16,000 off his production budget. And why not.

❄ *White Christmas (1954)*

Not many people know that this film's star ***Bing Crosby*** was so allergic to snow that his nose and ears would go a bit red if he came into contact with it. Director ***Michael Curtiz*** was forced to used a substitute, and dumped over 600 tons of flaked white asbestos on the Burbank lot. Sixty years on, many of the people who worked on the film have died. And why not.

❄ *Home Alone (1990)*

For this movie, set at Christmas in the suburban streets of Chicago, director ***Chris Columbus*** racked his brains for a way of making the snow look genuinely cold whilst shooting at the height of the summer. Special effects experts eventually came up with the idea of burying the set in two feet of ice cream. A million tubs of Ben & Jerry's Vanilla Thriller were ordered, but due to a mix-up at the factory it was New York Fudge Chunk flavour that was actually dispatched. Before shooting on the outdoor sequences could begin, the crew had to sit up all night picking out almost 40 million fudge chunks - weighing a cool 80 tons. And why not.

❄ *Citizen Kane (1941)*

Often feted as the greatest movie ever made, the plot of ***Orson Welles***'s masterpiece begins with the film's central character Charles Foster Kane playing in the snow with his beloved sledge Rosebud. But believe it or not, it's not real snow you see on the screen - it's mashed potato - 800 lorry loads of the stuff. Ever the philanthropist, after filming, the director had 300 lorry loads of sausages stuck into the mash, which was then handed out to the bums, vagrants and hobos of Depression-hit Tinseltown. And why not.

❄ *Miracle on 34th Street (1947)*

This early Hollywood feelgood movie may have had a sickly sweet script, but the plot was nowhere near as sickly sweet as the snow on the set, which was made from 5,000 tons of lemon sherbet. The kayli, specially shipped in from the Haribo factory in Pontefract, UK, was bright yellow in colour but this didn't matter as the film was shot in black and white. And why not.

More What they used for Snow in the Movies next week! *Barry*

NOW 28

THAT'S WHAT I CALL EXCUSES FOR TRAIN DELAYS

20 Original 'Tracks'

NOT AVAILABLE IN THE SHOPS!

The latest collection of the best excuses for train delays. Swear along under your breath and promise to take the car next time, as the most disinterested voices inform everyone that the train is subject to delay.

Available from: **Beeching Records, Unit 2, Manchester Ind. Est., Devon.** Please note: In the likely event that we lose your order, we reserve the right to throw all further correspondence straight into the bin.

20 All-Time Favourites including:

- ✻ *We apologise for the late running of this train. This is due to engineering works in the Basingstoke area...*
- ✻ *All suburban services are subject to speed restrictions at this time...*
- ✻ *An incident on the line near Reading is affecting all services to and from Euston...*
- ✻ *We have been advised to wait here until a platform becomes available...*
- ✻ *Apologies for this unscheduled stop. As soon as I have more information, I will let you know when we are able to proceed...*

...and many more!

Hen
Cabin

How much?
Five pee a bloody bird!
FUXTED CHICK

Batter this shit up we'll make a fucking mint!
• Chicken • Burgers • Kebabs • Halal •
9 pieces
Hen Cabin

400 chicken, ten piece a piece, that's 444 nine piece meals...

Meal £1.99, four pence of fries, 20p can – quid and half profit a pop!
Yeah...

...but it's condemned.
Not a problem.
FUXTED CHICKEN

Bloke said this spray stain is designed to wash right off.
Really?
Of course!

So fuckwits further down the chain can get fed it.

However
Bollocks!
Basic Bleach
Basic Bleach

Must be a dodgy batch.
Pass us that brush.
Soon
Any joy with the pumice stone?
It's just riving off the skin –
Basic Bleach

– and the meat inside is bright green too.
I know what we need here.

Scouring powder.

Later
Bit more Vim and these'll fly out!
Basic Bleach
Basic Bleach

Chance of steady supply too, he reckons – so long as no fucker dies we're laughing!

Until
There, see? Nobody'll tell it from the old fresh stuff.
I can.

No you fuckin' can't.
Easy.

Hmmm.
Might be best to play it safe...

Get rid ten 'til midnight, shit-faced cunts only.

DAD in a MILLION!

£35 MILLION a week!

MEET Terry Crumbhorn, who is a dad in a million ... quite literally. For the unemployed Wednesbury hod-carrier has fathered an amazing ONE MILLION children. And next week his partner Sandra is due to give birth to the million-and-first addition to their record-breaking brood.

By our Rabble-Rousing Correspondent
Daley Mael

"Cheers for all the handouts," says £35 million-a-week Terry

EXCLUSIVE!

100,000 HOUSES!

Litter Lout: Superdad Terry (top) has spawned a million strong-brood. And (above) a few of the 100,000 council houses where the Crumbhorns reside.

You might expect that feeding and clothing such a vast family would leave the couple out of pocket. But it doesn't cost them a single penny, since the pair coin in a whopping *£35 MILLION* in benefits *... every WEEK!*

And their freeloading antics at the taxpayer's expense don't stop there. The Crumbhorns live in 100,000 council houses which have been knocked through into one to provide accommodation for themselves and their seven-figure litter.

baby

And with yet another baby on they way, the greedy couple have demanded that Wednesbury Borough Council move them somewhere even bigger.

arse

"We've got four hundred thousand teenagers, and it's simply not fair to expect them to share bedrooms," says Crumbhorn. "At their age they need privacy, and it's up to the local authority to provide it for them."

Terry, 45, has not worked for nearly 30 years after suffering a work-related injury in 1984. But whilst he has claimed BILLIONS of pounds in incapacity benefit over the intervening decades, his 'bad back' has not stopped him fathering an ever-increasing tally of children.

"People call me irresponsible for having so many kids, but they don't know what they're talking about," he says. "Me and Sandra have only actually had nought point eight million kids together. The other two hundred thousand of them are from previous relationships."

screen

The couple openly admit that they have considered family planning in the past. "We decided to call it a day when we reached half a million and I went for a vasectomy," he continues. "But it didn't take."

"If anything, I became even more fertile than before."

"We're just like any normal family, only a little bit bigger," says Terry. "We have our ups and downs and our fair share of arguments. For instance, I had rows with twenty-five thousand of my teenage daughters last week when they wanted to go to discos wearing make-up and skirts that I considered too short."

driving

Terry admits that he doesn't feel guilty about accepting state handouts to bring up his enormous clutch of offspring. "I can't work because of my back," he says. "If I only had one kid, the council would meet the costs of bringing it up, so why should the system discriminate against me just because I've got a million of them?"

aptitude

However, the Crumbhorns' cushy, benefits-funded lifestyle was last night slammed by Conservative MP Sir Anthony Regents-Park. He told us: "It's a national disgrace that these scroungers and their verminous brood of rat-like feral spawn are living high on the hog whilst the ordinary, decent man in the street is footing the bill."

MOT

"People like Mr Crumbhorn don't want to work. He'll never get on his bike and find a £35 million-a-week job while the rest of us are foolish enough to hand it to him on a plate," Sir Anthony, who was recently criticised by the Parliamentary Standards Committee after claiming £6 million expenses to build a luxury, moated 48-bedroom duckhouse at one of his French holiday homes, added.

Supermarket Sweep

THE WEEKLY shopping list for a typical family of four is big enough. But when you have 500,000 times as many children as the average, it becomes enormous. Here's just a fraction of what the greedy Crumbhorns load up on every seven days... *at our expense!* We must be off our trolleys.

- ***10 million disposible nappies***
- ***3.5 million loaves of sliced, white bread.***
- ***5 million tins of Heinz Bangers 'n' Beans.***
- ***5 million tins of spaghetti hoops.***
- ***900,000 pats of butter.***
- ***1000 tons of Turkey Twizzlers***
- ***1.5 million gallons of fizzy blue pop***
- ***10,000 PlayStation 3s***

Have Your Say

NOTHING in life is black or white. There are always two sides to every story and how someone choses to live their life is no concern of ours. So we went on the streets to find out what the Great British public had to say about the scrounging bastard Crumbhorns and their fucking freeloading lifestyle.

I THINK the local authority only has a duty to look after these children's welfare until they turn eighteen and not a day longer. By my calculations, they must be reaching that age at a rate of more than a thousand a week, saving the council considerable sums in benefits.

Doreen Freebird, fluffer

BEFORE they can claim another penny in benefits, Mr Crumbhorn and his common law wife should be forced to undergo compulsory sterilisation. If they refuse, their payments should be stopped, it's as simple as that.

Jerry Tintwhistle, vet

I THINK that the previous commenter ought to be ashamed of himself. In suggesting a policy of forcible sterilisation for economically unproductive people, he is behaving no better than Adolf Hitler and his Gestapo henchmen when they came up with their so-called Final Solution. Perhaps he would like Mr Crumbhorn and his family to be made to wear yellow stars on their clothing every time they leave the house.

Edna Spermbubble, welder

I THINK Mr Crumbhorn and his family should be made to wear yellow stars on their clothing every time they leave the house, so that anyone who disapproved of their lifestyle could easily identify them in the street and berate them or spit on them.

Dolly Vitriol, dinner lady

THE Crumbhorns look to me like a lovely family and they clearly love their children - all one million of them. If there were a few more lovely families like the Crumbhorns about, this country wouldn't be in the state it is. It would be much lovelier.

Ada Chelstrom, Mahout

TO SUGGEST that Mr Crumbhorn goes out and finds a job is ridiculous, simply looking after a million children is a job in itself. Making a million poached eggs on toast every morning must take him months.

Herbert Pocket, Cottager

THERE'S nothing to stop him getting a job at night. Mr Crumbhorn could easily fit in a shift in a bar, heading out to work each evening after reading his children a million bedtime stories.

Gloria Transit, Chiropodist

PEOPLE should stop criticising them. They have a difficult job and, from what I can see, they do it wonderfully well. Admittedly, they perhaps do have rather too many children, and some of the older ones should be made to make their own way in the world, but overall I don't begrudge my tax money going to their upkeep.

June Mortice, plumber

WITH reference to my previous comment *(above)*, I apologise. I thought we were talking about the Royal Family. I think Mr Crumbhorn should be castrated and his family put in care.

June Mortice, plumber

TO SAVE money, couldn't the council pay a strange man in a gaily-coloured harlequin costume to play a pipe outside the Crumbhorns' house, luring the children out and leading them into a secret cave in a nearby mountain? Once all the million children were inside the mountain, it could close up and they would never be seen again. At a stroke, this would save the local authority £35 million a week, which could be spent repairing potholes, funding the Wednesbury Mobile Library and subsidising the Meals-on-Wheels service for senior citizens.

Ray Turdbridge, Lord Mayor of Wednesbury

BIFFA BACON

Archbishop Slams Gay High Interest Rates

***What a gay pay day:** Welby declares holy war on unscrupulous homosexual moneylenders*

THE NEW Archbishop of Canterbury *Dr Justin Welby* has slammed same sex payday loans as being "a sin against God, the Church and society." And he called for the practice of same sex couples lending money on a short-term, high-interest basis to be regulated by the government.

Addressing members of the Church of England General Synod at Lambeth Palace, Dr Welby said: "As the law stands at the moment, there is nothing to stop homosexuals in a civil partnership from lending money to married couples and charging them extortionate rates of interest."

interest

"It is all too easy for a heterosexual man and wife to get into a vicious spiral of debt after borrowing a relatively small amount of money from same sex loan sharks," he continued.

exchange

"One particular couple in my parish borrowed £100 off a pair of homosexual loan sharks without realising that interest was accruing at a rate of 2500% APR. After a month, the shark and his

Stop same sex loan sharks, says Archbishop

civil partner arrived at their door demanding in excess of £300 to settle the debt."

mart

Welby called upon the government to look into the activities of homosexual money lenders and bring in legislation that would prevent gay couples profiting from the financial difficulties of men and women within conventional Christian marriages.

"This usurious and unnatural blight must be cast out," he told his fellow bishops. "When God made credit extension providers, he made Adam and Eve at around 5% APR, not Adam and Steve at an exorbitant four figure interest rate," the Archbishop added.

TERRY FUCKWITT
HE'S A THICK TWAT
DJ '13

HI READERS, I'VE HAD THIS GREAT IDEA! IT'S A LOVELY SUMMER'S DAY...
...SO I'M GOING FOR A NICE WALK!

NO TERRY, YOU ARE NOT "GOING FOR A NICE WALK".
EH?
DAD!

WHAT YOU'RE DOING THERE, SON, IS LYING FLAT ON THE GROUND AND WAVING YOUR LEG IN THE AIR LIKE A DAFT CUNT.
OH... YEAH
SO I AM.

WHAT THE HELL ARE YOU TWO SHIT-FOR-BRAINS PLAYING AT?!
EH?
FUCK ME - IT'S GRANDAD!

COME DOWN OFF THAT WALL AT ONCE! HAVEN'T YOU EVEN GOT THE SENSE TO KNOW WHICH WAY IS UP?

WHAT'S GOING ON HERE?!
MUM!

HONESTLY! YOU REALLY ARE A TRIO OF UTTER COCKWITS!
IT'S A LOVELY DAY, AND YOU'RE ALL COOPED UP INSIDE THIS ENORMOUS REVOLVING WOODEN BOX!

FOR GOODNESS SAKE, TERRY, WHY DON'T YOU GO FOR A WALK, OR SOMETHING?
HEY! THAT'S A GREAT IDEA, MUM!

MUM'S ALWAYS HAVING GOOD IDEAS! I WISH I COULD COME UP WITH A GOOD IDEA...
UNFORTUNATELY THOUGH, I'M AS DENSE AS DOGSHIT.

BROWN'S ACCESSORIES
WE'RE NOT GOING TO SELL THESE UMBRELLAS ON A LOVELY DAY LIKE THIS!
I MAY AS WELL JUST THROW THEM OUT WITH THE RUBBISH.

PHEW! IT'S HOT!
YES, I'M IN DANGER OF GETTING SUNSTROKE!

IF ONLY WE COULD HIRE SOME KIND OF PORTABLE ACCESSORY WHICH WOULD ACT AS A SUN-SHADE!
!
YES! I'D PAY GOOD MONEY TO HIRE A HAND-HELD DEVICE WHICH RESEMBLES A PARASOL RIGHT NOW!

WAIT A MINUTE... THIS IS QUITE UNBELIEVABLE...
I DO BELIEVE THAT I'M HAVING AN IDEA!

OWN'S
SSORIES
YES.. YES, I AM!
SPRINT
AND IT'S A BRILLIANT IDEA!

TATTOO PARLOUR
BROWN'S HATS & ACCESSORIES
TATTOOS
ZOOM!

SOME TIME LATER
TATTOOS
ACTUALLY, READERS: ON SECOND THOUGHTS, HAVING A BIG PICTURE OF JIMMY SAVILE TATTOOED ON MY CHEST WASN'T SUCH A GREAT IDEA.
IN FACT — WITH HINDSIGHT — IT WAS PROBABLY THE WORST IDEA IN THE WORLD!

SURELY I MUST BE CAPABLE OF PRODUCING ONE GOOD IDEA IN MY LIFE
PERHAPS IF I TRY TO THINK REALLY HARD... GNNNNNN!

IDEA
THERE! I'VE DONE IT! I'VE HAD A BRAINWAVE!

NO, YOU HAVEN'T, TERRY...
WARNING! IT'S A REALLY BAD IDEA TO STICK A FORK INTO A LAMP SOCKET
DEPT OF HEALTH
YOU'RE MERELY STANDING IN FRONT OF THIS LARGE POSTER WHICH HAS A PICTURE OF A LIGHT BULB AND THE WORD "IDEA" ON IT.

WARNING! IT'S A REALLY BAD IDEA TO STICK A FORK INTO A LAMP SOCKET
DEPT OF
SHALL I PLUG THIS LAMP IN FOR YOU, TERRY?
YES PLEASE, DAD!

ZAP!
KILL!

MOST OF US have two, others have just one and some lucky individuals have none at all. We're talking about Grannies... and if you've got any, chances are they're winging their way to your house right now to spoil your Christmas. But how much do you really know about these wrinkly little old racists who sit farting and snoring their way through the festive season each year in your living room? You might think you know everything there is to know about the Great British Grandmother, but do you really? Here's our festive rundown of...

20 *GRAN-TASTIC* Things You Never Knew Abo GRANNIES

1 IN the past, a granny could easily be recognised from her drab, beige clothing. But these days, she'll more likely be found sporting apparel of much funkier hues, such as taupe, fawn, eau de nil or mouseback, all of which are a sort of mushroomy-beige colour.

2 YOU might expect a 'Great-Grandmother' to be an extra-special sort of grandmother - perhaps one who has no idea how decimal currency works and gives you a thousand pounds each Christmas in the mistaken belief that it's worth about a tenner. But you'd be wrong Because a great-grandmother is simply a much older sort of granny who refuses to die.

3 CHILDREN of lesbian couples who go on to marry will have children who have ***three*** grandmothers. And if both marital partners are the children of lesbian couples, their offspring will boast no fewer than ***four*** - that's twice as many as everybody else.

4 BELIEVE it or not, the grannies of today were young women who played an active part in the Second World war. Some worked at Bletchley Park, breaking the Enigma code; many worked in munitions factories or as land girls on the farm. Many more kept up the morale of US bomber crews by fellating them in air raid shelters, but whatever they did they all played their part in defeating the Nazi menace.

5 THE nation's favourite grandmother was Her Royal Highness Queen Elizabeth the Queen Mother. Until her untimely death at the age of 102, she received an amazing sixty million soaps on a rope each Christmas from us, her adoring "grandchildren".

6 THERE are many things that are suitable to buy as a gift for your granny at Christmas. You can't go wrong with a gift of bath salts, fleecy slippers or jellied fruits.

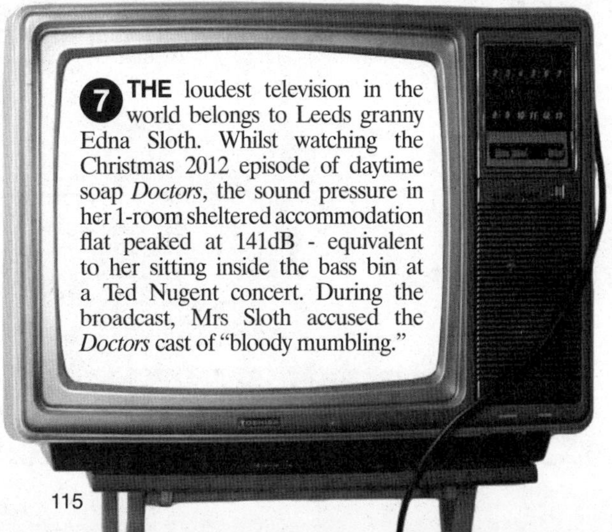

7 THE loudest television in the world belongs to Leeds granny Edna Sloth. Whilst watching the Christmas 2012 episode of daytime soap *Doctors*, the sound pressure in her 1-room sheltered accommodation flat peaked at 141dB - equivalent to her sitting inside the bass bin at a Ted Nugent concert. During the broadcast, Mrs Sloth accused the *Doctors* cast of "bloody mumbling."

8 OR a calendar with a cat on it.

9 THE legal minimum age to be a granny in Great Britain is $33\frac{1}{2}$. However, in many southern states of America and on Jeremy Kyle, they can be much younger.

10 IT'S a shocking fact that Grannies are forever getting mugged by youths for 20p. But the world record for the lowest amount a granny has been mugged for is held by 82-year-old Marketa Benes of the Czech Republic, who was mugged by a youth for a paltry 1 CzK - equivalent to just 0.03p.

11 JUST like sloths, grannies are notoriously slow movers and rarely exceed a speed of 1.5mph, unless they are falling down the stairs, when their velocity can peak at around 20mph.

12 OVER the years, grannies have been the subject of an endless succession of hit records, including *Grandma We Love You by* the St Winifred's School Choir and *Grandma's Party* by Paul Nicholas.

13 HE also did *Reggae Like it Used to Be*, but

that didn't really mention grannies.

14 AND *Dancing With the Captain*, which didn't mention grannies either.

15 AND he was also in *Just Good Friends*, with Jan Francis who, at the age of 66, is old enough to be a great grandma, or even a great-great grandma in some southern states of America.

Some Like it Hot: 87 Year Itch star Marilyn would keep her house like a bloody oven and still go on about how cold it was.

16 THE vast majority of grannies are quite small, between 4'6" and 5'2". But last year, *Nature* magazine reported that scientists from the University of Lapaz had caught an 8'3" tall monster on an expedition to the rain forests of Peru. The giant gran was lured into a spring-trap baited with a bag of Werther's Originals, an old copy of the *People's Friend* and a nice Shacklelton's High Seat Chair.

17 THEY might look old and past it, but according to the lurid covers of several DVDs in the Gilf Interest rack at the Sven Adult store in Newcastle, many grannies still enjoy active and energetic sex lives.

18 OVER the twelve days of Christmas, the average granny produces 12.5 cubic metres of silent flatus - that's enough flammable gas to fill a three berth caravan or keep a 1kW methane-powered stove burning for 38 hours.

19 PAUL Nicholas has been in *Doctors* three times, playing Martin Stockton in 2000, a character called Terry in 2006 and Pete Power in 2012.

20 AMAZINGLY, if Marilyn Monroe were alive today, she would be a granny of 87. And the blonde bombshell star of *Some Like it Hot, Gentlemen Prefer Blondes* and *The Seven Year Itch* would have her gas fire on even in the summer and would lay the blame for all the country's problems squarely at the door of immigrants.

RAY of the JACKAL

GAVRILO PRINCIP... JOHN WILKES-BOOTH... LEE HARVEY OSWALD... A chilling catalogue of cold-blooded assassins who ruthlessly took aim and pulled the trigger at a succession of kings, presidents and heads of state. In doing so, these ruthless marksmen changed the course of world history and ensured that their names would never be forgotten.

Showbiz world breathes easy as Ray's catalogue of murder comes to an end

But these hitmen are rank amateurs compared to one professional killer who claims to have "rubbed out" hundreds, if not thousands of A-listers from the world of showbiz. *"Believe you me,"* says ***Ray 'the Jackal' Pustule***, now retired and living in Holbeck near Leeds. *"The roll-call of people I've taken out reads like a Who's Who of famous names."*

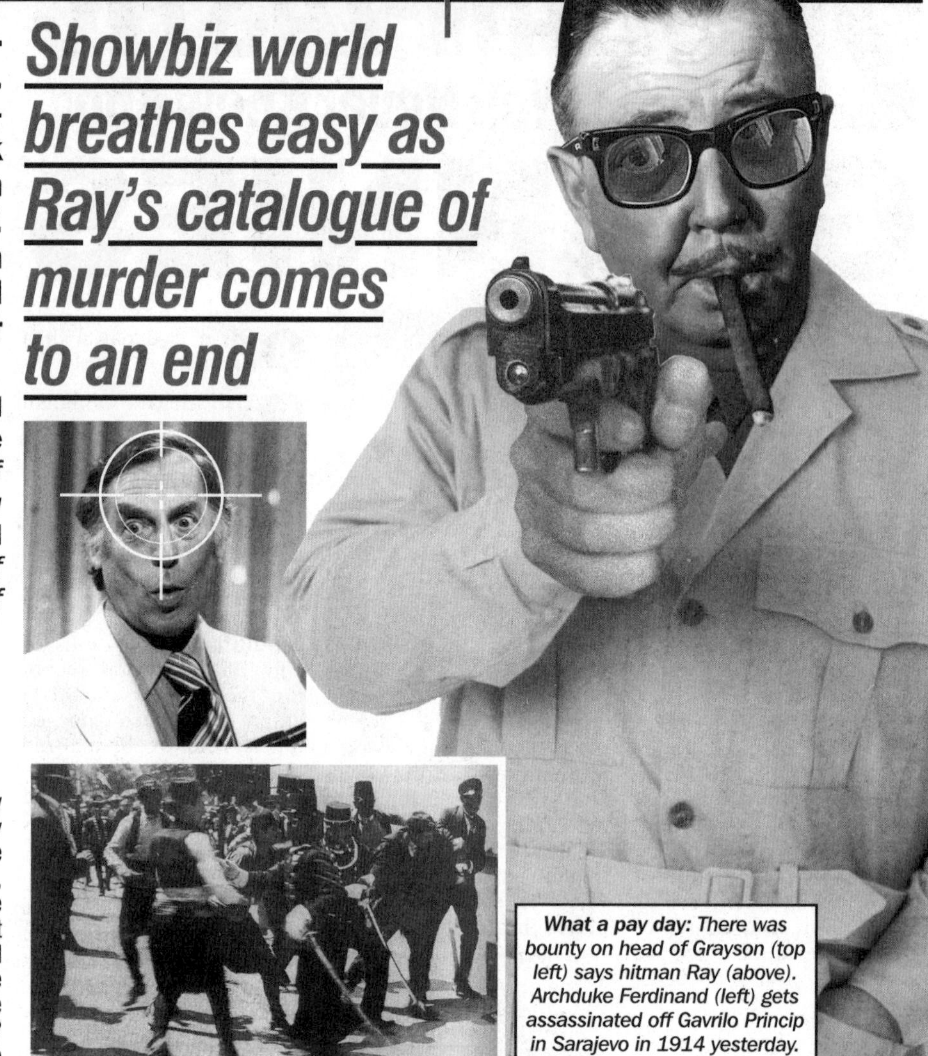

What a pay day: There was bounty on head of Grayson (top left) says hitman Ray (above). Archduke Ferdinand (left) gets assassinated off Gavrilo Princip in Sarajevo in 1914 yesterday.

And now, with his career behind him, Ray, 64, is finally free to tell his shocking story. "All the stars I assassinated are dead and buried," he told us. "And a bloke in the pub told me that according to British law, once they're six feet under nobody can be charged with their murder."

"People may think I'm a cold-blooded killer, but believe you me, all my victims had it coming to them. I was only doing my job and they were fair game."

paymasters

Pustule is now set to lift the lid on the murderous world he inhabited. He is presently looking for a publisher for his new autobiography *The Ray of the Jackal*, which runs to 38 sides of A4. This sensational document details many of the most high-profile of his "hits" and even hints at the identities of his shadowy paymasters. "The people who put up the money were the real criminals," he told us. "And it's time they were named and shamed."

modern majors

"There'll be plenty of twitching arseholes in the world of showbiz when this book hits the shelves, I can tell you," he added.

Now, in these exclusive extracts, Ray gives us a sneaky peek into the sinister yet exciting life of a celebrity hitman.

The Assassination Game.....

OVER THE YEARS many celebrities have died suddenly and unexpectedly. Often, the reason given is old age or illness, and that was certainly the case when *Generation Game* host ***LARRY GRAYSON*** was found dead in his dressing room at the age of 71 in 1995. But was there a sinister plot behind his demise? "The cause on the death certificate was given as a perforated appendix," says Ray. "But what the coroner didn't mention was that it was perforated by a 9mm slug from my gun!"

"You wouldn't have thought that a mild-mannered entertainer like Grayson would have had an enemy in the world, but he'd stepped on a lot of toes on his way up the showbiz ladder. There were many people who wanted him dead and one of them was prepared to put hard cash on the table to have him rubbed out. And that's where I came in.

The camp *Generation Game* host was well known for his love of flowers, so nobody at BBC Television Centre thought twice when they saw a helmeted motorcycle courier carry a big bouquet towards his backstage dressing room. He'd left the door open, and smiled when he saw the roses, chrysanthemums and lilies. What he didn't know was that nestling amongst the pretty blooms was a 9mm automatic pistol. And in that pistol was a bullet with Grayson's name on it.

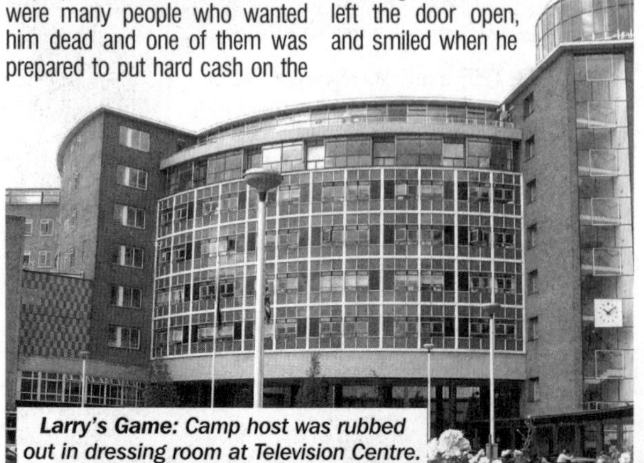

Larry's Game: Camp host was rubbed out in dressing room at Television Centre.

'Sorry Lal, nothing personal,' I said as I squeezed the trigger. There was a dull thud as the silencer did its work, the slug found its mark and the entertainer went down like a sack of spuds. I escaped on a motorbike and threw my gun into the Thames as I went over Tower Bridge. I couldn't help reflecting that if only Grayson had taken his own advice and 'shut that door', perhaps he'd still be alive today.

directors

Of course, the BBC hushed everything up. They hurriedly organised a funeral before the press and public started getting suspicious. But even now, one big question remains: Who had paid for the hit?

I'm a professional, and I'm not going to name any names. Suffice to say that when Grayson took over a certain high-profile Saturday night family show, he displaced another star, who was left bitter and angry. It was this man - a household name to this day - who told me: 'If you play your cards right, Ray, the price will be right.' And when he handed over the cash I have to admit, it was nice to see the money, to see the money nice."

Shooting Star.....

WHEN HE DIED last year at the age of 89, boggly-eyed astronomer ***PATRICK MOORE*** had been a fixture on our television screens for over a century. But it took less than half a minute for Ray to bring that remarkable career to a close.

"I got a phone call from a famous academic who claimed Moore had taken credit for discovering

Telescopic sight: Astronomer's regular routine made him easy to pick off with high-powered rifle.

Crater love: Moore's life was laid downdue to jealousy over lunar feature.

a crater on the Moon that he had seen first. He told me he wanted the *Sky at Night* presenter offed, as a warning to other boffins who were thinking of following suit.

best bitter

I booked myself into a B&B near Moore's home in Selsey, Sussex and watched him over the course of a week. Regular as clockwork every night at 9.30 he would finish his xylophone practice and make his way down to the small observatory at the end of his garden. The irony was, while he was looking at heavenly bodies through his telescope, I was drawing a bead on him through my telescope ... attached to the barrel of my Remington 700.

It was almost too easy. The ancient starspotter was so slow-moving and presented such a big target through my sights that I couldn't miss. He never stood a chance; it was like hitting a cow's arse with a banjo. One dum-dum bullet through his trademark monocle was all it took to dispatch him to the heavens he'd been observing all his career.

dark mild

As to the identity of the embittered boffin who called the hit? I couldn't possibly say. If you think you can get his name out of me, you can D;Ream on. But I will say this: with Moore out of the way, things could only get better for this former keyboard player turned TV physicist."

The Hitman and Hird.....

IF YOU DREW up a list of celebrities least likely to get assassinated, surely ***THORA HIRD*** would have been at the top. When she died at the age of 91 in 2003, the papers were full of heart-warming tributes to the *Last of the Summer Wine* and *Songs of Praise* star. But not everybody shared the nation's affection for this much-loved character actress. Indeed, one nameless celebrity hated her so much he was willing to pay The Jackal to take her out. Permanently.

"Most jobs start the same way and the hit on Thora Hird was no exception. A picture of the target in a brown envelope left in the cistern of a toilet at a railway station, with a phone number written on the back. I made the call and said two words: 'Ten grand'. The reply was also two words: 'Do it', then the line went dead. As I walked back to my bedsit, I idly wondered what the star of *In Loving Memory*, *Hallelujah* and *Dinnerladies* had done to deserve the ultimate punishment.

Russian imperial stout

Perhaps she was head of a drugs cartel who had overstepped the mark and tried to muscle in on some yardies' territory. Maybe she'd been blackmailing someone or had got in too deep in the sex slave trade and had fallen foul of the vengeful father of one of her victims. Whatever the reason for the hit, I had ten thousand better ones for carrying it out.

It wasn't going to be an easy job, I knew that, so I spent a day in the woods getting my eye in, shooting at watermelons with National Health glasses perched on them. Then I set off for Holmfirth in Yorkshire, where Hird was filming an episode of *Last of the Summer Wine*. I sneaked into the West Yorkshire County Council School Book Depository and hid myself away on the third floor. I didn't have to wait long before my opportunity presented itself.

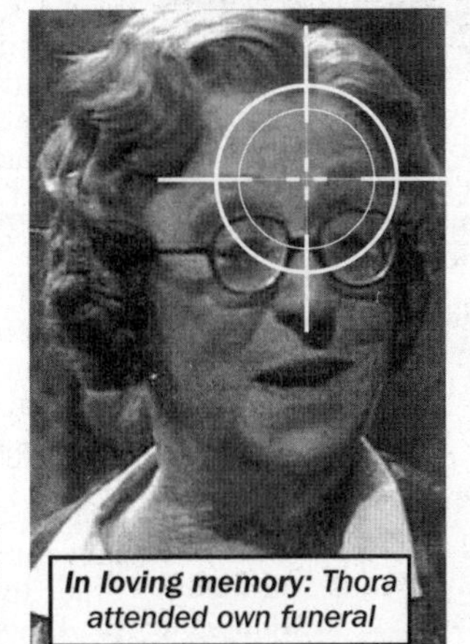

In loving memory: Thora attended own funeral

hill

They were shooting a scene where Hird's character Edie Pegden was riding down a hill in a bathtub on wheels. I knew she'd have to slow down to get the bath round the corner outside the depository, and that would be my one chance to get in a clean headshot. I lined up my rifle and squinted down the barrel, biding my time. Suddenly, Hird's face appeared in the crosshairs and I squeezed the trigger. My practice with the melons had paid off and the first round went in the back of her head and out of the front. I took a pre-paid mobile phone out of my pocket and dialled. 'Job done,' I said. The money was instantly wired into my numbered Swiss bank account.

To this day I don't know who my paymaster was. But if you ask me, there was only one person who stood to gain from Thora's premature death at 91. I'm not pointing the finger, but consider this: a new presenter took over on *Songs of Praise* that Sunday. A certain Welsh ex-boy soprano who was probably walking in the air with delight when he found out about his new job."

It Ain't Half Shot, Mum.....

IN 2003, the showbiz world was stunned to hear of the death of actor and singer ***DON ESTELLE.*** Aged 70, the papers reported that the *It Ain't Half Hot Mum* star had passed away peacefully in his sleep at his home in Rochdale. But there was no surprise for Ray "The Jackal" Pustule. For he already knew that Lofty was dead.

"This was one of my hardest hits, because I loved Estelle's show and I loved his voice. But I always made it a rule never to mix business with pleasure, so when I got my instructions to take him out, I put my personal feelings aside and went into assassin mode. He wasn't hard to find; he was signing LPs at the Co-op in Parliament Street, Nottingham. I followed him back to his hotel - a swanky Travelodge on the Ring Road.

edwards

I sat in my car on the opposite side of the street and got my gun ready. It was one of those that comes in a briefcase all in bits, and you have to put them together before you can use them. The magazine slid home with a satisfying clunk, I took off the safety catch and I was ready for another day at the office. But this was the office of death.

Moments later I was standing outside Estelle's door. I knocked.

He ain't half shot mum: Royalties dispute cost pint-sized Don his life.

'Who is it?' came the high-pitched voice from inside. 'Room service,' I replied. The door started to open and I made my move, pushing through the gap, keeping the element of surprise on my side. Once in the room, I knew I only had seconds to get the job done. I grabbed a cushion, pressed it across his face and emptied the chamber. There were feathers everywhere. I think I must have made quite a mess of him, because they could only identify him from the pith helmet he was wearing.

But why had such a mild-mannered, harmless man been targeted? It turns out that back in the seventies Estelle had recorded a duet with another actor who shall remain nameless. According to the recording contract, royalties were to be split fifty-fifty straight down the middle. However, in a double indemnity clause, if either party should die, the proceeds would go in their entirety to the surviving partner.

cricket

I can now confirm that it was indeed Estelle's former colleague who took out the contract and paid me to assassinate the pint-sized tenor. But my client can rest assured that I'm not going to speculate as to his identity. I'm not going to sing Lofty. I'm no whispering grass, lovely boy."

Shot Like That, Like That....

THE VIEWING public who tuned in to watch top-rated variety show *Live From Her Majesty's* on April 15th 1984 didn't expect to see one of the country's best-loved stars get assassinated right in front of their eyes on their TV screens, but that's just what they witnessed. And the truth of what happened that night has remained hidden until now.

"A famous television personality whose career had gone off the rails was holding funnyman ***TOMMY COOPER*** responsible for his downfall. It would be wrong of me to identify him now, let's just say he was a popular impressionist who had recently fallen on hard times. He was blaming Cooper because he couldn't really get the voice right, and he was prepared to pay good money to see the fez-wearing comedy magic star rubbed out ... just like that.

I decided to carry out the hit on live TV, so it was going to be a tricky job. Producers and directors don't like unauthorised personnel wandering about backstage during a broadcast, so I knew security would be tight. But I had a plan, and it was so audacious that if you saw it as part of one of those *Mission Impossible* films with Tom Cruise, you'd think it was far-fetched.

tarbuck

The morning of the hit, I made myself a rubber Jimmy Tarbuck mask. Wearing it, and doing an impression of the scouse comic's voice, I made my way backstage. Then, when the real Tarbuck introduced Cooper and he came on to do his act, I was able to sidle up behind the curtains and jab him in the arse with an umbrella that I had earlier tipped with deadly Amazonian tree frog poison.

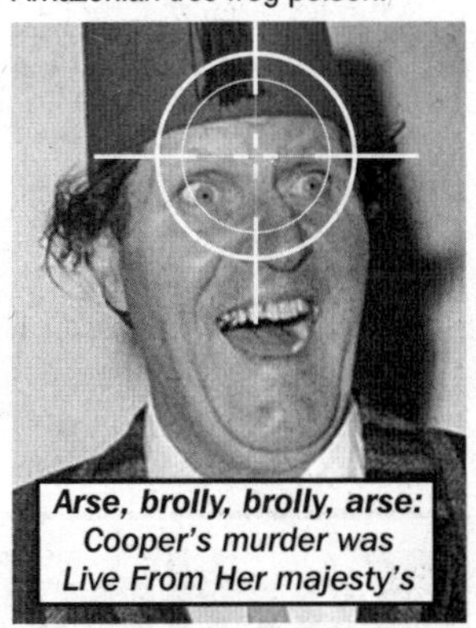

Arse, brolly, brolly, arse: Cooper's murder was Live From Her majesty's

Cooper went down almost immediately as the deadly toxin coursed through his veins. In the confusion, the director cut to an advert break. Meanwhile, all hell broke loose on the stage, and while everyone's attention was distracted, I pressed a secret button on my watch which shot out a grappling hook on a wire and zipped me up off the stage into the lighting gantry. From there, I managed to make my way onto the roof of the theatre, and then ran from roof to roof, halfway across London, doing forward rolls when I landed. Eventually I got to the top of the Post Office Tower, where I'd hidden a hot air balloon which I then escaped in."

• We showed the manuscript of Ray's book to police, who refused to confirm whether or not they would be re-opening investigations into any of the celebrity killings he claims to have committed. "Mr Pustule is known to us," said a spokesman. "We have spoken to him several times about cleaning up after his dogs in a public place and he has been cautioned twice after being caught standing on his neighbour's bins in order to look through her toilet window."

Kardashian to Tackle 'THE KNOWLEDGE'

LOS ANGELES 'It' girl *KIM KARDASHIAN* has revealed plans to relocate to the UK next month so she can begin studying for London taxi exam 'The Knowledge'.

Curvy Kim, 32 - who is best known for her role in reality TV show *Keeping Up with the Kardashians* - made the shock announcement during a recent interview with *Vanity Fair* magazine.

"Passing 'The Knowledge' is something I've dreamed of since

US socialite sets sights on London cab quiz

I was a little girl," she said. "I've been blessed with success in various fields - from modelling and clothing design to television production - but I don't feel my life will truly be complete until I've memorised all 25,000 London streets within a six mile radius of Charing Cross."

limousines

And while she's used to stepping out of stretch limousines in glamorous ball gowns, the sexy socialite admits her new venture will mean a downgrade in style for both her wardrobe and her means of transport.

"Riding around Lambeth on a battered moped whilst wearing a day-glo tabard will obviously be a bit of a change of pace for me," joked Kim. "But I'm prepared to do whatever it takes to commit the requisite 320 major central London routes to memory."

And Kardashian went on to reveal that, while she is eagerly anticipating the challenge of learning to navigate the capital without the use of a map or GPS, she does not expect the task to be an easy one.

She said: "My friends and family tried to persuade me to train as a suburban cabbie – known in the trade as a 'Yellow Badge' driver – but I've never been one for doing things by halves. Consequently, I've cleared a two-to-four-year gap in my schedule to tackle the full, all-London 'Knowledge', which demands an intimate awareness of more than 20,000 landmarks and places of interest within the Greater London area."

armstrongs

And it appears the trend for A-Listers swapping Hollywood stardom for less glamorous jobs within the British transport industry is spreading fast. According to recent reports, hotel heiress ***Paris Hilton*** has confirmed plans to move to Fleetwood, Lancashire, in order to qualify as a conductor on the Blackpool tramway.

You'll never guess who I had in the front of my cab: *IT-girl Kim (left) gets behind the wheel. (below) another cabbie hopeful studies 'The Knowledge'*

The PaRKiE
BEACH PATROL
EVERYONE IS A BASTARD!

...THERE YOU GO, SON.
WOW! CAN I STICK MY FLAG IN THE TOP NOW, DAD..?
YES. OF COURSE YOU...

STOMP!

NO BASTARD SANDCASTLES! BY ORDER!
CAN'T YOU FUCKING READ, TINKERBELL?
NO BASTARD SAND-CASTLES BY ORDER

...AND NO BASTARD FLAGS, NEITHER!
SNATCH!
AND NO BASTARD FLAGS NEITHER

I'M TRYING TO KEEP THIS BEACH TIDY. I'VE NOT SPENT ALL NIGHT RAKING AND ROLLING THE FUCKER JUST SO AS YOU CUNTS CAN DIG THE BASTARD UP WITH YOUR FUCKING BUCKETS AND TWATTING SPADES.

SHORTLY...
OOH, LOOK SIS! A LITTLE CRAB JUST WENT UNDER THAT ROCK...!
TEE-HEE!

BEEP! BEEP! BEEP! BEEP!
VEHICLE REVERSING! VEHICLE REVERSING!
?

FUCKING BASTARDS.
BLOIP!
QUICK DRYING CEMENT

KEEP OUT OF THE FUCKING ROCK POOLS

SHORTLY...
'ELLO... WHAT HAVE WE HERE..?
A FUCKING DOG ON MY BASTARD BEACH..?!
GIVE SOME PEOPLE A FUCKING INCH AND THEY TAKE A CUNTING MILE.
BEACH PATROL
RIGHT...
NO MORE MISTER NICE GUY!

OI! YOU THERE! YES, YOU...BILLY FUCKING BUNTER..!
I'M SORRY..?
YOU FUCKING WILL BE, PAL... DON'T YOU FUCKING WORRY.
WHAT? I...
ARP! ARP! ARP!

OFF SCHOOL THE DAY THEY TAUGHT READING, WERE YOU..?
WHAT ON EARTH..? THIS ISN'T A DOG... IT'S A COMMON HARBOUR SEAL, Phoca vitulina...
NO FUCKING DOGS ON THE FUCKING BEACH

I DON'T GIVE A FLYING WANK WHAT FUCKING BREED IT IS, JUST GET YOUR FUCKING SHITE MACHINE OFF MY BEACH BEFORE I PUT MY FUCKING BOOT THROUGH ITS FUCKING HEAD.
ALRIGHT?!

DOGS! FUCKING WET-NOSED HAIRY FUCKING BASTARD THINGS... SHITTING ON MY SAND AND CHASING BALLS INTO MY FUCKING SEA...
MUMBLE... GRUMBLE...
PUPPET SHOW 2pm

HELLO BOYS AND GIRLS!
WHO WANTS TO SEE A PUPPET SHOW?
WE DO!

HEY YOU! GET OFF MY BEACH, YOU LITTLE BASTARD OR I'LL BREAK YOUR FUCKING NECK!

AND THAT GOES FOR YOU FUCKERS AN' ALL... GO ON...
FUCK THE FUCK OFF!

CAN'T YOU FUCKING READ?!
NO KIDS
YOU HEARD ME
NO FUN
NO DECK-CHAIRS
NO ICE-CREAMS
FUCK OFF
FUCK OFF

LETTERBOCKS

Viz Comic, P.O. Box 841
Whitley Bay, NE26 9EQ
letters@viz.co.uk

☐ **I SEE** that scientists are now able to implant false memories into the brains of laboratory mice. The rodents are now able to recall something that didn't happen and believe it to be real. How amazing. As a reward for participating in the experiment, let's hope they implanted something fun, like driving a go-kart or beating up a load of cats in a Bruce Lee-style Kung Fu showdown.

Norman Fletcher, e-mail

☐ **THE** other week I made a conscious decision to accept the Lord Jesus Christ as my own personal saviour. The very next day I went arse over tit after a Special Brew binge and ended up in hospital. Explain that one, Bible cunts.

James Lennox, e-mail

☐ **I WENT** to the armed forces recruitment centre yesterday to sign up and join the infantry. I was told that I would probably be deployed to a conflict zone where there would be intense battles. When I pointed out that this sounded extremely dangerous in terms of health and safety, and that it would be better if I were sent to a non-combat zone, the vicious bullies laughed me out of the building.

Philip Halfwank, e-mail

STAR LETTER

☐ **ABOUT** 2% of the population of the USA have at some time been kidnapped by aliens. Well, we have space shuttles and astronauts, so why don't some of our spacemen go to these planets and kidnap a few aliens in return? Obviously I don't want to escalate the situation, but surely this might teach them a lesson and make them stop.

Alan Heath, e-mail

☐ **I READ** the other day that the Blakiston's Fish Owl is the largest owl in the world, reaching sizes of up to 72cm. They come from Japan, a country also known for videos of men spaffing over women's faces. You have to hand it to these guys. Personally, I'd be too worried about Alsatian-sized owls flying about to get a hard-on.

Simon Wingate, e-mail

☐ **CONSIDERING** that Bear Grylls is supposed to be ex-SAS and prepared for any eventuality during his regular forays into dangerous and inhospitable terrain, you'd think he might occasionally remember to pack a few sandwiches.

Brenford Nylon, Harpenden

☐ **I RECKON** Elvis might not have been so frivolous about serving a custodial sentence when he sang *Jailhouse Rock* if he had actually done a bit of bird. The last time I went away, I was too busy shitting in a bucket and picking the soap up with my toes to worry about Spider Murphy and his saxophone.

Decca Scruttock, Yorkshire

☐ **I'M** no Gregor Mendel, but wouldn't it be in women's interest to select a mate with a tiny head and narrow shoulders? It would revolutionise childbirth and in the future we'd all be a race of supersnakes.

Miko Stromstedt, e-mail

☐ **I'M** tired of hearing how the downturn in our economy has affected hard-working families and individuals. What about us lazy fuckers?

Gerry Patton, e-mail

☐ **THIS** scab on my mate's head looks exactly like HRH Queen Elizabeth II on a stamp.

Ronan McCarthy

UNLUCKY people. Prevent your bread always falling buttered side down by waiting until after you've dropped it to butter it.

Tom Ellen, e-ma

MAKE wild tigers and lions come closer to you on safa by making a "pspspsps" noise.

Ernest, e-ma

PRETEND you're a tennis player by going to the fruit bowl, picking up 3 oranges throwing one on the floor, putting one in your pocket and hitting the 3rd one up the stairs with a frying pan.

Matt Wray, e-ma

TRICK the man downstairs into thinking you have amoebic dysentery by flushir your toilet every three minute

Robin Znest, Perkle

ROLLS of chain-link fencing make ideal fishnet stockings for elephant glamour models

Mungo Chutney, Tru

☐ **I LOVE** that there's an empty square beside each letter on the Letterbocks page. I put a tick in each one after reading the letter so I know not to waste time reading it again.

Johnny Shields, e-mail

☐ **I WONDER** how Prince William and Prince Harry distinguished between their grandmothers when they were little. Do you think they referred to the Queen one and the other one? Or do you think they called them grandma Windsor and nana Shand-Kydd?

Hector Vuvuzela, London

☐ **"IS** there any bread or anything?" my girlfriend asked me last night. I had to laugh. Of course there was.

D Cooper, e-mail

☐ **WHILE** watching *Seven Ages of Britain* on the Discovery Channel, I noted Bettany Hughes alluding to

Duff Info

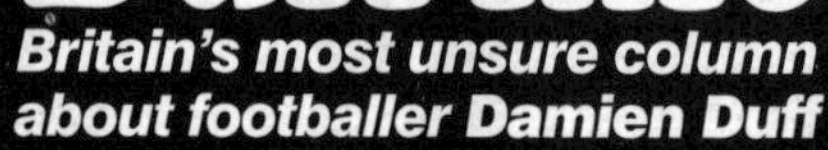

ONCE again we have been inundated with questions about the Republic of Ireland international from people who don't have access to the internet...

• **WHO** did Damien Duff play for before Chelsea?

Ada Lustgarten, Luton

* *I'm pretty sure it was Bolton Wanderers or possibly Wigan. Thinking about it, it could have been Blackburn, although to be honest i'm not 100% sure. It was one of those three.*

• **HOW** many Champions League appearances has Damien Duff made?

Dolly Adrenalin, Hants

* *Right, is this when he was at Chelsea? It's got to be more than 15, I would say, although he was on the bench a lot when he was there. Or was that Winston Bogarde? About 15, I reckon. Possibly a few more but not many.*

• **WHO'S** that actor who looks a bit like Damien Duff?

Hector Spam, Hull

* *You mean that bloke who looks like the one who played for Wimbledon? In that film? Blimey that's a tough one. It was on the other night as well. Gary something. It begins with a B I think. Is it Gary Busey?*

• **HOW** many goals did Damien Duff score in the 2002 World Cup?

Tarquin Bumfluff, Tring

* *Blimey, that's a tricky one. I think he made the squad, but was ruled out through injury. No, hang on, that was Niall Quinn. Wait, he did score a goal but it was ruled offside. Sorry, I'm thinking of David Dunn.*

That's all for this week. Keep your Damion Duff questions & queries coming in, offline DD fans.

IAKERS of driving gloves. Most cars now come quipped with a roof and vindows so it may be a ood time to branch out.
Dave Cossell, e-mail

START your own pay day oan company by lending omeone £5 and then hreatening them until they ive you £50.
Liam Campbell, e-mail

CHRISTIAN adulterers. eel less guilty by telling eople that God gave Mary ne when she was married o Joseph, and if it's good nough for Him it's good nough for you.
Tam Dale, e-mail

PARENTS. Don't waste ood money on expensive rams. Simply take a hopping trolley from your ocal supermarket. When the ttle nipper can walk, send im back to the supermarket o retrieve your hard-earned ne pound.
Ben Joseph, Brghton

SUPERMARKETS. Encourage even more people to use the self service tills by printing a guide on how to get away without paying for items for people who have not figured it out yet.
Rick Howarth, e-mail

CONVINCE friends that you own a snake by attacking your hand with a staple removing tool.
Matt Haines, e-mail

LONDON businessmen. Save the government billions of pounds building a high speed rail link to Birmingham by arranging your meetings in Birmingham 20 minutes later.
Andy Johnson, e-mail

BEEKEEPERS. Avoid being stung by keeping flies instead. **Richiepops, e-mail**

FOOL people into thinking you're a notorious serial killer by getting into the back of your car with a blanket over your head.
Nibs Minton, Chigley

a painting of 'a blacksmith fitting a shoe onto a horse'. I had to laugh as everybody knows that a blacksmith only fashions the horseshoe, and it's the farrier who then fits it onto the horse. Call yourself an expert historian, love? Pull the other one! In future, I suggest you let the real historians like Dan Snow educate me and you can stick to making the tea and doing some ironing, sugar-tits.
Matt McCann, e-mail

** Woah, Mr McCann. That is an extremely sexist attitude that has no place in a family magazine like Viz. Just because women are good at making tea and ironing doesn't mean that they can't do history as well. In fact we're sure that some women are every bit as good at history as many men.*

WHILST on holiday abroad recently, I came across a young British lad in a restaurant who was wearing a full Chelsea strip, had some temporary tattoos and was screaming *"I want chips. I want chips."* Can any other readers come up with a finer example of Britishness abroad than that?
Simon Hoffman, e-mail

WHY don't these hearse drivers put their foot down a bit? I mean no disrespect, but for all I know the guy in the coffin could have been up to his bollocks in unpaid speeding fines before he snuffed it. Does he really want to meet his maker as a hypocrite?
Max Gentleman, e-mail

HAVE you ever thought what it would be like if cows were the size of guinea pigs? It would be a very different world indeed. Milk would cost an arm and a leg and steaks would be fucking tiny. So let's all just be thankful cows are actually the size that they are.
Lee Hooper, e-mail

COP a load of the giant shit my goldfish is curling down in this picture. If a man were to lay a cable this length in comparison to his body size, it could easily jump over the Albert Hall. And that's a fact. Does 'Shelby' win £5?
Pat Doyle, London

IS it just a coincidence that you only ever print my letters or tips around the time of my subscription renewal? Cheque's in the post by the way.
Mike Tatham, e-mail

IF David Attenborough is so clever, can he please tell me how a wasp does a shite when its got a stinger coming out its arse?
Tam Dale, e-mail

** Well, readers. Do YOU know David Attenborough? Maybe you're his next door neighbour, or perhaps you deliver his milk in the morning. Or maybe you run the post office where he pops in to collect his pension every Thursday. If so, ask him how a wasp does a shite with a big stinger coming out its arse and write and let us know. Mark your envelope 'I've seen David Attenborough and asked him how wasps do a shite.' Actually, no, don't.*

AT MY wedding I was terribly bozz-eyed after being kicked in the head by a horse on my hen night, and I accidentally put the ring on the vicar's finger. Luckily, it turned out that my groom didn't like me much anyway and the vicar was quite happy to be my husband instead, so it all worked out for the best in the end. We have now been happily married for more than forty years.
Yootha Trowel, Lincoln

A HORSE that I'd bet 50p on at 10/1 just won its race. Do I win £5?
Robert Doherty, e-mail

WHILST on the London to Leeds train after a long day of meetings, I was watching people get off at Wakefield Westgate and I found myself thinking, "look at all those cunts getting off at Wakefield." The thing is, I've got nothing against Wakefield and all the people getting off seemed perfectly reasonable. So I'm not quite sure why I thought it to be honest. I'd had four cans of Grolsch on the train though, and a packet of Cheese Moments (which are quite hard to get hold of these days), and a Peppermint Cream which is one of my favourite chocolate bars. Sorry, I seem to have wandered off topic a bit.
Jarrod Hollingdrake, e-mail

THE London 2012 Olympics left some wonderful legacies, but this skip by the Olympic Stadium is one of which our nation can be truly proud.
Quinn Fraglen, e-mail

I WAS excited to see that the *Daily Mail* are running a competition to have a Spitfire fly over the winner's house. I wonder if the Editor of *Bild* might consider running a similar competition with a Messerschmitt? If I win both, they could then have agood old-fashioned dogfight above my house.
Angela Knox, e-mail

14,000 Rabbits Removed from Woman's Bum

IT WAS THE ROMANS who first introduced rabbits to Great Britain, but who was it that introduced them to Mrs Edna Hibbs's anus? That's the question that's puzzling scientists and veterinary experts alike after some 14,000 rabbits were removed from the retired dinner lady's bottom during a 9-hour operation on Monday.

The procedure, which involved all three emergency services, the RSPCA and more than a dozen doctors and nurses, is believed to be the first of its kind to be undertaken in this country.

Mrs Hibbs, 68, lived what neighbours describe as a normal life in Reading with her husband before noticing that her bum was completely full of rabbits.

surprise

Mr Hibbs, 67, says he no idea how his wife's arse came to be stuffed with so many bunnies. "To be perfectly frank, it came as a surprise to both of us," he told us. "Edna thought she had indigestion after eating too many crisps, but when we went to the doctors they said her back passage was totally overrun with carrot-munching rodents. We didn't know what to think."

But the mystery is how the mischievous burrowing creatures came to be there in the first place.

blind

"The trouble with rabbits," explained a representative for the RSPCA, "is that they breed like rabbits."

"We think that a single pair of rabbits must have somehow found their way into Mrs Hibbs's arsehole, and begun to reproduce. With no natural predators to control their numbers, the rabbit population soon reached 14,000."

"Of course we've no idea how they got there. We've spoken to her friends and family members, and none of them think she was the sort of woman who would stuff rabbits up her bum. It's a complete mystery," the expert added.

Bum bunnies: two of the rabbits removed from Mrs Hibbs, yesterday and (left) Mrs Hibbs in happier times.

ice cream

The procedure for removing the unwanted cotton-tailed pests was far from simple. Professor JG Harding, head of the Department for the Removal of Undesired Things from People's Arseholes at Cambridge University, was involved from the start.

halen

"We had a number of options, including flushing them out with terriers or simply pumping Mrs Hibbs's arse full of myxomatosis," he said. "But in the end it was decided to remove them humanely by hand. We assembled an elite team, specialising in the removal of unwelcome rectal intruders of the genus *Leporidae* and I do not think the operation could have been more successful."

Mr Hibbs had never seen anything like it. "I was aghast," he told us. "They just kept pulling one rabbit after another out of her bum. I'd never seem anything like it."

The RSPCA spokesman said: "However it happened, at the end of the day this poor lady's bum was completely full of rabbits and they needed to be removed. This has been a difficult time for Mrs Hibbs and her family, but our principle focus has necessarily been on the welfare of the rabbits."

morrison

"She was not a large woman and her bottom was insufficiently commodious for the happy accommodation of such a huge population of big-eared rodents," he added.

Sadly, Mrs Hibbs did not survive the operation.

Bunny Peculiar!
The FACTS about Rabbits

- **SCIENTISTS** believe that if rabbits continue to breed at the current rate the entire surface of the earth will be nine feet deep in bunnies by March 2014.
- **ALWAYS** wash your hands after contact with pet rabbits, say doctors. It's all too easy to swallow one and end up with an arse full of them if you're not careful.
- **ACCORDING** to a half-remembered feature on *Blue Peter* in the 1970s, rabbits are biologically more closely related to elephants than they are to mice or rats.
- **AUSTRALIA** doesn't have any rabbits in it, preferring kangaroos and wallabies instead.
- **RABBITS** are copraphagic. This means that after having carrots for their main course, the filthy beasts tuck into their own turds for pudding.
- **RABBITS** come in two different sizes - normal rabbits and hares.
- **IF YOU'RE** concerned that innumerable wiggly-nosed vermin have taken up residence in your shitter, call your doctor and the Fire Brigade.

NORMAN the DOORMAN
14

SOB

WOAH-WOAH-WOAH-WOAH... WHERE D'YOU THINK YOU'RE GOING..?
INTO THE CHURCH.
OH NO YOU'RE NOT.

BUT IT'S YOUR GRANDAD'S FUNERAL, NORMAN.
COME ON... I.D.

I'M NINETY-FOUR, NORMAN.
PLEASE LET US IN... WE'RE ALREADY RUNNING QUITE LATE...

YOU - GET BACK IN LINE AND WAIT YOUR FUCKIN' TURN!
BUT YOU DON'T UNDERSTAND... I'M DOING THE SERVICE...
TOUCH

PHYSICAL CONTACT! THAT'S ASSAULT, IS THAT! YOU SAW IT, DIDN'T YOU..? YOU SAW HIM ATTACK ME!

REASONABLE FORCE! THIS IS REASONABLE FORCE! YOU'RE MY WITNESS!
AARGH! JESUS!
SNAP!

STOMP! STOMP!
AN' YOU DON'T GET IN ANYWAY, WITHOUT A FUCKIN' TIE!
GAK!

RIGHT, SUNSHINE. PROOF OF AGE OR YOU CAN DO ONE. THERE'S PEOPLE WAITING HERE.

ERM... I THINK I'VE GOT ME PENSION BOOK HERE SOMEWHERE...

...YES! HERE IT IS... THERE YOU GO, NORMAN.

IT'S QUITE AN OLD PICTURE...
...I WAS EIGHTY-EIGHT.

ALRIGHT, IN YOU GO.

...NOT YOU, TWINKLETOES...
THAT FUCKIN' COFFIN'S CASUAL.

SEX in the STORE CUPBOARD!

A SOUTH YORKSHIRE school janitor could be on the verge of signing a four-figure Hollywood deal for his life story, after a letter outlining his lust-filled on-the-job antics caught the eye of top Tinseltown movie moguls. And now, with a studio bidding war well underway, *REG HARPIC* is preparing to hang up his brown dustcoat and consign his mop and bucket to history.

"Schoolma'ams took lessons in love from me" says Casanova caretaker

Taking care of dirty business: Janitor Reg's sexy story off 44 years at school is set to become Hollywood blockbuster

EXCLUSIVE!

"I'm no great looker, I've got to admit. But there's clearly something about me that drives the birds wild, because they're all over me like flies round shit," said Harpic, 60, who started caretaking straight from school in 1969.

"In my 44 years as a comprehensive school caretaker, I've seen a lot of women teachers come and go," he told us. "Mainly come, if you catch my drift."

torn

"Some of the things I've got up to over the years with these young teachers read like something out of one of the porn mags I occasionally find torn up in the bushes behind the bike sheds."

Harpic was reluctant to spoil any surprises for moviegoers by revealing too many details of his saucy adventures. But he did outline a few episodes from his sex-packed caretaking career to whet viewers' appetites...

"I remember one incident when a third-former knocked on the door of my windowless disinfectant storeroom-cum-office and handed me a note from a teacher. It read: *'Please come to Chemistry Room 3. VOF.'* I knew immediately what it meant; VOF is caretaker code for 'Vomit On Floor'. I picked up my equipment and set off.

van winkle

When I got there, the classroom was empty except for the science mistress - a slim brunette supply teacher who smiled at me shyly as I came in, pointing to a small pool of sick on the floor in front of the fume cupboards. She explained that some of the boys had been doing an experiment to make a gas that smelled

like bad eggs and one of them had thrown up. I knew exactly what to do; vomit is a caretaker's bread and butter.

I covered the pile in sawdust, explaining to the teacher that it would take about 45 minutes for the wood shavings to soak the excess liquid out of the spew. I told her that the offending matter could then be easily shovelled off the lino like a cowpat. She seemed fascinated by my conversation, hanging onto my every word, looking deep into my eyes and licking her lips.

'Well,' she said, coquettishly playing with the top button of her crisp, white labcoat. 'I wonder what we're going to do while we wait for that sick to thicken up. I've got a free period. Why don't we go in the stockroom and see if we can come up with something.' I didn't need asking twice, I can tell you.

To cut a long story short, she dragged me into the stockroom, stripping herself naked before undoing my dustcoat, loosening the front of my bib and brace and allowing it to drop. She had an amazing body, like a sexy model out of one of the porn mags I occasionally have to confiscate from the boys.

> **"She dragged me into the stockroom, stripping herself naked before undoing my dustcoat and loosening the front of my bib and brace."**

She gasped when she saw my manhood. Then she became like a lust-crazed animal, sweeping bottles of chemicals off the bench to make room for us. Dangerous acids, poisons and solutions mingled amongst the broken glass on the floor, causing brightly coloured clouds of gas to billow up all around us.

There was certainly a lot of chemistry going on on that floor, but not as much as what was going on on the bench. The lady teacher rode me like the rampant stallion that I was until she collapsed in a crescendo of orgiastic passion. The whole sexy episode had taken exactly 45 minutes, so when I went back in the classroom and slipped the dustpan under the vomit, it came up in one piece. The only sign it had ever been there was a slight damp stain on the lino, which I quickly removed with some Jeyes Fluid and a cloth.

off Britain

Just then, the bell went and in rushed the class for the next lesson. Emerging from the stockroom, the now fully-dressed teacher looked at the floor. 'You've done a wonderful job there, Mr

School for Scandal: Sutcliffe Lane Comprehensive in Dungworth, scene of Reg's saucy adventures.

Harpic,' she smiled. The kids probably all thought she was talking about the sick, but the satisfied glint in her eye told me otherwise. ”

Harpic's reputation as a lover was the talk of the staff room, and to be serviced by him became almost a rite of passage for freshly-appointed female teachers at the school. So he was not at all surprised when he received a summons to meet the newly-appointed deputy headmistress...

“ She was quite a looker - a real MILF type in her late thirties like you get in *Readers' Wives* - and I'd had the distinct impression she'd been eyeing me up ever since she arrived. The day before I'd been picking up some dog's mess from the playing fields outside her office when I'd caught her looking at me through the window. It was hot work and I'd left my bib and braces hanging loose round my waist. So it was no surprise that she sent for me the very next morning.

tide

Apparently, I must've missed a dog dirt and the art teacher had stepped in it and then trodden it into the staff room rug. The deputy head explained that she needed it cleaned up - and pronto.

The temptation when dealing with excrement on carpet is to go in hard with a scrubbing brush and detergent. But after forty years in this game I can tell you that the best way to lift turd is to scrape in from the outside edges with a kitchen knife. Next you blot up what's left with damp paper towels. Only then is it safe to move in with the brush and detergent.

flash

I finished the job in about ten minutes and stood up to admire my handiwork. I was pretty pleased with the results. Even I couldn't see where the feeshus had been. The deputy head looked impressed, and got down on her knees to see if she could sniff it from close up. She couldn't; the job was a good'un.

Barker's egg: Dog's mess had been trod into pile on staffroom carpet.

'Well done, Mr Harpic,' she said, kneeling in front of me. 'You sorted that dog's mess out a treat. Now it's my turn to see if I can't sort you out.' As she spoke she was seductively undoing the flies on my dungarees and licking her lips, also seductively. What happened next was like something from the readers' letters pages of one of those mucky magazines I sometimes find stuffed down behind the cisterns in the boys' toilets. Suffice to say there was nothing 'deputy' about the 'head' I got that day! It was the real deal, I can tell you.

commissioner

I went off at the same moment as the bell for break and it wasn't long before the rest of the teachers began flooding into the staff room. From the raised eyebrows I spotted, I think a few of them must have guessed what had been going on just moments earlier. My reputation as the Casanova of Dungworth Comp was growing by the day. ”

Although many lady teachers gave into temptation as soon as they arrived at the school, others took a little longer to succumb to Reg's overpowering animal magnetism...

“ I'll never forget this one time. I was sitting in my office, filling in a requisition for a new tin of Vim, when a lady's face poked round my door and announced: 'There's an emergency in the girls' toilets, Mr Harpic.' It was an English teacher who I'd never really spoken to in the two years she'd been at the school. To tell the truth, I'd never really given her a second look. She wasn't really my type at all; she had her hair up in a bun and wore severe, dark-rimmed glasses.

station

I followed her down the corridor to the girls' bogs; she went in first to check there was no-one in there. She said it was okay and I followed her in, hanging an 'Out of Order' sign on the door and closing it behind us. 'It's in there,' she said, pointing at trap three. I went inside to find the pan full to the brim with bangers and mash.

The first move by an amateur in such a situation would be to try to flush it down. But I've got years of experience dealing with blocked lavs on a daily basis. I knew that one pull on the handle would cause the

Stalls: School lav was blocked with bangers and mash

mess to simply cascade over the rim, making a crisis out of a drama. A single glance told me all I needed to know; that mountain of paper and excrement was in no hurry to go anywhere, I can tell you.

“As I put my bucket of cat turds down they both removed their tracksuits, revealing that they were wearing nothing underneath except stockings, suspenders, peephole bras and high-heeled shoes.”

Any caretaker worth his salt will tell you; the only way to shift a heap like that is to break and flush, break and flush. It's not rocket science, it's just a war of attrition. Man versus beast.

constable

The teacher watched me as I set to work with my special stick. In the end, it took more than a dozen cycles of mashing and flushing before that toilet was good to go. By the time I'd finished I'd worked up quite a sweat, but that was nothing compared to the sweat that the English teacher had worked up watching me. My gladiatorial combat with that lavatorial foe had really turned her on, and she had taken off her specs and let her hair down.

sargent

I couldn't believe the transformation that had come over her. From a dowdy frump, she had turned into the sort of ravenous, sexually-insatiable piece that wouldn't have looked out of place across the middle pages of a Scan mag that I once found in some lockers at the end of term. I gave my hands a rinse as they'd been down the pot and we stripped off and made mad, passionate love on the floor of the toilet.

sewing machine

After we had finished, she put her glasses back on, did her hair up and re-buttoned her starchy blouse. Before my eyes she once again became the dowdy English teacher I had known before. But it was clear from the wanton glint in her eye that I had ignited a spark of sexual passion deep within her. And as it turned out, I was right, for this was only the first of many trysts that we enjoyed together whilst on school premises. ”

During his tenure as caretaker, the school had a high turnover of female staff. Eventually Reg realised that if he was to stand any chance of getting round to pleasuring them all, he might have to start doing them two at a time.

“ I'd been called down to the athletics field where some cats had been using the long jump sand as their litter tray. It was an easy job I'd done many times before; the turds get covered in sand and

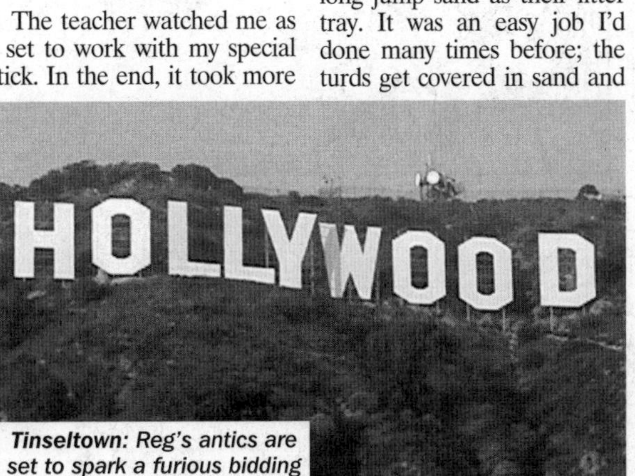

Tinseltown: Reg's antics are set to spark a furious bidding war in the movie capital.

you just flick them into a tilted bucket with a stick. Bish-bosh - as far as I was concerned it was just another day at the office.

songwriter

To be fair, it was probably a bigger job than I'd been anticipating. There must've been a few cats using the pit as I'd half-filled my bucket with sandy rissoles by the time I was done. Anyway, I was just carrying them back towards the main school building when a voice called me from the sports gear storage pre-fab at the end of the field. 'Coo-ee! Mr Harpic! Could you just give us a hand in here, please?'

No man's sand: Neighbourhood cats had been using athletic facilities to perform their bodily functions.

I'd always assumed that these two lady games teachers were lesbians, so I thought they probably just wanted some help lifting some medicine balls onto a higher shelf or something. But even if they were that way inclined usually, they weren't beating about the bush that afternoon. They got straight to the point. 'We want you to come in here and have sex with both of us, right here and now in the sports gear storage prefab,' they said.

gazelle

I didn't need asking twice. As I put my bucket of cat turds down they both removed their tracksuits, revealing that they were wearing nothing underneath except stockings, suspenders, peephole bras and high-heeled shoes. Honestly, they looked like a centrefold out of one of those mucky mags I occasionally find abandoned on the top shelf of my local newsagent.

It was game on, and let me tell you I gave those two lady PE teachers the aerobic workout of their lives. To this day, I don't know if they were lesbians, but they were certainly 110% back on solids for the duration of our afternoon sex marathon, and that's for sure. If sex was an Olympic sport, we would have won Gold, Silver and Bronze in the Team Threes-Up event that afternoon, I can tell you. ”

Major studios in Hollywood were last night tight-lipped about their plans to commit Reg's story to celluloid, and refused to confirm rumours that George Clooney was being lined up to play the title role.

"Reg who?" said MGM production chief Hymen T. Brookhymen.

Meanwhile the head of Sutcliffe Lane Comprehensive confirmed that a member of the auxiliary janitorial staff had recently been disciplined for storing pornographic magazines on school premises.

The Viz Careers Officer

MOST PEOPLE probably imagine that vicars have it easy, working for a couple of hours on a Sunday morning before taking the rest of the week off. But nothing could be further from the truth, for church ministers are actually on call 24-7, 365 days a year, tending to the spiritual needs of their parishioners. If you fancy becoming a man of the cloth, you'll have to be prepared for long hours, plenty of hard work and precious little reward... in this life at least! So, before you rush down to the church recruiting office and sign on the dotted line, let's take a behind-the-screens peek at the life of a typical vicar.

MONDAY is our vicar's day of rest, a chance to put his feet up and recov from his gruelling Sabbath schedule. Here, he relaxes in front of the televisio enjoying a cup of tea and a selection of pastries brought in by his housekeepe But, just like a fireman he is still on duty. He knows that he could be called out a moment's notice to provide spiritual succour or moral guidance to a trouble member of his flock. For the moment, he hopes that the hardest work he'll hav to do today is pick which sticky bun to eat first.

IN TOWNS and villages the length of the country, the local church isn't merely a place of worship; it's a hub around which the whole community revolves. Today the vicar is chairing the parish council meeting. There are a mountain of jobs on the agenda; the graveyard needs weeding, the vicarage windows must be cleaned, the vicar's car could do with a wash, his toilet is blocked and his dog needs taking for a walk. Luckily, an army of volunteers is ready and wiling to take on all these responsibilities, leaving the vicar free to do what he does best - tending to the pastoral needs of his flock.

COMMUNITIES often find themselves united in grief, particula when a terrible tragedy occurs in their midst. Here an express train h derailed and fallen down the embankment. Casualties are mounti and the vicar is quickly on the scene to offer what comfort he c to the unfortunate victims. Because the accident has occurred sor distance from the village, the vicar has to make do with tea from flask, which is never as good as tea from a pot. Also, the selection of cakes is quite poor and he must choose between a squashed eclair, an unappetising scone and a rather tired Danish that has seen better days.

A VICAR cares about the wellbeing of all the people in his parish, whether they attend his services or not. Indeed, he will often go out of his way to bring a lost sheep back into the church's fold. Every Wednesday, the vicar makes a special trip to a well-known local house of ill-repute, where he meets fallen women, tending to their pastoral needs for 15 to 20 minutes at a time. He also tries to help them in other ways, leaving them money from his collection plate.

So you want to be... a VICAR?

VICARS are there for the happy times in our lives, such as village fetes, veddings and christenings, but equally they are also there for the sad times. oday our busy curate is visiting the home of a parishioner whose husband of i0 years has just died, in order to sort out arrangements for his forthcoming uneral. Naturally, after nursing her ailing spouse through the final days of is illness, the poor old lady hasn't had a chance to go to the shops. As a esult, there is an extremely poor assortment of cakes to accompany the icar's tea. But understanding as ever, he waits patiently whilst she pops into own to fetch him a more inspiring selection.

THE UPKEEP and maintenance of church buildings is a constant worry for the vicar. Despite the C of E sitting on assets running into trillions of pounds, the vicar must somehow get the money for repairs from his parishioners. Here a "thermometer" board, which charts the progress of a fund-raising drive to fix the vestry's leaking roof, has fallen into disrepair. The vicar immediately launches an urgent appeal to raise funds to get it fixed.

THROUGHOUT history it has been the principal duty of men of the cloth to pray for their flock. Many parishioners ask their curate to entreat God on their behalf, amongst them the lost, the lonely and the bereaved. But often the vicar makes a special prayer for a member of his community without being asked. Today, a local jockey is riding a horse in the 3.15 at Chepstow. The vicar takes a moment to close his eyes and offer up a prayer, beseeching the Lord to ensure that the man has a safe and successful race.

IT IS A myth that vicars can only preach inside a church. These days, you'll find them giving spiritual guidance the unlikeliest of places - in shopping centres, on oil rigs, in the street ... even in your local pub! Here our vicar ls in at a neighbourhood lap-dancing club to spread the good news about God and Jesus. The £50 entrance fee mes courtesy of the collection plate, but if a single soul is saved then it will be money well spent.

ALTHOUGH his main concern is looking after his parishioners' spiritual wellbeing, a modern man of the cloth is often called upon to deal with much more down-to-earth problems. Here a member of the parish, whose identity is known only to the vicar, has run up huge debts gambling, drinking and going with prostitutes. Despite this catalogue of sinful behaviour, the vicar knows that God will forgive the man, and organises a summer fete - with every penny of the proceeds going towards keeping his creditors, including bookies, pimps and payday loan companies, at bay.

Next Week the Viz Careers Officer asks: So you want to be... a Wank Booth Jizz-mopper?

THE REAL ALE TWATS
DJ '13

FULL STEAM AHEAD TO THE FULCHESTER ARMS, CASKETEERS!
MINE HOST DOTH SERVE AN EXCELLENT PINT OF OWLD GERVAIS'S FULMINATING TWEET.

A LIGHT, GOLDEN ALE, IT IS REMINDFUL OF THE COLLIER'S SHIVERING WHIPPET WHICH I SAMPLED AT THE PIG AND BUCKET IN OSWESTRY, IN '92.
THE FULCHESTER
FINE ALES
BAR
THE LANDLORD'S NAME WAS COLIN.

OH, TUT TUT AND THRICE TUT!
GUEST ALES
IT WOULD APPEAR THAT OUR BELOVED HOSTLRY IS SUFFERING FROM AN INFESTATION OF "STUDENTUS UNIVERSITYUS".

THE DREADED "FRESHERS' WEEK" MUST BE UPON US AGAIN
WHISTLING DIXIE
HUNDREDS OF PIMPLY-FACED YOUNGSTERS, AWAY FROM HOME FOR THE FIRST TIME, BRINGING ROWDINESS AND MAYHEM INTO OUR PEACEFUL LITTLE WATERING HOLE.

TSK! STUDENTS EH, LANDLORD? THEY ARE THE PROVERBIAL PAIN IN THE RECTUM.
THEIR MONEY'S AS GOOD AS ANYONE ELSE'S...

ANYWAY, OUR NEW BARMAID'S A STUDENT...
OHO! WE HAVE A FRESH SERVING WENCH BEHIND THE BAR!

SO, MY DEAR, YOU'RE STUDYING AT COLLEGE, ARE YOU?
YES, I AM...
BUT I EXPECT YOU ALSO FIND TIME TO INDULGE IN DEBAUCHED BACCHANALIAN PARTIES, DON'T YOU?

ERM... NO, NOT REALLY...
COME NOW, MY DEAR! I KNOW WHAT STUDENT LIFE IS LIKE — I WAS ONCE ONE MYSELF, WAY BACK IN THE MISTS OF TIME!

OH YES, I WAS SOMETHING OF A "PARTY ANIMAL" BACK IN MY WILD AND UNTAMED UNDERGRADUATE DAYS
INDEED, I WAS KNOWN TO BE A BIT OF AN AFICIONADO OF THE OLD "WACKY BACCY"!!

THIRTY YEARS PREVIOUSLY
HMM, A LIGHT, MELLOW SMOKE WITH A HINT OF SENSIMILLA ON THE NOSE...
J.R.R. TOLKIEN
ZZZZ
HAWK WIND
IT IS REMINDFUL OF THE LEBANESE SQUIDGY BLACK I ONCE SAMPLED AT A PARTY IN LEVENSHULME IN '81. THE DEALER'S NAME WAS REG.

OF COURSE, I AM OLDER AND WISER, NOW.
THESE DAYS, I CONFINE MYSELF TO A FEW PINTS OF CASK-CONDITIONED NECTAR, AND SOME JOVIAL BANTER WITH MY FELLOW IMBIBERS.

TSK!
ALAS, I FEAR THAT SOME OF YOUR FELLOW STUDENTS HAVE YET TO LEARN THE RULES OF SOCIAL DRINKING.

THERE'S A FINE LINE BETWEEN HAVING A GOOD TIME AND JUST MAKING A NUISANCE OF YOURSELF.
SEASONED PUB-GOERS SUCH AS OURSELVES ARE WISE TO THAT DISTINCTION.

YES MY DEAR, YOU'LL FIND THAT WE, YOUR LOYAL REGULARS, HAVE MUCH WISDOM TO IMPART
AND YOU SHALL BE OUR PUPIL!

WE WILL TUTOR YOU IN THE SUBJECTS OF BARMAIDOLOGY AND ALEHOUSE ETIQUETTE...
..AND SHOULD WE EVER FIND YOUR PROGRESS TO BE AT ALL UNSATISFACTORY...

..WE WILL PUT YOU OVER OUR KNEES AND SPANK YOUR BOTTOM!
ARF! SNORT! SNURFLE! TITTER!

AND, IN COURT
...FURTHERMORE THIS INJUNCTION FORBIDS YOU TO APPROACH OR COME WITHIN 200 YARDS OF MISS SMITH OR HER PLACE OF WORK, THE FULCHESTER ARMS PUBLIC HOUSE...
HMM! THIS IS REMINDFUL OF THE RESTRAINING ORDER I RECEIVED AT DARROWBY CROWN COURT IN '97 IN RESPECT OF THE BARMAID AT THE HARE AND CLOPPER. THE JUDGE'S NAME WAS KEITH.

Further Arrests in Operation Zootree

A NATIONWIDE police investigation into historic non-human abuse has led to more arrests under Operation Zootree this weekend, bringing the total number detained or questioned to 19.

You're knicked: Grace Brothers stalwart Mrs Slocombe's pussy has been smeared, says lawyer.

The first of the new arrests came when Mrs Slocombe's pussy was taken into Paddington Green police station in the early hours of Saturday morning. It is believed that the ageing feline was being questioned by officers investigating obscenity allegations dating back to the early 1980s.

The pussy was released on Sunday morning, but was bailed to appear before Brentford magistrates in October.

hairy

Standing beside his client, solicitor Hampton Wick read a statement on behalf of the hairy pussy, saying that his client strenuously denies all allegations. He said the charges were malicious and without foundation.

"Mrs Slocombe's pussy has been fingered without good reason. I am confident that when the police probe into it they will find nothing to interest them," he said.

kellog's

Meanwhile, friends of Mrs Slocombe's pussy were shocked by the latest arrest. Many close associates of the old lady's pussy said they could not believe it capable of being obscene or lewd. "It smells a bit fishy to me," said one.

Numbers rack up in animal abuse clampdown

Others commented on the pussy's honesty. "I've known Mrs Slocombe's pussy for 40 years, and it has always been completely open with me," said another. "It would bend over backwards to accommodate anyone."

crunchy nut

The arrest came on the same day that a 52-year-old emu was taken into custody by Hampshire police. Although no charges have yet been brought, it is believed the bird is being questioned over a series of assaults committed in the 1970s and 80s. The animal has not been officially named, but news of the arrest sent the Twittersphere into a frenzy with several prominent users speculating on the identity of the flightless bird in question.

Former *That's Life* presenter Esther Rantzen said the arrests sent out a strong message.

chewy cock

"There was a culture of untouchability around celebrity animals in the 70s," she said. "I remember very well a dog on my programme that could say 'sausages' when its owner wobbled its jaw. And believe me, that's not all it could say," she added.

"With its owner moving its mouth it would constantly make obscene suggestions to young women on the crew. Everyone knew about it and did nothing. Except me. I didn't know about it," she added.

...ZOOTREE ARREST TIMELINE...

...JUNE 3RD...

Lulu, the *Blue Peter* Elephant, arrested in relation to a public order offence dating from 1969 in which the animal was alleged to have behaved in a manner that offended public decency. It denied the charges, but eventually accepted a caution after seeing that the incident was caught on camera and has had over 2,000,000 views on YouTube.

...JULY 14TH...

Hand-held canine ***Spit the Dog*** has his collar felt by West Midlands police. The showbusiness veteran was detained under the Dangerous Dogs act due to an alleged history of aggressive behaviour dating back until the early 1970s. The 32-year-old puppet (225 in dog years) refused to comment and spat at police officers when he attended Solihull police station, accompanied by his long term partner Bob Carolgees.

...AUGUST 9TH...

Following a dawn raid, detectives took ***Flash*** the *Fingerbobs* tortoise in for questioning over historic allegations of serious sexual misconduct. Speaking on the steps of the station, he told reporters that he "welcomed this opportunity to clear his name," although he later pleaded guilty to over 40 charges of indecent exposure dating back to 1972.

...AUGUST 25TH...

Tales of the Riverbank rodent ***Hammy the Hamster*** was sentenced to 3 years in prison after being found guilty of a series of aggravated sexual assaults on production staff which took place in his dressing hutch during filming of the popular BBC television series in the 1960s. The prosecution protested to the Attorney General about the leniency of the sentence, which was later increased to 6 years by the Court of Appeal.

...AUGUST 29TH...

Patriarchal cloth cat ***Bagpuss*** was questioned over a series of indecent assaults on hundreds of mice on the mouse organ stretching back 40 years. However, the Director of Public Prosecution, Keir Starmer decided to drop all charges. *"Mice only live for 18 months, so it is unlikely that enough witnesses could be found to bring about a successful prosecution,"* he told journalists.

"I'm a world famous sexy R'n'B diva... but only when I've got my wig on," says West Midlands mum-of-five

Rihanna Montana

Don't give up the day job: *Edna puts in a shift stripping wallaby pizzles on the dog-chew production line.*

IN A TWIST straight out of the plot of *Hannah Montana*, a Wolverhampton woman has revealed that she is living an amazing double life ... as pop star ***RIHANNA!***

As told to ***Fanny Gaslight***

"It's time the world knew my secret identity," says petfood factory worker *Edna Flatus*. "I am Rihanna and when you see her on the telly it's not her, it's really me." And just like the character played by Miley Cyrus in the TV series Edna, 58, assumes the identity of her red-hot alter-ego by taking off her specs and putting on a wig.

"The world knows me as Rihanna, with a string of hits including *Only Girl (In the World)*, *Disturbia*, and *Rude Boy*, but to the other girls in the dog meat factory I'm just plain old Edna," she told *Take A Shit* reporter ***Fanny Gaslight***. "If only they knew the truth, they wouldn't believe it."

Mrs Flatus's bizarre deception began when she innocently donned a bright red wig to take part in a karaoke contest at her local pub, The Turk's Head in Dunstall, Wolverhampton. "I did that song off *Titanic*. I did it with all the notes going up and down and I went down a storm," she said. "As it happens, the head of a big record company was in the audience and he offered me a million pound recording contract and a world tour there and then."

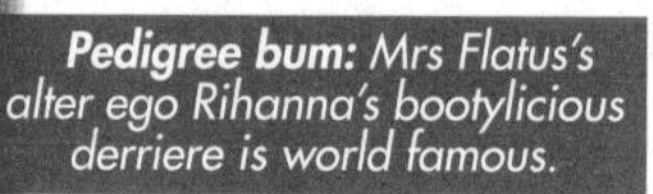

Pedigree bum: *Mrs Flatus's alter ego Rihanna's bootylicious derriere is world famous.*

"Of course I was tempted. Who wouldn't be? It's everyone's dream to be a superstar R'n'B diva, travelling the world in private jets and stretch limousines, partying into the early hours with A-listers and stopping in ten star hotel rooms."

"But at the same time, I loved my job in the dog food factory, and I'd just got promoted to stripping the skin off the kangaroo carcasses, which paid an extra fifty pence an hour. Giving all that up to go on the road was a step that I wasn't ready to take," she added.

> **"I'd just got promoted to stripping the skin off the kangaroo carcasses, which paid an extra fifty pence an hour. Giving all that up to go on the road was a step that I wasn't ready to take"**

"That's when I came up with the idea of a double life, combining the best parts of both my careers," said Edna. The record company boss explained to Mrs Flatus that Edna was no name for a sexy hip-hop diva, so she chose a pseudonym - Rihanna. "I don't know where the name came from, it just popped into my head," she told us.

"With my wig on, I would be glamorous Rihanna, 25-year-old bootylicious Barbadian beauty and international celebrity. Without it, I would be plain Edna Flatus, an unremarkable middle-aged mum of five working in the meat reclamation department of a large Wolverhampton pet food plant."

For the next five years, Edna juggled her two lives, jetting round the globe to perform her hits in front of thousands of screaming fans before returning to the West Midlands each morning to clock on for her shift in the kangaroo rendering section of the factory. And so far, although she's never got her two identities confused, there have been a few near misses.

"I remember one time, I was cleaning bluebottle eggs out of the de-boning machine when one of the other girls started humming my latest hit *We Found Love* on the radio," Edna told us. "I just went into Rihanna mode, strutting my stuff up and down the production line and shaking my booty. Everyone just stood open-mouthed. They couldn't believe what they were seeing."

Worlds apart: *The dog food factory wher Mrs Flatus spends her day and Madison Square Garden where she appeared last week.*

Edna told us: "It's a good job I didn't have my wig on or my secret would have been out!"

"Another time I was doing the backshift from midnight to eight. There'd been an outbreak of diarrhoea at the factory, and they'd asked me to do a double shift in the boil-down sheds. I checked in my diary and saw that I was appearing at the MOBO Awards in Rio de Janiero that night, but the bosses at the factory were offering me time-and-a-half so I said I'd do it."

"I knew the timings were going to be tight. I had just twenty minutes to get off the stage after my last encore and make it to the airport, where my private jet would be waiting on the tarmac with its engines running," said Mrs Flatus. "We landed in Wolverhampton just five minutes before midnight. I didn't want to be late, because last time when I'd missed the bus in and was ten minutes behind they'd made me work through my tea-break. I was already on a warning that if I was late clocking on again, I would be docked the full hour."

"I was appearing at the MOBO Awards in Rio de Janiero that night, but the bosses at the factory were offering me time-and-a-half so I said I'd do it"

"In all the excitement, there was no time to change out of my glamorous stage outfit, so I just pulled on a set of factory overalls, my wellies, rubber gloves and my hairnet, and got down to work scraping fat off kangaroo pelts to put in the boiling vat," she continued.

"If my co-workers had known that underneath my dowdy, offal-spattered work-clothes I was wearing a sexy diamond-studded leather basque, fishnet stockings and thigh-high leather boots, I think the game would have been well and truly up."

"That was a close one, but luckily they never suspected a thing!" she added.

Edna Flatus is presently on her Diamonds World Tour, her single Pour it Up (featuring Mikky Ekko) is out now and her new album Uncovered is released on August 5th.

Take a Shit

Hallelujah! It's a MIRACLE!

A GOOLE MAN who suffered an horrific accident pulled through against the odds only thanks to the quick-thinking of his wife, who prayed to God to save him. *Patrick O'Reardon*, 62, was shopping at a local precinct when he was dragged into the mechanism of an escalator.

Whilst passers-by and security guards at the Blackwater shopping centre rushed to operate the emergency stop switch and raise the alarm, wife Bernadette, 62, looked on in horror. She told us:

"He was dying in front of me. There was nothing anybody could do, so I got down on my knees and started praying to God to help him."

Engineers managed to dismantle the escalator and paramedics worked for four hours to free Mr O'Reardon, who had suffered severe injuries that had practically severed both his legs. "He was in a terrible state," said Mrs O'Reardon. "To be honest, I didn't think he was going to pull through. I knew that the only thing that could save him was to pray."

ambulance

Mr O'Reardon had lost more than half his blood in the accident, and was given three emergency transfusions on the sixteen mile trip to Hull Royal Victoria Infirmary. "I went in the ambulance with him," said Mrs O'Reardon. "I kept saying the Lord's Prayer over and over again and eventually it started to work. His blood pressure stabilised."

"It was a miracle," she added.

At the hospital, teams of doctors, nurses and anaesthetists battled for nearly 14 hours to re-attach Mr O'Reardon's legs. At one point, a specialist orthopaedic surgeon was flown in from London to assist in the re-connection of damaged nerve tissues. Mrs O'Reardon told us: "I was in the hospital chapel for the whole time, asking the Lord to spare my husband."

"After fourteen hours someone came and told me that he was going to be alright, although he was still very poorly. I must have said over a thousand Hail Marys and Our Fathers in that chapel, and those prayers had been answered," she said. "It was another miracle."

screw

Although he had come through the surgery, Patrick's doctors warned that a full recovery would take a long time. He was referred to a team of physiotherapists who worked on a rigorous twelve-month convalescence and recovery programme, involving exercise, drugs and remote muscle stimulation therapy. "I prayed to God every day that he would one day be able to walk out of that hospital," said Mrs O'Reardon. "And although it took nearly a year, the Lord saw fit to answer my prayers."

Hymn and her: *Mrs O'Reardon's prayers saved hubby Patrick*

Humberside man pulls through thanks to power of prayer

betty

"There were tears in my eyes when I finally saw Patrick back on his feet, surrounded by some nurses or doctors or something. I simply don't have the words to thank the Lord enough for what he did over those twelve months.."

"Not only had he let my husband live, he had let him walk again," she said. "It was a miracle."

As a token of her appreciation for her husband's recovery, Mrs O'Reardon set up a fund to help other people pray for injured relatives. She recently hosted a series of coffee mornings, sponsored walks and cake sales, raising more than £10,000, which she put in an envelope and sent to the Pope.

the BROWN BOTTLE

MILD MANNERED BANK CLERK BARRY BROWN IS ABOUT TO CLOSE UP FOR THE DAY...
WELL, THAT'S THE LEDGERS COMPLETED MR MORRISON
WELL DONE BARRY

SUDDENLY...
THIS IS A FUCKIN' STICK UP! PUT YOUR HANDS WERE WE CAN SEE 'EM!

GASP! WHAT AM I GOING TO DO?
PUT THE MONEY IN THE FUCKIN' BAGS!

I KNOW! UNDER MY DESK!
SILENT ALARM

CAREFULLY NOW...
...MADE IT!
SILENT ALARM
THIS IS A JOB FOR...

THE BROWN BOTTLE!
CLINKY TINK CLINK!

C'MON, GET A MOVE ON GRAMPS
YEH. AND NO FUNNY BUSINESS
KER-SHTIK!
GLUG GLUG GLUG GLUG!
SWAG

WHEN BARRY BROWN NECKS NEWCASTLE BROWN ALE, HE TRANSFORMS INTO THE INCREDIBLE BROWN BOTTLE!
OI! FUCKINN' YOOOOU!
GULP!

GASP! IT'S THE BROWN BOTTLE!
WE'RE DONE FOR!

YOU HEVINT GORRA LIGHT HEV YA SONN?
..JUSS A LIGHT. JUSS LENSS A LIGHT MANN THASS AAL A WANT
A LIGHT & A TABB...
SWAG

YEH, HERE LOOK...
CHEERS KIDDA

AAH. LIKE FUCKIN' MANNA FROM HEAVEN
BLISS!
..HOW. Y' COULDNT LENS US TWENTY PENSS? ITS FIR ME BUS MAN HOWAIRE. LENS TWENTY PENSS FIR ME BUS. ITS AWNLY TWENTY FRIGGIN PENSS MANN
HOWAIRE

OOH, ERM, HANG ON.. LET ME SEE WHAT I'VE GOT...
PSST: DONT GIVE HIM ANYTHING FOR CHRISTS SAKE!
SWAG

OI! YOU FUCKINN' KEEP OUTA IT! THISISS BETWEENN ME AN' 'IM!

NAH NAH NAH. AWNLY JOKIN' MATE. AWNLY JOKIN' YEH?
YER A GOODD LADD YOU. YOU AND YER MATE, EH?

CUMM ON FEEL THE NOYZE! CUMM ON FEEL THE NOYZE!
WYLDD WYLDD WYLDD!
..CUMM ON FEEL THE NOYZE...

CRASH!
POLICE!
FREEZE!!

DONT WORRY LADS. THE BROWN BOTTLE HAS GOT EVERYTHING UNDER CONTROL!
THANKS BROWN BOTTLE. WE'LL TAKE IT FROM HERE
WHAT?! I NEVVAH TOUCHED NEE FUCKAHH. GODS HONEST TRUTH

WELL DONE BROWN BOTTLE! YOU'VE SAVED ALL THE MONEY IN THE BANK. PLEASE - HAVE WHATEVER YOU WANT
YUH CUDNT LENS TWENTY PENSS CUDDJAH? ...AWNLY TWENTY PENSS
...AAH NEED IT FIR THE BUS, MAN
REYT! I'M FUCKINN' OFF! OFF T' FLY FASTER THANNA SPEEDINN' FUCKIN' BULLETT
...TO THE FUCKINN' CHIP SHOPP

SLIP!
WHOO-ARGH! YA FUCKAH!

WE MIGHT NEVER KNOW WHO HE TRULY IS, OR WHERE HE GOES, BUT THIS CITY OWES A GREAT DEBT TO ITS GUARDIAN. THE BROWN BOTTLE!
BANK
DONT LOOK AT HIM HELEN. I THINK HE'S SHIT HIMSELF

FRY 'T.' BUNN
THE MASTER BAKER AND HIS GINGERBREAD SEX DOLLS

YOU'RE SO LUCKY, FRUBERT... A WHOLE WEEKEND IN AMSTERDAM! I'VE ALWAYS WANTED TO GO THERE AND SEE ALL THE CANALS AND WINDMILLS AND CLOGS.
HMMM.
FERRY TICKETS
ARE YOU SURE ME AND CHELSEA CAN'T COME WITH YOU..?

NO! HOW MANY MORE TIMES? IT'S THE BAKEWARE EXPO 2013... WHICH PART OF "BAKERS ONLY" DO YOU NOT UNDERSTAND?!

SHORTLY...

HA! FUCK THE BAKEWARE EXPO! BOLLOCKS TO ITS BORING ROLLING PINS, WOODEN SPOONS AND PROVING BASKETS... I'M OFF TO HIT AMSTERDAM'S NOTORIOUS BREAD LIGHT DISTRICT!

SO...
HMM... WHAT HAVE WE HERE..? THE ONE ON THE LEFT IS TOO STALE FOR MY TASTES...
...AND HER FRIEND HAS SAGGY MERINGUES AND TOO MUCH SUET IN THE MIX...

THIS ONE, ON THE OTHER HAND, IS PERFECT!
SLURP!
FRESHLY-BAKED MODEL IN TOWN MASSAGE €20

GOOD EVENING, MY DEAR. I'D LIKE THE FULL BAKER'S BODY MASSAGE, PLEASE...

WHAT'S THAT YOU SAY..? I SHOULD POP THROUGH HERE, TAKE ALL MY CLOTHES OFF AND CLIMB UP ON THE TABLE..?

SHORTLY...
...OOH, YES! JUST THERE! YOU REALLY KNOW WHAT YOU'RE DOING. YOU'VE GOT THE MAGIC FINGERS ALRIGHT...
WHAT'S THAT YOU SAY..? TURN OVER? OKAY...

WHAT'S THAT YOU SAY..? THAT'S THE BIGGEST ONE YOU'VE EVER SEEN..? WELL, IT IS RATHER IMPRESSIVE, I HAVE TO ADMIT...

WHAT'S THAT..? WOULD I LIKE A HAPPY ENDING FOR AN EXTRA 20 EUROS..? OR HOW ABOUT A MERINGUE RIDE AND UNPROTECTED DOUGHNUT FINISH FOR ANOTHER 50..?
PHWOOAR!

...URGH! URGH! URGH! TAKE IT! TAKE ALL FOUR AND THREE-EIGHTHS INCHES OF IT, YOU DIRTY DUTCH PASTRY SLUT..!

MONDAY...
...I DON'T UNDERSTAND, FRUBERT... HOW HAVE YOU SPENT A THOUSAND EUROS AT THE EXPO BUT COME HOME WITH NO BAKING EQUIPMENT..?
WELL... EVERYTHING IS VERY EXPENSIVE IN HOLLAND. A CUP OF TEA IS TWO HUNDRED EUROS!

DIDN'T YOU EVEN HAVE ENOUGH LEFT TO BUY CHELSEA A LITTLE SOUVENIR..?
NO. LOOK, I'M VERY SWEATY AFTER THE JOURNEY. I'M OFF FOR A SHOWER.

SO...
OOH... WHAT A DIRTY WEEKEND YOU'VE HAD, YOU NAUGHTY OLD BAKER, YOU...
...BUT NOW IT'S TIME TO CLEAN YOURSELF UP A BIT...

OH MY GOD! THAT'S NOT RIGHT! CHRIST... I MUST'VE CAUGHT A DOSE OFF ONE OF THOSE DUTCH PARKIN PROS..!

I'D BETTER GO AND SEE A DOCTOR.

AND...
...WHAT'S THAT YOU SAY, DOCTOR..? YOU'VE GOT THE RESULTS OF MY TESTS AND IT LOOKS LIKE A FEW CURRANTS STUCK ON MY BOBBY'S HELMET WITH ICING SUGAR..?!
OH MY GOD.

...YOU CAN BE STRAIGHT WITH ME, DOC... HOW LONG HAVE I GOT?
SURGERY
WAITING ROOM
SKRIT! SKRIT!
SKRIT! SKRIT!

letterbocks

Viz Comic, P.O. Box 841, Whitley Bay, NE26 9EQ • letters@viz.co.uk

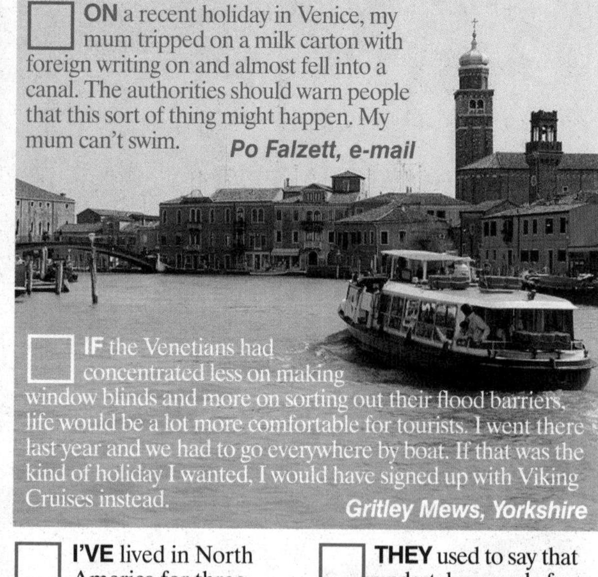

ON a recent holiday in Venice, my mum tripped on a milk carton with foreign writing on and almost fell into a canal. The authorities should warn people that this sort of thing might happen. My mum can't swim.

Po Falzett, e-mail

IF the Venetians had concentrated less on making window blinds and more on sorting out their flood barriers, life would be a lot more comfortable for tourists. I went there last year and we had to go everywhere by boat. If that was the kind of holiday I wanted, I would have signed up with Viking Cruises instead.

Gritley Mews, Yorkshire

STAR LETTER

I'M glad that the Sellafield Visitors' Centre has made it clear that it is open all year round EXCEPT Christmas Day. It would be sad, for so many reasons, to imagine some family turning up bright and early to spend December 25th looking round a decommissioned nuclear facility only to find the gates firmly shut and padlocked.

Leonard Prodworthy, e-mail

I'M beginning to think that the cheetah is a very aptly named animal. I watched one on a wildlife programme today chasing a young gazelle and it blatantly tripped it up to catch it. It was bang out of order. If there was ever some kind of animal Olympics, I'm sure it would have been disqualified and sent back to the Serengeti in disgrace.

Leyland Palmer, Twin Peak District

IN the documentary *Bin Laden: Shoot To Kill*, Barack Obama said that taking out Bin Laden was the greatest day of his life. I was rather saddened by this comment as I was hoping he remembered his visit to our cheese factory in Fakenham in 2010.

Jethro Chewcud, Norfolk

I WATCHED a pornographic video the other night where the lead actress involved was described in the title as a 'beautiful woman.' I thought this was rather a nice, romantic touch in what is usually a harsh, gritty industry. The fact that the full title of the film was *Beautiful Woman Fucked Senseless* rather spoiled the sentiment.

Perceptive Paul, e-mail

THEY say that if you 'die' in your dreams then you die in reality. Firstly, if this were the case, how would anyone be able to say they had dreamt they had died? And secondly, I dreamt I was run over by a steamroller last night and I'm fine this morning. So everyone everywhere can just fuck off then, can't they?

Michael Coffeetable, e-mail

I WONDER if there is someone somewhere that doesn't have a mate called Dave?

Ross Kennett, e-mail

** Well, readers, have you not got a mate called Dave? If not, would you like one? Perhaps there are some Daves out there who haven't got any friends who we could put you in touch with. Or perhaps you are called Dave yourself and have or haven't any namesake pals. Write and let us know.*

IT was a bit out of order when, during a documentary about the blonde one from Abba recently, the interviewer asked her about her split. Admittedly, I would have preferred more focus on that famous arse of hers, but like a true lady she declined to comment anyway.

Torbjorn Magnussen, Luton

IT'S funny that Saint George was canonised after slaying all those dragons. It would be interesting to hear what the RSPCA of the day thought about him.

Ada Fiddlesticks, Cromer

I'VE lived in North America for three years and it still makes me laugh every time the people here say fanny instead of bottom. What a place.

Neil Shand, e-mail

WHY is it when the door bell rings, dogs always assume it's for them?

Ross Kennet, e-mail

WHITE wine isn't really white is it? It's more of a yellowy piss colour. But asking people if they prefer red or yellowy piss wine wouldn't work either, so I'm at a loss as to what to call it. Perhaps we could just refer to it as wine.

Tim Pavey, e-mail

I AM the father of two young girls who are learning to read. As I leave copies of *Viz* lying around my house, I was wondering if you wouldn't mind toning the language down a bit from now on. Thanks in advance.

Shaggus Meatfart, e-mail

IN *Alien*, if John Hurt had been bending over to tie his laces with the facehugger egg behind him instead of looking at the top of it, we would have had both a much funnier, yet much darker film.

Matt Neave, e-mail

HAVING just watched the film *Prometheus*, I noticed that, as per usual, we engineers are portrayed as the villains of the piece. Okay, we occasionally charge for a new boiler when all that is required is a 13 amp fuse. But I personally would draw the line at seeking to destroy humankind by storing weapons of mass destruction on some distant planet several million light-years away, and then taking someone's arm off with an oily tentacle. That would be going too far in my book.

Dave Barmcake, Leeds

THEY used to say that undertakers made fortunes during the lawless days of the Wild West. However, the amount of times I have seen cowboys smashing windows with their rifle butts for a shoot-out rather than simply opening them makes me think that glaziers didn't do too badly either.

Mable Syrup, Peterborough

THE RSPCA would like us to save the beavers, yet Friends of the Earth would like us to save the trees. They need to get together and sort out what they want.

Bert D'Angelo, Hampton

I KNOW Dracula is forever painted as a villain, but at least he was always very smartly dressed, with his white shirt, bow tie and all. When you consider what a scruffy bugger that Frankenstein was with his ill-fitting, Norman Wisdom jacket and half-mast ragged trousers. Eeh, fancy his creator letting him go out looking like that.

Ada Prolapse, Bethnal Green

FOLLOWING a check-up, my dentist told me that my teeth were extremely healthy and didn't require any treatment. He then presented me with a bill for £18. I couldn't beleive it. I wouldn't pay a mechanic for not working on my car, so what on earth is going on? The man was an absolute rob-dog. Mind you, his nurse had got huge tits.

Clement Fistula, Truro

KEEP looking for lost items for a few moments after you've found them. That will prevent them being in the last place you look, therefore making them easier to find.
Robert Forrest, e-mail

MAKE your cheese and wine party more appealing by having no cheese or guests.
Thirsty Jack, e-mail

HIGHJUMPERS. Wear platform shoes to get an immediate 2 or 3 inch advantage over your competitors.
Neil Mainey, e-mail

CYCLISTS. Turn your trip into a full body workout by using your handlebars to do push-ups whilst the pedalling does the trick for your legs.
Thomas McColl, e-mail

WOMEN drivers. Save money on expensive frocks by jamming a long piece of floral material at the bottom of your car door.
Colmando, e-mail

H out of Steps. Get married by civil partnership to Mr C out of The Shamen and save £££s on expensive personalised taps for your new home together.
James Brown, Edinburgh

ADULTERERS. Clear your conscience by having sex with your mistress in the dark whilst thinking about your wife.
Daniel Rigglesby, Preston

DOG lovers. Convince your neighbours you have a Chihuahua by carrying around a cocktail sausage in a freezer bag. For a Great Dane use a Cumberland ring.
Sir Winnalot-Prime, e-mail

STYLE-conscious gents. Give yourself a tidy swagger by only wearing one shoe.
Daniel Goree, Sendshire

CONVINCE your neighbours that you are from North Korea by hiring a flatbed truck once a year and driving a missile down the street.
David Herron, e-mail

KERB crawlers. Simply find an equally perverted driving instructor, book a few driving lessons, and Hey Presto! Cruise your local red light district with complete impunity.
S. Mesophyll, Luton

DOWN and outs. Restore some semblance of self-respect by using a 'Noel Coward' type cigarette holder to smoke those discarded dog ends that you find on the street.
Chesney Walnut, Harrow

NEW parents. Save money on expensive weights by bench pressing your child 50 times a day. The weight of the baby and your ability to lift heavier loads increases simultaneously.
Ross Kennett, e-mail

I BANGED a girl in a hotel in Crawley 22 years ago, and then dumped her in the morning. Furious, she told me that one day she was going to be on the telly, and then I'd be really, really sorry when she was rich and famous. However, I haven't seen her on anything yet, certainly not on the BBC or ITV. I don't even think she's been on Dave. I wonder if any of your other readers have seen her.
Dave Weathercock, e-mail

* *Well readers, have YOU seen the girl that Dave Weathercock banged 22 years ago in a Crawley hotel on the telly? If you have, write and tell us what she was in.*

"WHAT goes up must come down" said Sir Issac Newton. Well I bet he's feeling a bit silly now, what with *Voyager 1* leaving the solar system and carrying on forever. Well he would be, had he not died in 1727.
Christopher Hampshire, e-mail

I DON'T understand why in Britain we have to keep putting the clocks backwards and forwards and backwards and forwards. Someone told me it's to do with the farmers in which case they can all fuck off. Just because they have to be up at the crack of dawn to toss some cows off, I don't see why we all have to follow suit.
Albert Sclereids, Mablethorpe

I HAVE just watched the swallows fly off to Africa, and I have to say good riddance. They spent all summer shitting on my car and lawnmower and I for one hope they fuck off somewhere else for their holidays next year.
Ian Pinchess, e-mail

RAISING the subject of oral intimacy can be a challenge in a new relationship. I'd like to advise your readers (and my ex-boyfriend Martin), that singing *"Scrotal fruits, made to make your mouth water"*, whilst jiggling your hips and grinning, may not always be the best approach to take.
Ellen, Penge

THE other day, for the first time I used the expression 'cooking with gas' to mean 'achieving a high level of performance.' It so happened that I was standing in front of a propane-powered barbecue at the time. Imagine my delight at this unexpected coincidence.
C Hanson, e-mail

THE Welsh have a cheek claiming to have invented cheese on toast and calling it Welsh Rarebit. I was looking at some 2000-year-old cave drawings in Guanajuato, Mexico recently, and although the tour guide said it was a depiction of human sacrifice, it looked very much to me like they were simply making a bit of cheese on toast.
Hector Xylem, Luton

WHY do we need another referendum on EU membership when I can distinctly remember voting in the one on June 6th 1975? If they had told me then that I would have to vote again, I would have stayed in the pub.
John Steer, e-mail

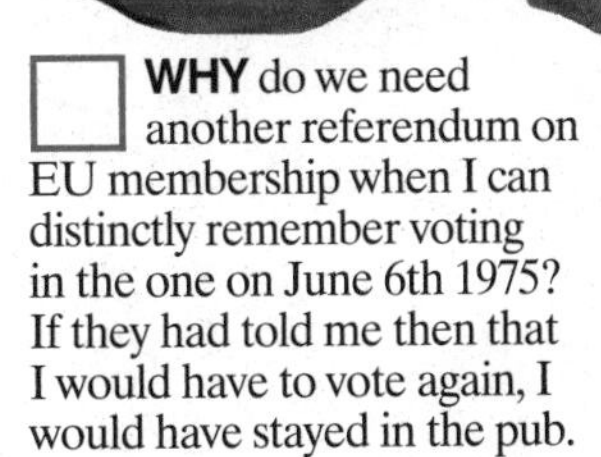

WHILST at the supermarket the other day, I purchased a bottle of 'value' bubble bath. When I came to use the product, I discovered that not only was I expected to provide my own water, warmed at my expense, but also the air to fill each bubble to boot. AND the bath tub to put it all in. When I returned the product to the store I was given short shrift and escorted from the premises.
Norman Hovercraft, Truro

WHY is it that moaning rush hour commuters always describe their trips on the London underground as being 'squashed like sardines'? I was watching a David Attenborough documentary the other night and he explained that sardines are in fact a fish, and regularly migrate around the entire ocean. In my book that gives them a good deal more space than most creatures on the planet.
Clive Metatarsal, Bumbridge

HAS anyone recently lost a house key? I have found one in the back lane. It is silver and has a pattern that goes two jaggedy bits, a dip, three more jaggedy bits, a smaller dip and then straight.
Irvine, e-mail

ROGER MELLIE
THE MAN ON THE TELLY
ROGER IS FILMING HIS NEW FTV TRAVELOGUE MELLIE COUNTRY...
I DO APOLOGISE FOR THE HOLD UP... ROGER IS VERY PUNCTUAL AS A RULE
NO PROBLEM

VROOM!
SCREECH!

SORRY I'M LATE, TOM... A FEW TOO MANY SCRUMPIES LAST NIGHT AND I SLEPT THROUGH THE COCKEREL
WELL WE DIDN'T, ROGER. WE GOT HERE AT 7:00 AM

WELL DONE. HEY, WHO'S THE FUCKING VILLAGE IDIOT, TOM?
ROGER!.. THAT'S MR CARTER, THE FARRIER...

WE'RE DOING A PIECE ABOUT DYING COUNTRY TRADITIONS, AND HE'S KINDLY OFFERED TO SHOW US HOW TO SHOE A HORSE.
HMM!

LISTEN, YOU COULDN'T MAKE ME A CUP OF COFFEE FIRST, COULD YOU?... MILK AND FOUR SUGARS
NO, ROGER. HE'S A FARRIER, NOT A BARISTA
BUT I NEED MY KICK START, TOM

LOOK, WE'RE TWO HOURS BEHIND SCHEDULE ALREADY... WE'VE GOT TO BE OVER THE VALLEY AT TEN TO DO THE PIECE ON DRY STONE WALLS
DRY STONE WALLS?... FOR FUCK'S SAKE...
...NOBODY'S GOING TO WATCH THIS SHIT, TOM

WHEN I TOOK THIS ON I THOUGHT I'D BE DOING STUFF LIKE SHOOTING RABBITS OR CHASING SHEEP ROUND ON A QUAD BIKE...

NOT PLAITING FUCKING CORN DOLLIES OR TYING FISHING FLIES.
JESUS CHRIST...
NO WONDER THE SUICIDE RATE'S SO HIGH IN THE STICKS... I'D TOP MYSELF FOR SOMETHING TO DO

THERE MUST BE SOME STRIP CLUBS OUT HERE WE COULD FILM, TOM
LOOK, ROGER...
WHERE'S ALL THE DOG FIGHTS AND THE FARMERS FUCKING SHEEP IN THE BACK ROOM OF THE PUB FOR A BET?

WE'D HAVE TO EDIT A BIT FOR THE PRE-WATERSHED, BUT...
ROGER, IT'S SHOEING A HORSE AND DRY STONE WALLING TODAY, AND THAT'S THAT
...NOW LET'S GET ON WITH IT

SHORTLY...
CUE ROGER... AND ACTION!
AT THE TURN OF THE CENTURY THERE WERE 70,000 FARRIERS IN BRITAIN. TODAY THERE ARE FEWER THAN 250... AND TODAY I'M WITH ONE OF THEM... SILUS CARTER

SILUS... THAT LOOKS VERY BRUTAL... DOESN'T IT HURT THE HORSE AT ALL?

OH, NO, ROGER...
HIS HOOVES ARE MADE FROM THE SAME STUFF AS OUR FINGERNAILS

I SEE... AND HOW OFTEN WILL YOU HAVE TO SHOE A HORSE ON AVERAGE, SILUS?
IT DEPENDS ON THE WORK HE DOES, ROGER, BUT IT'S USUALLY EVERY 6 WEEKS

SIX WEEKS? AS OFTEN AS THAT, EH?
YES. WOULD YOU LIKE TO HAVE A GO?
WOULD I FUCK!
CUT!

SORRY, I'M NOT GOING ANYWHERE NEAR THAT BASTARD THING, TOM...
FUCK THAT...
TEETH ONE END, SHIT THE OTHER AND FOUR METAL FEET IN BETWEEN.

MATE OF MINE GOT KICKED IN THE HEAD BY ONE OF THEM THINGS AND HE WAS AWAY WITH THE FAIRIES FOR THE REST OF HIS LIFE, POOR CUNT...
NEVER ATE SOLIDS AGAIN, TOM

CAN'T I DO SOMETHING A BIT MORE EXCITING... LIKE GASSING SOME BADGERS?.. OR NECKING A CHICKEN?
NO ROGER... YOU'VE GOT TO SHOE A HORSE. THE VIEWERS EXPECT IT

HE'S RIGHT. ALAN TITMARSH WAS HERE YESTERDAY AND HE HAD A GO... AND ADE EDMONDSON THE DAY BEFORE
AND I'VE GOT PAUL O'GRADY COMING TO DO IT TOMORROW MORNING, THEN MARTIN CLUNES IN THE AFTERNOON

OKAY, OKAY... BUT I'M NOT HAPPY
GIZ THE FUCKING HAMMER

SO...
GET THE CAMERA ROLLING, TOM... I'M ONLY DOING THIS ONCE SO GET IT ON THE FIRST TAKE, OKAY.
FTV
SURE... OH, CAN YOU GET RID OF THE CIGARETTE, ROGER? JUST FOR CONTINUITY

RIGHT-HO, TOM
FLICK!
FSSSST!
POP!
POP!

A WEEK LATER...
HERE WE GO, ROGER
JUST IN TIME, TOM... IT'S ON
SKY
COMING UP NEXT...

GOOD EVENING... AND WELCOME TO RURAL A&E
SKY
Rural A+E
with Matt Baker

ON TONIGHT'S SHOW... A FARMER DIALS 999 WHEN HE BECOMES TRAPPED UNDERNEATH HIS OVERTURNED TRACTOR...
SKY
OO-AAR!
...AND A SHEPHERD IS AIRLIFTED TO HOSPITAL AFTER BREAKING HIS LEG OUT ON THE FELLS...

BUT FIRST... PARAMEDICS ARE CALLED OUT TO A FARRIER'S WHERE A MAN HAS BEEN KICKED BY A HORSE IN A VERY SENSITIVE AREA...
THERE I AM, TOM
SKY

SKY
OH BLEEP! ME BLEEP! KNACKERS! CHRIST!.. I BLEEP! TOLD YOU, TOM! THE BLEEEEEEEEEEEP! ANIMAL!

OH BLEEP! TOM... I'LL NEVER BLEEP! AGAIN!.. JESUS!
I HOPE I'M GETTING AN APPEARANCE FEE FOR THIS SHOW, TOM

HOW ARE THE OLD CLOCKWEIGHTS TODAY, ROGER?.. STILL SWOLLEN?
SIZE OF FUCKING COCONUTS THEY ARE, TOM... AND YOU SHOULD SEE THE COLOUR OF 'EM...
...BLUE AS A BABOON'S ARSE!

HOLD ON... I WONDER IF THEY FANCY DOING AN 'EMBARRASSING BODIES' CELEBRITY SPECIAL... HAVE YOU GOT DR. CHRISTIAN JESSEN'S PHONE NUMBER, TOM?
ACTUALLY, THAT DR. PIXIE McKENNA WOULD BE BETTER...
I WOULDN'T MIND HER GIVING MY NUTS THE ONCE OVER, I CAN TELL YOU

ROYAL FLUSH

"It was me what give the Queen the shits," says Palace milkie

IN MARCH, the nation held its breath as her majesty the Queen succumbed to a severe bout of gastroenteritis. The monarch was forced to cancel several engagements as the diarrhoea bug took its toll on her regal nipsy. For two weeks the country's head of state fought a brave rearguard action against the stool-loosening bacillus before finally getting the upper hand.

Gold top: But Milkman Ken's bottom was in a right old state.

Happily, the 86-year-old head of state is now back to full health, and is once again able to undertake official engagements free from the constant fear of following through. The country rejoices as one at her remarkable recovery, but one man who is breathing a bigger sigh of relief than anyone is milkman Ken Gripewater. For Ken, 62, fears that it was he who was responsible for passing the serious tummy bug on to her majesty.

"Buckingham Palace has been on my rounds since I took it over 40 years ago. Three pints of semi-skimmed every day and a couple of yoghurts at the weekend," he told us.

terrible

"Then, one Sunday at the end of February I came down with terrible squirts," he continued.

"My guts was rotten. Not to put too fine a point on it, I was shitting through the eye of a needle. I had the worst trumpeter's lips I've ever had, and that's saying something, because I did national service in Malaya."

no

"I'd been up and down all night, and by rights I shouldn't have gone into work on the Monday morning. But there's an old saying in my business - the milk round must go on."

"I just couldn't bear the thought of my customers, including the Queen, eating dry cornflakes or drinking black tea, so I dragged myself in to the depot."

EXCLUSIVE!

Gripewater set out on his rounds as usual, but as he approached the Mall, he started experiencing dreadful gripping pains in his abdomen.

Phibes

"It was the thirty-second warning before the bomb bay doors opened. I pulled the float up and started pulling my trousers down as I headed for the nearest litter bin. And I only just made it. It was about four in the morning, so luckily there was nobody about to witness my predicament."

"There must of been a pint of chicken gravy come out of me, I can tell you. And when it finally stopped, I had to use a crisp packet for the paperwork. After the action my tea-towel holder had seen the night before, it really did smart."

No squitters: Her Majesty in happier times.

standards

After four decades working in the dairy industry, Gripewater is only too well aware of the importance of good hygiene. But after being caught short in the middle of his round, even he had to let his usual high standards slip.

"Unfortunately there was nowhere to wash my hands after I'd wiped. As it happens, they weren't too bad and I managed to wipe the worst of it off on the front of my apron. But I have to admit there was perhaps a germ or two left on my fingers judging by the smell of them."

posts

The rest of Ken's round took in Buckingham Palace where he dropped off the

ANUS HORRIBILIS!

WHEN THE bug that causes a bout of gastroenteritis strikes, it strikes very quickly. And sadly, not even royalty is immune from its devastating effects. Here's a timeline of the key events as the Queen Elizabeth II's recent tragic bout of diarrhoea unfolded...

Timeline of Rectal Horror for HM Queen

Ⓐ Fri 28.02.2013 08:35
HM Queen awakes in her Buckingham Palace bedroom with violent stomach cramps and a monkey's toe...

Ⓑ Fri 28.02.2013 08:38
Her majesty rushes to en-suite bathroom where she releases a pace car

Queen's order on the step. And it is from these bottles that he now fears her majesty picked up the stomach bug that laid her low and left her in hospital.

"When I heard that her Royal Highness had been struck down with the old rusty arse water, I felt really bad," he told us.

houses

"If her bubblepoo was half as bad as mine was, it could easy have finished off a woman of her age. So I'm really relieved that she made a recovery."

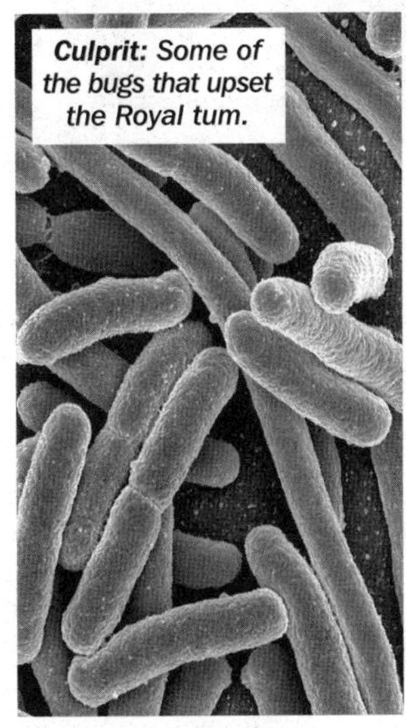

Culprit: Some of the bugs that upset the Royal tum.

Ken comes up for retirement in 2016, and after supplying milk to the royal household for more than four decades, he had been hoping for a token of official recognition for his loyal services.

"Word at the dairy was that I was in line for a gong," he told us. "But I suppose any chance that I had of getting an MBE has now went down the fucking pan."

Bad Guts Science

.......with Dr Ben Goldacre

Bowel upsets have been around as long as Kings and Queens, but modern Royals can take simple precautions to avoid being laid low on the throne, says media medic Dr Ben Goldacre.

"The majority of regal tummy upsets are caused by improperly-cooked poultry. Any swans that you eat should be thoroughly cooked to kill any salmonella-causing bacteria. Make sure your palace chef tests the meat by piercing it with a gold skewer to make sure the juices are running clear before serving it on a priceless, solid silver platter. If a solid silver platter is not available, a solid gold or platinum one will do.

Many bouts of gastric illness are the result of a poor hygiene regimen; scrupulous cleaning after every toilet trip is the best way to prevent harmful bacteria from spreading between anus and mouth. So make sure that your butler washes his hands thoroughly after wiping your bottom. Better still dismiss your butler following each lavatory visit and replace him with a new one wearing a clean pair of white gloves.

Often, stomach bugs are caused by eating contaminated food, so always check the sell-by dates on anything you are intending to eat. If in any doubt about the freshness of a product you find in the palace fridge, such as an opened pot of caviar or some leftover pheasant under glass, feed a small amount to one of your ladies-in-waiting, eg. Lady jane Fellowes, and wait 24-hours to see if she comes down with the squirts.

Many infections are transmitted by simple social contact, such as shaking hands. So, when out on an official engagement and required to meet common people, ensure that they have first been soaked head to foot for at least two hours in a strong solution of disinfectant such as Parazone or Jeyes Fluid.

More Bad Guts Science next time."

Ben X

followed by around two pints of fizzy gravy...

C Fri 28.02.2013 09:02

After an extensive clean-up involving 42 sheets (folded) of Charmin Ultra and 8 Hackle moist wipes, her majesty returns to bed...

D Fri 28.02.2013 09:03

Queen returns to the toilet after sharting the bed. Butler called to change sheets...

E Fri 28.02.2013 09:32

The Queen's surgeon, Sir Humphrey Bell-Tawse arrives and diagnoses acute gastroenteritis. He recommends immediate admission to hospital...

F Fri 28.02.2013 10:48

Her majesty is taken to the King Edward VII Hospital in the gold-encrusted State Ambulance, drawn by four white horses. The route is lined by thousands of cheering well-wishers...

G Fri 28.02.2013 11:05

En-route, her majesty disembarks in Oxford Street to go on an informal walkabout, chatting with her subjects, accepting flowers and Get Well cards...

H Fri 28.02.2013 11:06

Gripping her buttocks, the Queen dashes up Poland Street and into the Ali Kebaba takeaway, where she asks to use the toilet...

I Fri 28.02.2013 11:07

A footman arrives with a white ermine toilet seat and fixes it to the pot in the small WC behind the kitchen and her majesty rushes in...

J Fri 28.02.2013 11:38

Her majesty emerges and awards shop proprietor Mr Tibor Szakacs the Queen's Empire Medal for services rendered to the crown...

K Fri 28.02.2013 11:39

The Queen breaks wind and re-enters the lavatory for a second sitting...

L Fri 28.02.2013 12:02

The State Ambulance arrives at the hospital where her majesty is greeted on the steps by chief hospital administrator Sir Norman St.John-Mosley, who presents her with an engraved solid silver tea service commemorating her admission to the hospital with diarrhoea.

RULING CL~ARSES

HER MAJESTY THE QUEEN is not the first British monarch to suffer from Montezuma's revenge. Here are FIVE more crowned heads who've had trouble with their tails.

AFTER losing a bet with Cardinal Wolsey, the famously gluttonous **Henry VIII** *once ate sixty hard-boiled goose eggs and was laid low with constipation for twelve weeks - a royal record that stands to this day. It was during this period that he posed for painter Hans Holbein's iconic portrait, which shows the Tudor king bloated and standing wide-legged due to three months of backed-up foulage.*

A LOVER of black pudding, **Elizabeth I** *constantly suffered from wet buttocks on the toilet, caused when her large, dense stools hit the water. However, the Virgin Queen's problem was solved when Sir Walter Raleigh or possibly Sir Francis Drake gallantly laid his cape across the surface before she sat down for a poo, creating a pap baffle to protect her regal mudflaps from splashing.*

LIKE a mouse, **Queen Victoria** *had no anal sphincter and consequently had no control over where or when she stooled. A series of specially-trained servants - known as turdie-ghilies - were charged with following the monarch 24-hours-a-day and using a dustpan and brush to discreetly sweep up any tods which emerged from under her voluminous skirts.*

WHEN his relationship with hermaphrodite American divorcee Wallis Simpson threatened to engulf the monarchy in scandal, **Edward VIII** *took to the airwaves to abdicate. But few people realise that whilst giving up his throne, Edward was sitting on another one - in his bathroom. For, at the time of his historic broadcast, the King was suffering from a bout of violent squitters as a result of the four packets of Smints he had chomped through whilst writing his fateful address.*

ASK any schoolboy what **King Alfred** *was famous for and they'll tell you: "Burning the cakes." But few people know how this famous historical event came to pass. Hiding in an old peasant woman's cottage, the incognito monarch was charged with watching the oven. Left alone and feeling the urge to break wind, Alfred attempted a one-cheek-sneak and followed through catastrophically, the result of eating four packets of Smints earlier in the day. Leaving his post to throw his ruined ruined doublet and hose in a nearby bush and wipe himself clean with some dockleaves, he returned to find the cakes burnt to a crisp.*

THE HORSEPOWER & THE GLORY!

Top Gear-style makeover planned for the C of E

SUNDAY MORNING services at Westminster Abbey could look very different in future, if plans by the newly appoionted Archbishop of Canterbury to give his church a *Top Gear*-style makeover come to fruition.

EXCLUSIVE

For in a bid to boost flagging congregations, **Justin Welby** has decided to make his sermons more like the top-rated BBC2 motoring show. And the radical makeover is set to completely change the face of Sunday worship at the 1500-year-old cathedral.

worthy

Welby explained: "The Church of England's got a reputation for being dull-but-worthy, a bit like *Top Gear* was in the eighties, with stuffy reviews of hatchbacks and boring items about seatbelts."

"I want to do for the church what Jeremy Clarkson did with that tired old format, grabbing it by the scruff of the neck and making it relevant for the new millennium. With its high octane mix of fast cars, smoking tyres, and controversial, laddish humour, Top Gear is now a must-watch for millions of people," he continued.

"And I'm going to do the same for the C of E."

REVS PER MINUTE: Mystery holy man "The Bish" will provide speedy thrills.

- **OUT will go old-fashioned pews. The congregation will mill around the abbey behind the Archbishop and his two co-presenters as they lounge on leather chairs, discussing topical ecumenical issues in an irreverent manner.**
- **IN will come light-hearted features, including *Star in a Reasonably-Priced Pulpit*, where guest celebrity clerics will compete to deliver one full Eucharist in the quickest time.**
- **OUT will go choirs, organists and fuddy-duddy lay preachers talking about Jesus and the Ten Commandments.**
- **IN will come "The Bish", a mystery prelate who will silently officiate at religious ceremonies with his face hidden behind a dark visor on his mitre.**
- **OUT will go boring hymns, prayers and communion, to make way for wacky *Top Gear*-style challenges.**

Welby told us: "We've got some great stuff coming up. In our first service, me and my fellow curates will be given a budget of £50 each to go and buy a second hand font. Then it's a race to see who will be the first one to get it back into the Abbey and carry out a christening."

"On future Sundays, we're going to dig a grave with some dynamite and fit nitrous injection to the organ pipes to see if we can break the 14th Century stained glass windows in the transept."

AMEN & MOTORS: Juzza, The Gerbil and Chaplain Sensible yesterday.

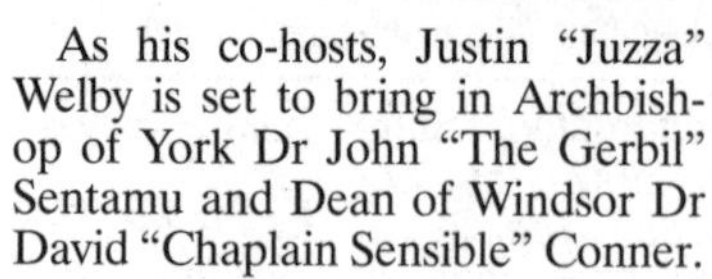

As his co-hosts, Justin "Juzza" Welby is set to bring in Archbishop of York Dr John "The Gerbil" Sentamu and Dean of Windsor Dr David "Chaplain Sensible" Conner.

animal

"We make a great team," said Welby. "There's an on-altar chemistry between us that I think the congregation's going to love."

But the Archbishop refused to reveal the real name of The Bish. He told us: "I dare say internet forums will be abuzz with people speculating about the identity of our tame man of the cloth."

"But there's only two people who know who's hidden behind that visor, me and Him upstairs," he joked.

gonzo

And the Archbishop promised even more surprises for members of his congregation.

"At the end of each service, me, the Gerbil and Chaplain Sensible will run down the church steps, leap into three high-powered sports cars and drive round really fast with all smoke coming off the tyres, doing doughnuts," he added excitedly. "I'm really looking forward to it."

The General Synod had been in talks with the BBC to broadcast the re-vamped services on Sunday evenings, in place of outdated hymn show *Songs of Praise*. But negotiations reportedly broke down when Welby demanded £1 million a sermon and full copyright on the format, in case it transferred to other faiths and international markets.

watersports

"The BBC has lost a massive opportunity. Anyone who continues to tune into *Songs of Praise* deserves to be dragged out of their house and stoned to death in front of their family, in accordance with the scriptures," Welby added, controversially.

Drunken bakers

"Hi, Andy Serkis here. You probably know me best from doing a sort of Donald Duck voice for that Gollum thing in them Lord of the Rings films. But I bet you didn't know that I've also played lots of monkeys in films, a couple of Ians - moors murderer Brady and rockstar Dury - and Tintin's seafaring sidekick Captain Haddock. But in all the films I've been in, I've never played anyone who likes piccalilli, which is ironic, because I absolutely love the stuff. I can't get enough of this delicious, pale yellow, spicy vegetable pickle. And judging by all the letters you've sent me on the subject, neither can you. Here's the pick-alilli of the bunch..."

MY HUSBAND absolutely adores piccalilli, and insists on having it with every meal. However, he doesn't like the cauliflower in it, which he picks out and puts on the side of his plate. He does the same with the onion and the marrow. And the gherkins. In fact, by the time he's finished there's only the sauce left, and he doesn't like that very much either.

Ada Branston, Ross

MY WIFE and I love to feed the birds in our garden and one day last summer we thought we'd give them a little treat. So we filled half a coconut with piccalilli and hung it off the bird table. Unfortunately none of them liked it and a couple of the sparrows that did try it died in some distress. Looking back, my wife thought it might have been a bit too acidic for their delicate gizzards, so next time we're going to try them on chutney instead.

Albert Doorstop, Tring

THESE days people throw their unopened jars of piccalilli into the bin after only a couple of years sitting in the back of the pantry. But I've got an unopened jar from 1945 in the cupboard which I've never fancied. It certainly puts these modern piccalillis to shame.

Dolly Earnshawn, Hull

MY HUSBAND and I are in our 80s and recently watch the film 9½ *Weeks* on the telly. Inspired by the scene where the man smears the contents of his fridge onto a bare lady and licks it all off, my husband

suggested we did the same to put a bit of a spark into our sex life. However, we only had a half jar of piccalilli in our fridge, and the thought of having such an acrid, vinegary sauce full of cauliflower rubbed into my intimate crevices didn't do anything for me sexually. When I explained my concerns to my husband, he was forced to agree. So we had a cup of tea and did a sudoku instead.

Mable Gunt, Torquay

MY HUSBAND is colour blind, so I like to put bright blue food colouring into his piccalilli, and he doesn't notice a thing. If I run out of food colouring I use fountain pen ink or Toilet Duck.

Joice Fibroids, Gloat

AS THE father of a new-born baby, I couldn't help noticing a similarity between the contents of my child's nappy and a large pile of piccalilli. - so much so that I thought I'd play a cheeky trick on my wife. I emptied half a jar of piccalilli into a clean nappy and when she came into the room I showed it to her. "Look at this, dear," I announced, before scooping it out and starting to eat it. I was expecting her shock to turn into helpless laughter when she realised my ruse, but instead she went hysterical and began to shake. Then she vomited and started shouting: "Oh my God! Oh my God! No!" I stuck my tongue out at her to show her that it was piccalilli and tried to kiss her, but that just made things worse, and she seemed to suffer a sort of breakdown, slipping on the vomit as she tried to back away across the landing and falling down the stairs. My wife's in a neckbrace and I've been sleeping on the sofa for the last two weeks. In fact, with hindsight I'm beginning to wish I hadn't carried out my little practical joke.

Charlie Barnfeather, Lower Dingwall

PICCALILLI TIPS

DON'T waste money buying jars to put home-made piccalilli in. Jars of chutney, relish and pickle can be emptied, washed out and used to store your piccalilli.

Dolly Lungbutter, Cheam

WHY NOT use piccalilli as an ingredient in a savoury trifle? Simply put layers of bread, red onion jelly and piccalilli "custard" into a glass bowl, then top it off with salad cream. Garnish your trifle with cracked pepper 'hundreds and thousands.' Different and delicious!

Ciccy Oerstryke, Hull

RUN OUT of vegetables for Sunday dinner? Simply empty a jar of piccalilli into a sieve and run it under the tap to rinse off the sauce. Hey presto - a portion of tasty, if slightly yellow vegetables that can be heated in the microwave and served with your roast.

Edna Chelstrom, Luton

NO MILK for your tea? No problem - simply stir in a spoonful of piccalilli instead. But remember, only do this if you've run out of milk and you don't mind your tea tasting quite unpleasant.

Mavis Polyps, Kent

How Much Do YOU Like Piccalilli?

YOU EITHER love it or you hate it. Either that, or you can take it or leave it. Nothing splits people into three camps like Piccalilli. But which of those camps are YOU in? It's often very difficult to tell. It would be a waste of money buying ten jars of piccalilli if you can't stand the stuff. Similarly it would be a shame to refuse to have it on a sandwich if it's one of your favourite foods. So how do you know? Take Andy's Scientific test to see if you're Piccalilliphilic or Piccalilliphobic. Or Piccalillinonpartisan. Answer each question truthfully *a*, *b* or *c* then tot up your score to discover your Piccalilli Rating.

To piccalilli, or not to piccalilli; that is the question.

1 WHILST out shopping, you spot a "Buy One Get One Free" offer on a range of food products at the supermarket. What do you add to your basket?

a. Two jars of sweetcorn relish
b. A jar of chutney and a jar of piccalilli
c. Two jars of piccalilli

2 YOUR house is on fire. Your family and pets are safe, but you have the opportunity to run back in and get one thing. What single item do you choose to rescue from the flames?

a. Your photograph album, full of precious memories
b. The teddy bear you treasured throughout your childhood
c. A half-empty jar of Tesco "Everyday Value" Piccalilli

3 YOU ARE at a finger buffet with some friends and you load up your plate with a slice of quiche, a couple of sausage rolls, a piece of pork pie, a Scotch

AT SCHOOL I was always being given the cane for spelling the word piccalilli incorrectly. So my grandad taught me a handy rhyme to help me remember. Unfortunately, I could never remember the rhyme either, and so I continued getting six of the best on a daily basis. But it never did me any harm.

Hector Pidgeon, Wrexham

WITH reference to Mr Pidgeon's letter *(above)*, I wonder if the rhyme was the same rhyme that my grandfather taught me? It went;

Piccalilli, Iccalilli,
Ciccalilli, Coo,
Alibillybongo,
Lilly, Lilly, Loo.

You simply take the initial letter of the first five words, remove the last letter of either the fifth or sixth word and replace it with an 'i', and ignore the seventh word completely. I never forgot this little poem and when I left school I got a job designing labels for a major manufacturer of piccalilli.

Albert Fart, Notts

DOES anyone know if it's against the rules for Jews to eat piccalilli? Only I'm thinking of becoming Jewish, but I love piccalilli. I don't mind having my foreskin removed, but I draw the line at giving up my favourite condiment for religious reasons.

Hector Bile, Deeside

IF YOU ask me, there are far too many programmes about singing on the television these days and not enough about piccalilli. Why don't they do a show where members of the public have to make piccalilli for a panel of celebrity judges, and they get through if their piccalilli is the best or if their granny is dying or they've had cancer? I'd certainly tune in, and they could call it X-Piccalilli or The Piccalilli Factor. Or Britain's Got Piccalilli.

Mavis Churns, Oakham

PICCALILLI had always been one of my favourite foods until a septic cyst burst on one of my wife's labiums. I don't know why, but I've never really fancied piccalilli since then.

Dr F Treves, Dundee

Piccalilli Lost & Found

LOST. In Croydon area. Nearly full jar of piccalilli. Small tear on top of label and scratch on lid. Kids distraught. Reward for information leading to safe return. *Box 306.*

MISSING in N.Yorks Leyburn/ Masham area. Jar of piccalilli. Last seen in pantry 4/5/2013. Has gone walkabout before but never this long. Please check outhouses and sheds. *Box 4.*

FOUND in Wednesbury/ Bromsgrove area. Jar of Heinz Piccalilli, almost full. Obviously a well-loved family jar. If not claimed within a week will put on pork pie and eat. *Box 83.*

egg, lettuce and tomatoes. At the end of the table is a selection of relishes and sauces. Which one do you choose?

a. Salad cream
b. Red onion marmalade
c. Piccalilli

4 **YOU ARE** going on holiday to a place where they eat foreign food, so you pack a jar of chutney, a jar of burger relish and a jar of piccalilli in your suitcase. At the airport check-in, your baggage is overweight and you have to leave behind two out of the three jars. Which ones do you bin before boarding your flight?

a. The chutney and the piccalilli
b. The piccalilli and the burger relish
c. The burger relish and the chutney

5 **YOU ARE** going out for a meal on a first date. What kind of restaurant do you choose?

a. An informal carvery with a set menu
b. A small bistro that is cosy and intimate
c. Somewhere where they do piccalilli

How did YOU do?

Score 1 for every answer a, 2 for every answer b and 3 for every answer c...

0-5: *Oh dear. You don't seem to like piccalilli at all. Perhaps it's the of-putting colour or maybe it's the unpleasant taste, but whatever the reason, you and piccalilli don't see eye to eye. Better call it a day with this relish and move on.*

5-10: *Hmm. You just don't seem able to make up your mind whether you like piccalilli or not. Our advice is, don't rush things. Take it steady, try adding a little bit of piccalili to your food occasionally and see how it goes.*

10-15: *Congratulations, you're a sod for the piccalilli, stuffing it down your face morning, noon and night. As far as you're concerned there isn't a meal in the world that couldn't be improved by adding a generous dollop of this lumpy yellow condiment.*

Dear C.S.I. Miriam

Solves YOUR forensic piccalilli pickles

Piccalilli on collar gave hubby away

Dear Miriam

RECENTLY my husband has been spending a lot of time working late. But yesterday he came home at nearly midnight with a small blob of piccalilli on his left shirt collar.

He is 32 and I am 31 and we've been married for 5 years. I wouldn't worry normally about such a small food stain on his collar. But he doesn't like piccalilli and I think he might be having an affair, because his secretary loves piccalilli and she's a fairly messy eater. I'm concerned that she must have got some of the stuff on her chin at lunch, which has then got wiped onto my husband's collar when they were smooching.

I have tackled him about it, but he says it happened at lunchtime when he was out for a meal with some clients. He claims that his ploughman's lunch came with a piccalilli garnish which he tried to remove with a spoon. He swears that it sprang up and landed on his collar.

He has previously had an affair which he initially denied, before eventually admitting everything when I discovered some chutney in his pubes. I don't believe he is telling the truth this time, and I don't know which way to turn. Please help me out of this piccalilli, Miriam.

AB, Norwich

Miriam says...

You are right to be suspicious. I don't buy this story about how your husband got piccalilli on his collar. Any forensic scientist will tell you that a spoon would not project piccalilli onto a shirt collar unless the victim was spooning it towards himself and upwards with some force. When removing unwanted food from a plate we naturally push it away and downwards; it's elementary psychology. Even if he did remove the stuff as he said, a spoon would not have the 'spring' necessary to project piccalilli two feet into the air, unless it was made of plastic. And what businessman holds an executive lunch in a joint with plastic cutlery?

Also, your husband is right-handed, so any food flicking up could not land on the left side of his collar. What's more, you say he arrived home at midnight - a full 12 hours after his lunch when the incident was supposed to have happened, yet the piccalilli was still in a blob. After such an interval any sauce or pickle would have spread into a large patch.

No, that piccalilli was fresh, and it looks like this wiseguy's alibi has got more holes that a Swiss cheese in a goddamn string vest. Face it honey, your man's screwing around with a broad who's got piccalilli on her chin.

Miriam's CSI Piccalilli Help Lines

The piccalilli advice lines you can trust

Husband claims to have eaten alone, but wife found 2 spoons covered in piccalilli in sink:
018 118 055

Dropped piccalilli blamed on accident, but splatter patterns just don't add up:
0 181 18055

Wife claims to have been out all day, but piccalilli on table was 8° below room temperature:
01811 80 55

Piccalilli missing from jar, but ham salad undisturbed in fridge:
0 1811805 5

Vaginal dryness:
0 18 11805 5

Call cost $1.50 per minute and terminate in Jerry Bruckheimer's house, Hollywood

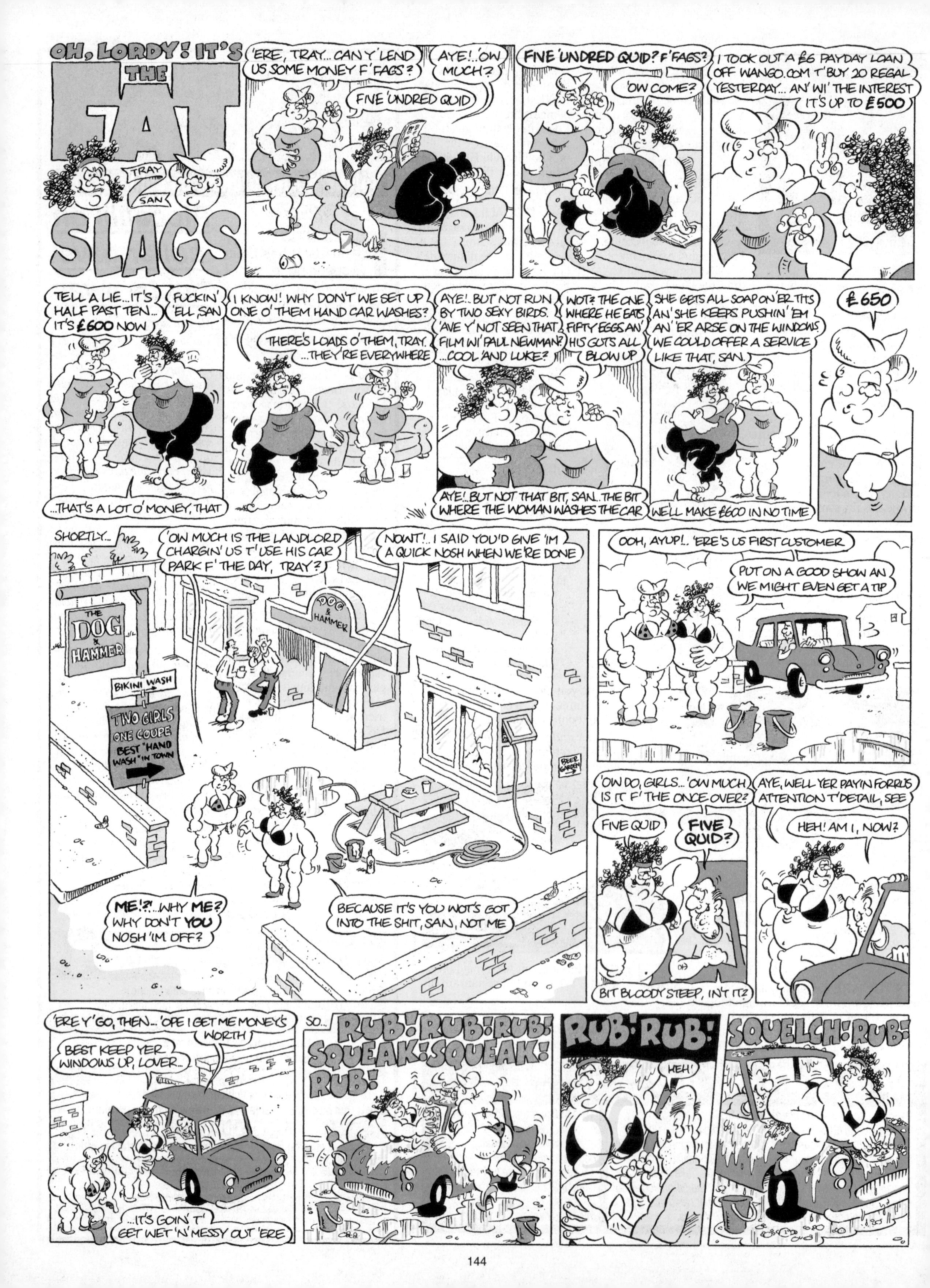
OH, LORDY! IT'S THE FAT SLAGS
TRAY
SAN
'ERE, TRAY... CAN Y' LEND US SOME MONEY F' FAGS?
AYE!.. 'OW MUCH?
FIVE 'UNDRED QUID
FIVE 'UNDRED QUID? F' FAGS?
'OW COME?
I TOOK OUT A £6 PAYDAY LOAN OFF WANGO.COM T' BUY 20 REGAL YESTERDAY... AN' WI' THE INTEREST IT'S UP TO £500
TELL A LIE... IT'S HALF PAST TEN... IT'S £600 NOW
FUCKIN' 'ELL, SAN
...THAT'S A LOT O' MONEY, THAT
I KNOW! WHY DON'T WE SET UP ONE O' THEM HAND CAR WASHES?
THERE'S LOADS O' THEM, TRAY. ...THEY'RE EVERYWHERE
AYE!.. BUT NOT RUN BY TWO SEXY BIRDS. 'AVE Y' NOT SEEN THAT FILM WI' PAUL NEWMAN? ...COOL 'AND LUKE?
WOT? THE ONE WHERE HE EATS FIFTY EGGS AN' HIS GUTS ALL BLOW UP
AYE!.. BUT NOT THAT BIT, SAN.. THE BIT WHERE THE WOMAN WASHES THE CAR
SHE GETS ALL SOAP ON 'ER TITS AN' SHE KEEPS PUSHIN' 'EM AN' 'ER ARSE ON THE WINDOWS. WE COULD OFFER A SERVICE LIKE THAT, SAN.
WE'LL MAKE £600 IN NO TIME
£650
SHORTLY...
'OW MUCH IS THE LANDLORD CHARGIN' US T' USE HIS CAR PARK F' THE DAY, TRAY?
NOWT!.. I SAID YOU'D GIVE 'IM A QUICK NOSH WHEN WE'RE DONE
THE DOG & HAMMER
BIKINI WASH
TWO GIRLS ONE COUPE BEST "HAND WASH" IN TOWN
DOG & HAMMER
BEER GARDEN
ME!?!... WHY ME? WHY DON'T YOU NOSH 'IM OFF?
BECAUSE IT'S YOU WOT'S GOT INTO THE SHIT, SAN, NOT ME
OOH, AYUP!.. 'ERE'S US FIRST CUSTOMER
PUT ON A GOOD SHOW AN WE MIGHT EVEN GET A TIP
'OW DO, GIRLS... 'OW MUCH IS IT F' THE ONCE OVER?
FIVE QUID
FIVE QUID?
BIT BLOODY STEEP, IN'T IT?
AYE, WELL YER PAYIN FORRUS ATTENTION T' DETAIL, SEE
HEH! AM I, NOW?
'ERE Y' GO, THEN... 'OPE I GET ME MONEY'S WORTH
BEST KEEP YER WINDOWS UP, LOVER...
...IT'S GOIN' T' GET WET 'N' MESSY OUT 'ERE
SO...
RUB! RUB! RUB! SQUEAK! SQUEAK! RUB!
RUB! RUB!
HEH!
SQUELCH! RUB!

SQUE-E-E-E-E-K!

RUB! RUB! RUB!

RUB! SPLASH! SQUEAK! RUB!

THAT'S IT, LOVER. I'LL RINSE THE SUDS OFF AN' Y' CAN 'AVE A LOOK
GOOD SHOW, THAT, GIRLS... I'LL 'AVE T' SLIDE ME SEAT BACK T' GET OUT

IF Y'VE DONE AS GOOD A JOB ON THE CAR AS Y'AVE ON ME COCK I'LL BE WELL CHUFFED
WE AIM T' PLEASE

FUCKIN' NORA! WOT Y' DONE!? LOOK AT THE FUCKIN' STATE OF THE FUCKER!
AYE!.. NIPPIN', IN'T IT?

Y'VE FUCKIN' WRECKED IT... I WANTED Y' T' WASH IT, NOT FUCKIN' SQUASH IT!
THEM LITTLE DINGS WAS IN IT BEFORE WE STARTED
WERE THEY FUCK!

AN' IT'S THE WIFE'S CAR... SHE'LL 'AVE ME BOLLOCKS IN THE TOASTER WHEN SHE SEES THIS!
D'Y' WANT YER FIVER BACK?

AYE! AND THE REST!... 200 QUID THIS'LL COST T' PUT RIGHT
200 QUID!?!

WE AIN'T GOT 200 QUID, MISTER... MAYBE WE COULD PAY Y' BACK IN SOME OTHER WAY, EH!?!
'OW D'Y' MEAN?

WELL... WE COULD GET IN THE CAR AN' GIVE YER GEARSTICK A BIT OF A BUFFIN' UP... Y'KNOW... GET YER BIG END LUBRICATED
AYE... THEN FUCK YER
WELL... I S'POSE I COULD TELL THE MISSUS SOMEBODY DUNCHED ME IN LIDL'S CAR PARK... HEH! HEH!

SHORTLY...
BOING! BOING! BOING! BOING! BOING! BOING! BOING! BOING!
UGH! UGH! UGH!

CLUNK!!
OOF!
I 'OPE THAT WEREN'T 'IS BACK

OH, CHRIST AN' A BEAR... LOOK WOT Y'VE FUCKIN' DONE...
BEST HAND WASH IN TOWN

FUCKIN' 'ELL... THE SUSPENSION... THE EXHAUST... Y'VE FUCKED IT... OH CHRIST!
IT WERE LIKE THAT WHEN WE GOT IN

THERE A THOUSAND FUCKIN' QUID'S WORTH O' DAMAGE THERE
'OW ABOUT WE LET YOU DO US UP THE SHITTER THIS TIME?
NO! YOU TWO ARE GOIN' T' PAY T' GET THIS SORTED!... CASH!

SHORTLY...
SEE... Y' JUST ADJUST THIS SLIDER 'ERE TO 'OW MUCH Y' WANT T' BORROW... AN THIS ONE TO 'OW LONG T' PAY IT BACK...
RIGHT...

...SO I'LL PUT THIS UP TO £1000.?
BEST MAKE IT £1006... WE'VE RAN OUT O' FAGS.
Wango .com
APR = 28 x 10¹⁴ %
CALL THE SAMARITANS

You've Been Changed!

Clipsters: Beadle, Riley, Hill and the other one whose name we can't remember (not shown).

THE GOVERNMENT last night put forward plans for a major overhaul of the *You've Been Framed* clip payments system. The shake-up, whereby each home video will be assessed according to a strict sliding scale, represents the first variation in the television show home video blooper allowance system, which has been set at a flat rate of £250 since 1990.

By our Entertainment Economics Correspondent
Rick Spangleton-Jones

From next April the single £250 payment will be scrapped, and viewers sending in footage of their comical mishaps, cute babies and adorable pets will be subject to a brand new assessed payment scale, depending on the quality and type of clip submitted.

flat

"When the programme was first introduced twenty-three years ago, members of the public were paid a flat rate of £250 for each clip of a fat woman breaking a swing, a dog stealing an ice-cream or a small child being catapulted off a bouncy castle," said Chancellor of the Exchequer George Osborne. "It is time to face up to reality. That system is no longer workable in the current economic climate."

baseball

The cap on the maximum amount payable is to be raised to £350, restoring the top clip rate back to its 1990 value in real terms. But it is understood that the vast majority of claimants will receive significantly less under the new proposals. So, while the new system

will be good news for men in vests riding monkey bikes into fences and sleepy babies falling face-first into their dinners, it will be bad news for toddlers kicking footballs into their dads' knackers.

phrygian

According to the Chancellor, rather than a 'one size fits all' approach of the type presently operated, clips are to be graded against to a strictly-enforced tariff. "Of course, there will be winners and losers," said Osborne. "But it's a much fairer system, a much more equitable system and it is a system that offers value for money for the hard-working British taxpayer."

dutch

To accompany the changes, the Treasury is setting up a so-called "Whistleblowers' Hotline", a freephone number where members of the public can anonymously voice their suspicions about staged clips.

"For too long, *You've Been Framed* fraudsters have been helping themselves to £250 payouts," said

Downing St announces shake-up to clip show payment system

Osborne. "It's time to stamp out this *You've Been Framed* free-for-all once and for all."

"We want people to report any suspicious behaviour. Maybe you've seen your neighbour in his back garden, practising tripping over whilst carrying a birthday cake, or perhaps you think he's deliberately chopped a tree down onto the roof of his old shed," the Chancellor continued.

"Have you seen a toddler rehearsing going over his tricycle handlebars into a paddling pool while his dad sets the camcorder up? Whatever your suspicions, even if you have no proof, you can call anonymously and we will stop their money immediately."

And Mr Osborne had this message for the video clip cheats caught out in the new clampdown: "You've Been Named and Shamed."

How the new system will affect home video clip claimants:

The Scoopers

MIDDLE-aged woman swings out on rope over river and branch snaps

SMALL toddler kicked in face by jiving auntie at wedding — £310

NAN loses false teeth whilst blowing out candles on birthday cake — £290

CHRISTMAS pudding sets fire to napkins/paper hat/silly string — £275

MAN sticks foot through plasterboard ceiling — £260

The Bloopers

SCENERY collapses onto back of child's head during school production of "Annie"

WOMAN dragged face-first across beach by motorboat before getting airborne on paraglider

SMALL cat falls into a swing bin or fish tank

HUNGOVER best man/groom faints during wedding service — £38

CHILD at petting zoo spat at by llama and cries — £15

THE ADVENTURES OF
8
ACE

EIGHT! EIGHT!
WORRISSIT, LUV..? WOT'S F-FFUCKIN' UP?
WAH! WAH! WAH! WAH! WAH! WAH!

IT'S BABBEH, EIGHT.
GIZ IT 'ERE. A'LL BRAY IT FOH YER.

THAT'S YOUR FUCKIN' ANSWER TO EVERYTHING, IN'T IT... ...BRAYIN'.
NO IT F-FFUCKIN' IN'T.
WAH! WAH!

YES IT IS... FUCKIN' BRAYIN'!
NO IT IN'T, Y'F-FFUCKIN' B-BB-BB...

BB-BBITCH!
WAH! WAH! WAH! WAH!

THERE Y'FUCKIN' GO, EIGHT. TRYIN' TER FUCKIN' BRAY US... AGENN.
THAT?!
THAT WOHN'T PROPEH BRAYIN'...

THAT WOH JUSST A PLAYFUL F-FF-FF-FFUCKIN' TIFF, LUV...

ANYWEH... WOT'S UP WI' F-FFUCKIN' BABBEH? WHY'S IT F-FFUCKIN' ROARIN' FOH?
IT'S GOT SLUGS ON IT, EIGHT.

F-FFUCKIN' SLUGS?
AYE. THEH CUMMIN' INTEH TH'OUSE AN' BITIN' IT IN ITS FUCKIN' COT.

YER WANT T' POISON TH'CUNTS... A'LL GO AN FETCH YER SUM PELLETS FROM SHOP... THEH... ONE FORTEH-NINE...
FUCKIN' PELLETS..!? Y'CAN'T PUT PELLETS IN A FUCKIN' BABBEH'S COT, EIGHT!
WAH! WAH!

NO. A WANT T'PUT A SLUG TRAP IN'T FRONT YARD, EIGHT, T'CATCH 'EM BEFORE THEH CUM IN.
WOT THE F-FF-FFUCK'S A F-FF-FFUCKIN' SLUG TRAP?

IT'S JUST A SHALLOW DISH O'BEER, EIGHT. FUCKIN' SLUGS CAN'T RESIST SMELL AN' THEH THAT FUCKIN' SIMPLE THEH FUCKIN' DROWN IN IT.
OH, REYT.

'ERE'S ONE SIXTEH EIGHT... GO DAHN PATEL'S AN' FETCH NINE TIN OF ACE. YOO CAN 'AVE EIGHT ON 'EM, AS LONG AS I CAN 'AVE NINTH FOH ME FUCKIN' SLUG TRAP.
WAH! WAH! WAH! WAH! WAH! WAH!

SO...
...ACE... NOT... ERM... NOT NOT ACE... ACE... NOT NOT ACE... NOT NOT ACE... ACE...
EXTRA ACE.

AND...
NINE ACE.
ONE SIXTY SEVEN POINT SIX TWO FIVE.

LATER...
REYT... THIS'LL CATCH BASTODS. THEH'VE GOT REYT PRIMITIVE BRAINS AN' INSTINCTS, Y'SEE, AN' THEH CAN'T RESIST SMELL.

IN THE MORNING...

SIZZLE!
FIZZ!
SALT

LeTTeRBocks

letters@viz.co.uk

I THINK the answer to all Britain's problems lies in making Brian Blessed Prime Minister. He can bellow at the EU until they inevitably back down on every issue. And when faced with a crisis in the NHS, he'd simply throw his head back and laugh like a marauding angel-winged Viking. Problem solved. Financial crisis? Massive fucking beard. Sorted.

Brendan, e-mail

WHY don't we have drag kings? In the name of equality, I think there should be women who dress in ostentatious men's clothes and go on stage singing Frank Sinatra and Tom Jones songs.

Neil Email, e-mail

THIS so-called 'global warming' is a load of ruddy nonsense. I bought some chips and a battered sausage on the way back from the bingo the other night, but when I got home they were stone cold. Once again the so-called experts know nothing.

Bunty Titwillow, Cornwall

PERSONALLY, I have always found those *Harry Potter* films a little far-fetched. It might be a school of witchcraft and wizardry, but Hogwarts is still an English public school at the end of the day. Perhaps if Harry or Ron were caught wanking in the dorm, or maybe Argus Filch was accused of trying to bum the Weasley twins, then the plots might be a little more believable.

Hampton Bland, Croydon

MY dog walks round in circles for about a minute before he curls one off. If I did the same it would take seven minutes, according to the dog years formula, meaning I would probably shit myself and faint.

Karl Djizm, e-mail

WHY are people always so scared of Zombies? They're so slow that it'd be just like fighting with someone who'd drunk fourteen pints and smoked a quarter of weed. A Werewolf, on the other hand, seems pretty nifty on his feet, and I definitely wouldn't want to meet him on a dark, moonless night.

Brandon Took, Luton

STAR LETTER

IT'S true what they say about "What doesn't kill you makes you stronger." My fitness instructor is a very nice man who has never tried to murder me, and he has indeed helped me to improve my overall strength and muscle tone.

Banberry Cross, Cambridge

WHY is it that tabloid newspapers always refer to the appearance of scantily-clad, attractive young women as "leaving little to the imagination"? It's precisely that sort of thing which gives my imagination a thorough workout.

Phil Kitching, Jura

DO you think it is possible to train a Hedgehog to walk up and down a table with cubes of cheese stuck to the end of its spikes? It's just that I'm having a dinner party soon and would like to impress my guests.

Helmet Cheese, e-mail

PEOPLE often define a person's disposition with reference to whether they view their glass half empty or half full. Speaking as an alcoholic, it's panic stations either way for me, I'm afraid.

Bartram Fibreboard, Hull

THEY say life is full of surprises and I can't disagree. Yesterday I was diagnosed as having acute Bilharzia, a parasitic worm infection of the digestive tract. Then two hours later I won a tenner on the lottery.

Tam Dale, e-mail

I WAS just reading that letter *(page 134)* about the blonde one from Abba's split, when Abba came on the jukebox. I could only sigh and be reminded that He does indeed move in mysterious ways.

Richard Carr, e-mail

IN this modern age of smart phones and social media, It was heartening to see that at least one youngster could articulate his thoughts the old fashioned way by carving "Karen is a slag" into the paintwork of my local bus stop.

Ben Vowles, e-mail

I WONDER if the cameraman in the House of Commons would mind moving his camera up a bit during Prime Minister's Qustions. There's a female MP behind David Cameron with some pair of tits on her. As I have not seen her face yet, I cannot decide whether or not I would. So come on cameraman, get your finger out.

Danny Mulgrew, e-mail

HAVING watched *The Bounty* on telly recently, I was amazed by how many up-and-coming Oscar-winning actors appeared in it. Sir Anthony Hopkins, Mel Gibson and Liam Neeson all starred. Rather disappointingly, that bloke out of Men Behaving Badly being in it sort of takes a bit of the shine off.

Marvin Broom, Totnes

MY wife woke me up at five o'clock this morning to tell me that she had had a dream in which she burned our oven glove. She is now on the phone to her mother telling her the very same thing. Have any other readers' partners had a more mundane dream that they feel the need to keep banging on about?

Arlo Butterscotch, e-mail

I ALWAYS think of Barry Gibb as having the Bee Gee-est face out of the Bee Gees. But thinking about it, as his face constituted only one third of the faces of the Bee Gees, and the other two were identical, then I guess his face was only half as Bee Gee as the other two, if that makes any sense. Do I win five pounds?

Harry Scammel, e-mail

AS a tree surgeon and lay horticulturist, I am livid that the police decided to call the investigation into Jimmy Savile's exploits "Operation Yew Tree." The yew tree is a beautiful plant and would never even consider groping young girls or touching them up on *Top of the Pops*, even if it was physically possible.

William Hooker, Kew

WHERE ARE THEY NOW?

HOSTED BY JOE PESCI

HEY, HOW YA DOIN'?

TONIGHT WE'RE GONNA BE TALKIN' ABOUT A REAL CLASSY BROAD...

...MISS EARTHA KITT

NOW, MOST A YOUZE PROBABLY REMEMBER HER FROM THAT GOOFY FUCKIN' 'BATMAN' T.V SHOW...

OR THAT 'SANTA BABY' SONG WHERE SHE SOUNDS LIKE SHE'S JUST ABOUT TA FUCK JOLLY SAINT NICK

ON a recent visit to the Ageas Bowl to watch England play cricket, all pass holders were urged to make a choice. I never found out where N-X pass holders were supposed to go.

Jon, Hampshire

I WOULD like to warn your readers that there is no patient/doctor confidentiality clause with dentists. I put my hand up the hygienist's skirt whilst having a scale and polish and she grassed me up to the Old Bill.

Crompton Oldacre, London

WHY do dogs go mad when they see a postman? I'm the one getting nothing but bills and the occasional summons.

Ross Kennett, e-mail

FEMALE cabaret singers and people who are vomiting. Can any of your readers think of any other type of person that gets carried around by their elbows?

Dave Anderson, e-mail

I THINK it's bang out of order calling the Abominable Snowman "abominable." Nobody has ever actually met him and for all we know he could be a really top bloke.

Hampton Bluebird, Barking

AS an avid follower of all things green and environmentally friendly, I still find the smoking ban rather confusing. Surely it doesn't make sense forcing all smokers to smoke outside in the open air sending all their smoke up into the ozone layer. If we could have continued lighting up inside the pub, the smoke would be safely contained, and all the landlord would have to do is give the ceiling a lick of emulsion every now and then.

Mark Richards, South Queensferry

I'M BETTING that there are lots of blokes called Jimmy Savile up and down the country, and no doubt their parents thought it a quirky thing to do in the 70s and 80s. However, now it's become a terrible stigma and will plague them for the rest of their lives. One can only imagine how bad it would have been for the actual Jimmy Savile, had he lived.

Morton Pardew, Rugby

THEY say that if you gave monkeys a load of typewriters, eventually they'd produce the works of Shakespeare. Well I hope the zoo keepers of Britain hurry up and provide them, because in every zoo I've ever visited all they seem to be interested in is screeching like a bunch of lunatics and throwing handfuls of shit all over the place.

Bobby Bowels, e-mail

I DOUBT the Queen would get invited to half as many posh 'do's if she wasn't royalty. Nor would she get past the security at Buckingham palace quite so easily either.

Peter Busby, e-mail

EVERY single time I see an advert for Ariel or Persil, it's always 'New and Improved' or 'Brighter and Whiter'. Considering these products have been going for about fifty fucking years, it must have been like washing your clothes in soot in the early days.

Monty Bullhorn, Oakham

HOW come people on their deathbeds on telly and in films never stop talking? My grandad recently snuffed it and he never said a fucking word. Alright, he was in a coma on a life support machine, but a couple of profound, life affirming speeches wouldn't have gone amiss.

Rupert Cambium, Hastings

I CAN'T understand all the negative press about the big supermarkets. I recently bought some food from one of them and it was very tasty and competitively priced too.

Debbie Macintyre, e-mail

IS IT just me or are children getting more ungrateful? I spent 600 quid on my 3-year-old daughter's Christmas presents and all I got in return was a card and a World's Best Dad certificate. The selfish little fucker.

Tam Dale, e-mail

AS it's my husband's birthday next year, could you possibly print a photo of a man kissing a hot young lady's bottom for him? If not, is there any chance you could cater for your female readers and print a picture of my dream man, sweaty, darting sexpot Ted 'The Count' Hankey? Phwoar!

Harriet Kempton-Park, e-mail

** Once again, one our our female readers is guilty of overt sexism. Ted 'the Count' Hankey is a world champion darts player, and for you to look upon him lustfully as merely an object of your sexual desire is demeaning to him and indeed all men. Shame on you, Mrs Kempton-Park.*

WHAT'S wrong with people these days? I saw a sign pinned to a tree with a picture of a cat, and asking if I had seen it. I rang the number and told them I hadn't, and they hung up. Civility costs nothing.

Teviz, e-mail

I THINK roads would be much safer if all drivers wore big leather gauntlets, goggles and a backwards-facing cap when at the wheel. Everyone wore these items to drive in the 1920s and there were hardly any road deaths back then.

Azure Blue, Tooting

I READ a magazine article entitled '10 things you never knew about Spiderman'. But I knew at least 4 of them. I won't be reading their lists again, the lying shits.

Shoobert, e-mail

The MAN in the PUB

HERE'S a thing, mate of mine's a doctor and he told me spiders drink from the corners of your eyes while you're asleep. And here's another thing, on average you eat one spider every night, apparently. Or one a year. It might be one a year. Do you know what the most poisonous spider is? It's a daddy long-legs. I shit you not. A daddy long-legs. And snakes don't have ears, neither.

YOU could fit everyone in the world into Loch Ness. Or is it the Chinese? Aye, that's it. You could fit everyone in China into Loch Ness. Or everyone in the world into China. Something like that. Amazing, really, when you think about it. And if they all jumped up and down at once, the earth would jump out its orbit. That's a scientific fact, is that. It was on QI. 10 billion of them, there are, the Chinese. Imagine all that lot in Loch Ness, jumping up and down. It don't bear thinking about. Cheers, mine's a pint and a bag of chilli nuts.

I DON'T understand why, when the orchestra put all the hard work in, it's the conductor that gets all the applause. If they want to keep everybody in rhythm and in time, they ought to get behind a bloody drum kit and chip in a bit, the lazy sods.

Luke Newland, e-mail

HOW come Hari Krishnas are always so tall? I reckon that far from being the liberal, free-loving pacifists they purport to be, they have a strict height requirement for inductees, similar to that of most police forces around the world.

Hampton Strathmere, Cornwall

TOP TIPS

SIGN language speakers. Enjoy a peaceful life by always making your missus carry something so she can't nag you all day.

Ross Kennett, e-mail

TWO Wrigleys Extra chewing gum pieces make ideal emergency front teeth if yours get knocked out just before a photograph.

S McGowen, e-mail

FOR a cheap and eco-friendly hairnet, walk through a cobweb.

Ethel Burberry, e-mail

LADIES. Whilst waiting for a face-pack to dry, pop on a Sarah Millican DVD. If you like Sarah Millican, try Justin Lee Collins.

Beoufonia Rideaux, e-mail

BOVRIL can be used as 'placebo' Marmite in clinical trials.

Simon Schunt, e-mail

TARDY people. Avoid being late by simply setting your watch four hours ahead. Then, when you arrive at your destination early, you'll know how it feels to be waiting on someone who's fucking late.

Dylan Channon, e-mail

BOUGHT too many rolls of toilet paper? Simply pop a few in the freezer and defrost when you're running low.

C Miranda, e-mail

FROZEN garden peas make ideal cannonballs for the mouse branch of The Battle of Trafalgar Re-enactment Society.

Perkin Warbeck, Richmond

MOTORISTS. Fool other drivers into thinking you don't have electric windows by moving your arm in a 'winding' motion while operating your electric windows slyly with your other hand.

Steven Ireland, Manchester

PHOTOGRAPHERS. Save time by asking people to say 'ee' instead of the much more time consuming 'cheese'.

David Bailey, e-mail

mr Logic
COGITO ERGO SUM ANUS

OKAY EVERYONE...
PARACHUTE JUMP FOR CHARITY
...WE'RE OVER THE DROP-ZONE!

REMEMBER... COUNT TO THREE AND THEN PULL THE RIPCORD!

WHAT'S WRONG, LAWRENCE..? GETTING COLD FEET?
NO. THE AMBIENT TEMPERATURE OF MY PEDAL EXTREMETIES IS 98.6° FAHRENHEIT.

I MERELY REQUIRE FURTHER INFORMATION WITH REGARD TO YOUR INSTRUCTIONS...

FIRSTLY, NOTWITHSTANDING THAT YOU SPECIFIED AN END POINT IN THE COUNTING, ie 3, YOU DID NOT DEMARK A POINT FOR ITS INITIATORY COMMENCEMENT...
SHOULD I EMBARK UPON MY COUNT AT ZERO... OR MINUS FIFTY-THREE... OR INDEED AT ANY OTHER DISCRETIONARY LOCUS IN THE NUMERICAL LINE..? SECONDLY...

YOU FAILED TO ENUMERATE THE INCREMENTAL PARAMETERS TO BE EMPLOYED WHILST COUNTING TO THREE ... INTER ALIA, SHOULD THEY BE THE CARDINAL INTEGERS...
...THAT IS TO SAY ONE... TWO...THREE..?

...OR SHOULD I UTILISE SOME OTHER SUB-MULTIPLE EXPONENT OF THE INTEGER ... FOR EXAMPLE THUS... ONE POINT TWO-FIVE... ONE POINT FIVE... ONE POINT SEVEN-FIVE... AND SO ON..?

TERTIARARILY, YOU NEGATED TO DETAIL THE RATE OF THE COUNTING, TO WIT, AM I SUPPOSED TO LEAVE INTERVALS THAT ROUGHLY EQUATE TO A SINGLE SECOND BETWEEN SUBSEQUENT NUMERICAL INSTERSTICES, LIKE SO...
... ONE... TWO... THREE..?

OR SHOULD I ALLOW A GREATER OR LESSER INTERREGNUM BETWEE CONSECUTIVE SERIAL ALGORISMS..
...VIZ, ONE...

20 SECONDS LATER...
...TWO...

20 SECONDS LATER...
...THREE...

FURTHERMORE, ADDITIONAL CLARITY IS REQUIRED IN RELATION TO YOUR STATEMENT THAT WE SHOULD "COUNT TO THREE AND THEN PULL THE RIPCORD..."

IT IS CLEAR THAT THE PULLING OF THE RIPCORD SHOULD BE PERFORMED ONLY AFTER WE HAVE COUNTED TO THREE, BUT EXACTLY HOW LONG AFTER?
IMMEDIATELY..? ONE SECOND LATER..? THREE YEARS LATER..?
YOU HAVE ELUCIDATED INSUFFICIENTLY COMPREHENSIVE DATA.

WITHOUT BEING FURNISHED WITH FULL INFORMATION, HOW CAN I PROCEED TO JUMP..?
SORRY, LAWRENCE. I CAN'T HEAR YOU OVER THE ENGINES!

LET'S GO!

ONE... TWO... THREE..!
PLUMPF!
hmmm...

MINUS FORTY-SEVEN POINT TWO-FIVE...
MINUS FORTY-SEVEN...
MINUS FORTY-SIX POINT SEVEN-FIVE...

OUR BOXING DAY visit to the lavatory to pass our Yuletide log is the most relaxing 3 hours of the year. For 180 peaceful minutes, as we park our Christmas dinner in a state of quiet contemplation, it's a time to think about friends and family, reflect on the year gone by and make plans for the one to come. It's an experience we all take for granted, but how many of us have ever stopped for a moment to consider all the different elements that have to come together to make this post-festive motion the oasis of peace that it is? Let's undo our trousers, lower our underpants, sit down and take a few moments to consider what goes into...

The Perfect Boxing Day Turd

The Sliding bolt door lock

THE sliding bolt door lock is an obligatory part of any relaxing Boxing Day motion experience. With the house swarming with relatives over the Christmas period, having a good bolt fitted to the bathroom door is essential; no-one wants their granny wandering in for a piss when they're halfway through dropping off the turkey and all the trimmings. And holding the door shut with an extended leg, whilst it might be okay for a routine digestive transit during the rest of year, simply doesn't provide the reassurance we need over this festive period. The simple sliding bolt, examples of which have been founded on the toilet doors in the Great Pyramid of Cheops, is a timelessly elegant solution to the problem, making sure the room is secure for as long as you want it with no chance of being rudely interrupted whilst fouling.

The Toilet Tissue

LAVATORY paper is essential on any toilet visit, but it is immeasurably more so during the holiday season. A few sheets laid gently onto the water's surface before we sit down provide a handy baffle to prevent early splashback. At this chilly time of year, nobody wants to be sat for three hours in an unheated bathroom with wet mudflaps. And here's a handy hint - if your Yuletide stoolage is such that it requires a series of interim flushes at half-hourly intervals, don't forget to put a fresh baffle down each time. A quality toilet roll is also de rigueur when it comes to the final clean-up operation at the end of your Boxing Day foulage. Before the invention of the soft, absorbent tissue we take for granted today, harsh, shiny and crinkly papers were used, leaving olden days wipers dreading the denouement of any sit-down visit, not least the goose- and figgy-pudding-fuelled marathon of December 26th.

Reading Matter

DURING the rest of the year, we require only the lightest sorts of literature to peruse during our brief ablutions on the jobby engine. A casual flick through the latest copy of the *Autotrader*, the Scott's of Stow catalogue or a *Fred Basset* omnibus is usually more than sufficient to see us through a normal, run-of-the-mill sit-down visit. But our Boxing Day confinement calls for something a bit more substantial in the way of reading matter. Luckily, the previous day's presents will have provided us with a heavyweight literary cornucopia to choose from; The *Guinness Book of Records*, a compilation of Jeremy Clarkson's columns from the *Sunday Times* or a humorous tie-in annual based on a character from some adverts. Without one of these weighty tomes to get our teeth into, we'll be twiddling our thumbs before the first hour is up.

The Air Freshener

WE all over-indulge during the Christmas festivities, and the result of our excesses can often be a cloying stench in the smallest room. Worse, the stink typically turns up during the early rounds of our Boxing Day battle with Meatloaf's daughter, leaving us unhappily sat in a sulphuruous marinade of our own noisome flatus for the rest of our time on the shit pot. Amidst the eye-watering smell, it's all too easy to lose sight of the true meaning of Christmas - a celebration of the miraculous birth of the Christ child in a lowly stable more than two thousand years ago.There is, however, a solution to the perennial problem of a stink you could hang your duffle coat on; the simple, common or garden air-freshener. Whereas early versions simply masked bad smells, modern air fresheners actually eliminate them, replacing them with strong scents that can even overpower the foetid bouquet of a twenty-stone man's festive stool, leaving him comfortably ensconced in the WC for the whole of St Stephen's Day afternoon.

The Ash Tray

THANKS to political correctness, these days it's against the law to spark up a coffin nail practically anywhere. Thankfully, an Englishman's thunderbox is still his castle, so the Boxing Day turd provides a good opportunity to enjoy an uninterrupted twenty Benson whilst sat on the pan. But without an ashtray on hand, that relaxing smoke could easily turn into an anxious ordeal. Whilst it is true that ash can be flicked onto the carpet and slippered neatly into the pile, the dog-ends must be disposed of. If you're reduced to flicking them down the toilet, either way you run the risk of a sudden methane-fuelled arse cress forest fire flare up, or worse, a painful first degree burn on the bobby's helmet. Any ash tray, from a fancy, purpose-made heavy crystal affair to a simple foil tray off a mince pie, can bring peace of mind and make your three-hour festive sojourn the pleasure it was meant to be.

The Bog Brush

NONE of us want to spend our three hours on the toilet worrying that we're going to leave the U-bend looking the starting grid at Brands Hatch. But with our rich, festive diet of Christmas Cake, Guinness, dates and plum duffs, it's practically certain that our Boxing Day stools will sign the porcelain before making their way to the beach. That's why a sturdy lavatory brush is a vital piece of toilet kit to keep within arm's reach of the seat. They may seem expensive, and it's true that they sit there doing nothing for 364 days of the year, but we all know that on December 26th, these bad boys come into their own and earn their keep. Once the business of wiping and flushing is done, it only remains to call the wife and hand her the brush so she can get that trap clean as a whistle again. Relaxed, refreshed and a stone-and-a-half lighter, the best bit of Christmas is over all too quickly. But don't despair - we've got it all to look forward to again next year.

POPE ON A ROPE
IT IS THE FIRST DAY OF POPE FRANCIS'S PONTIFICAL REIGN, AND ALL THE CARDINALS HAVE BEEN CALLED TO THE VATICAN FOR A VERY SPECIAL AUDIENCE WITH THE HOLY FATHER.
I WONDER WHAT HIS HOLINESS IS GOING TO ANNOUNCE. PERHAPS HE INTENDS TO ALLOW THE USE OF RUBBER JOHNNIES.
MAYBE YOU ARE RIGHT. OR HE COULD BE ABOUT TO RESCIND THE CHURCH'S LONG-STANDING OPPOSITION TO BUMMING, RIMMING AND FELTCHING.
WHO KNOWS? BUT WE'LL SOON FIND OUT.
MY CHILDREN. I ASKED YOU HERE TODAY TO MAKE A VERY IMPORTANT ANNOUNCEMENT.
THE ROMAN CATHOLIC CHURCH'S YEAR-END RESULTS ARE IN, AND THE NET INCOME IS DOWN.
YEAR
MASS ATTENDANCES
GASP!
THE SAD FACT IS, WE'RE JUST NOT GETTING THE FAITHFUL BUMS ON SEATS ANY MORE. OUR POPULARITY IS AT AN ALL TME LOW...
WHEN THE CATHOLIC CHURCH HITS THE HEADLINES THESE DAYS, IT IS ALWAYS FOR THE WRONG REASONS.
NEW CATHOLIC ABUSE SCANDAL COVER-UP
PAEDO PRIEST RING SMASHED!
SHAME OF KIDDY-DIDDLING BISHOP!
PAEDOPHILE PRIEST MOVES TO NEW PARISH!
LAST NIGHT I SPOKE TO GOD, AND HE TOLD ME WHAT I MUST DO TO RESTORE THE CHURCH'S REPUTATION IN THE EYES OF THE PUBLIC.
I WILL GO ON A PILGRIMAGE ACROSS NIAGARA FALLS...!
...ON A TIGHTROPE!
WHAT IS MORE I WILL PERFORM A LATIN MASS HALFWAY ACROSS...WITHOUT A SAFETY NET...
...WHILST BLINDFOLD!
NO! THIS IS MADNESS, HOLY FATHER!
YOU WILL SURELY BE DASHED TO DEATH IN THE ICY WATERS BELOW. YOU MUST NOT ATTEMPT SUCH A CRAZY STUNT!
HAVE FAITH, YOUR EMINENCE.
THE LORD SPOKE TO ME IN MY DREAM. HE WILL GUIDE MY STEPS ALONG THE ROPE.
BY HIS GRACE I SHALL REACH THE OTHER SIDE.
THE CHURCH WILL BE IN THE HEADLINES ONCE MORE, AND THIS TIME IT WILL BE FOR THE RIGHT REASONS. NEW MEMBERS WILL FLOCK TO JOIN OUR CONGREGATIONS AND OUR PROFITS WILL GO THROUGH THE ROOF.
BUT IT'S TOO RISKY, HOLY FATHER.
WOULD IT NOT BE MORE WISE TO ATTEMPT A LESS DANGEROUS FEAT?
YES, SUCH AS TRIPLE SOMERSAULT ON THE TRAPEZE OVER A CAGE OF LIONS OR A KNIFE-THROWING ACT.
OR COULD YOU NOT FIRE YOURSELF OUT OF A CANNON IN THE SISTINE CHAPEL?
NO, MY CHILDREN. MY MIND IS MADE UP.
TOMORROW I WILL WALK A TIGHTROPE BLINDFOLD ACROSS NIAGARA FALLS. I SHALL REACH THE OTHER SIDE AND IT WILL BE A MIRACLE.

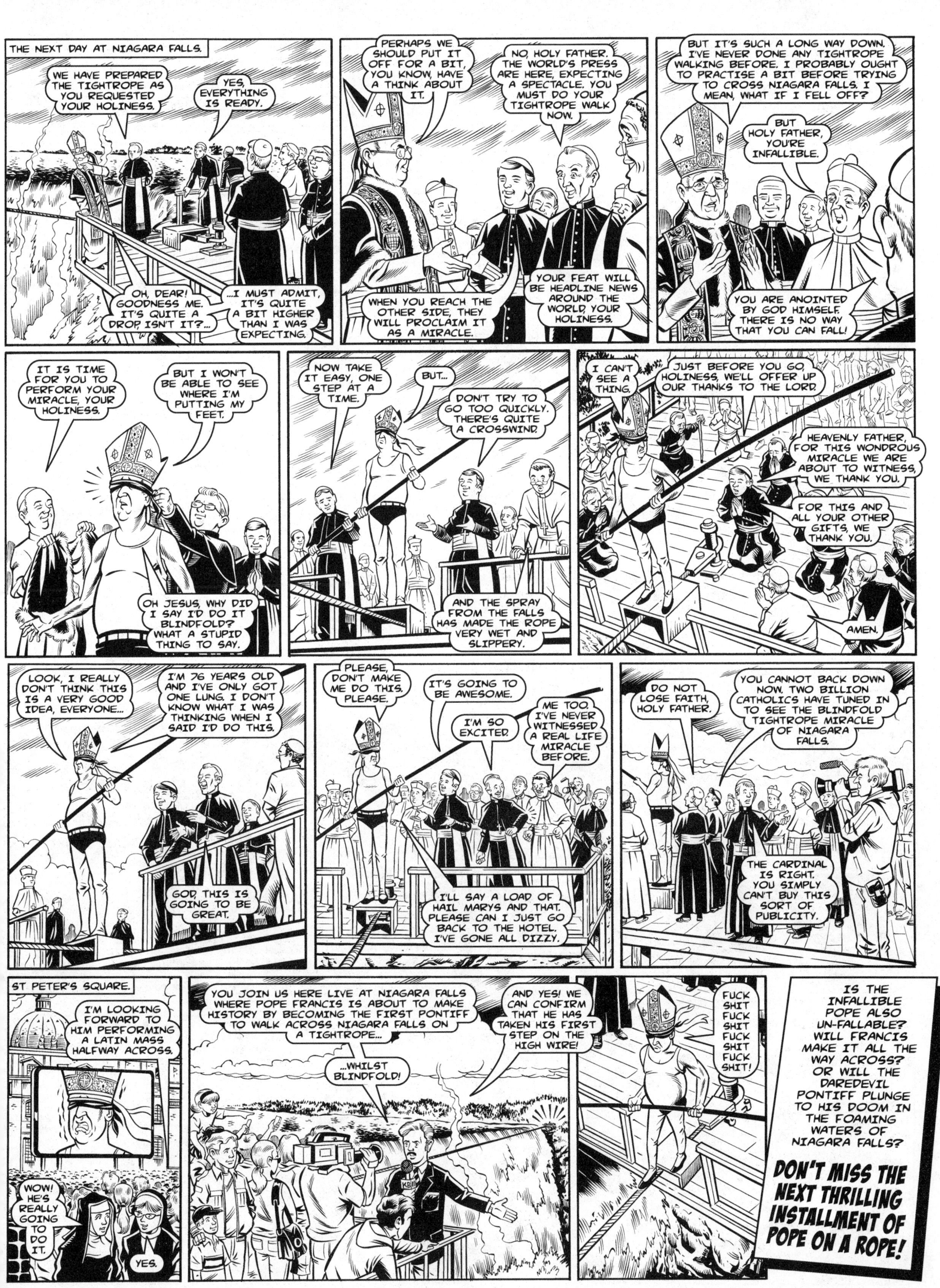
THE NEXT DAY AT NIAGARA FALLS.
WE HAVE PREPARED THE TIGHTROPE AS YOU REQUESTED YOUR HOLINESS.
YES, EVERYTHING IS READY.
OH, DEAR! GOODNESS ME. IT'S QUITE A DROP, ISN'T IT?...
...I MUST ADMIT, IT'S QUITE A BIT HIGHER THAN I WAS EXPECTING.
PERHAPS WE SHOULD PUT IT OFF FOR A BIT, YOU KNOW, HAVE A THINK ABOUT IT.
NO, HOLY FATHER. THE WORLD'S PRESS ARE HERE, EXPECTING A SPECTACLE. YOU MUST DO YOUR TIGHTROPE WALK NOW.
WHEN YOU REACH THE OTHER SIDE, THEY WILL PROCLAIM IT AS A MIRACLE.
YOUR FEAT WILL BE HEADLINE NEWS AROUND THE WORLD, YOUR HOLINESS.
BUT IT'S SUCH A LONG WAY DOWN. I'VE NEVER DONE ANY TIGHTROPE WALKING BEFORE. I PROBABLY OUGHT TO PRACTISE A BIT BEFORE TRYING TO CROSS NIAGARA FALLS. I MEAN, WHAT IF I FELL OFF?
BUT HOLY FATHER, YOU'RE INFALLIBLE.
YOU ARE ANOINTED BY GOD HIMSELF. THERE IS NO WAY THAT YOU CAN FALL!
IT IS TIME FOR YOU TO PERFORM YOUR MIRACLE, YOUR HOLINESS.
BUT I WON'T BE ABLE TO SEE WHERE I'M PUTTING MY FEET.
OH JESUS, WHY DID I SAY I'D DO IT BLINDFOLD? WHAT A STUPID THING TO SAY.
NOW TAKE IT EASY, ONE STEP AT A TIME.
BUT...
DON'T TRY TO GO TOO QUICKLY. THERE'S QUITE A CROSSWIND.
AND THE SPRAY FROM THE FALLS HAS MADE THE ROPE VERY WET AND SLIPPERY.
I CAN'T SEE A THING.
JUST BEFORE YOU GO, HOLINESS, WE'LL OFFER UP OUR THANKS TO THE LORD.
HEAVENLY FATHER, FOR THIS WONDROUS MIRACLE WE ARE ABOUT TO WITNESS, WE THANK YOU.
FOR THIS AND ALL YOUR OTHER GIFTS, WE THANK YOU.
AMEN.
LOOK, I REALLY DON'T THINK THIS IS A VERY GOOD IDEA, EVERYONE...
I'M 76 YEARS OLD AND I'VE ONLY GOT ONE LUNG. I DON'T KNOW WHAT I WAS THINKING WHEN I SAID I'D DO THIS.
GOD, THIS IS GOING TO BE GREAT.
PLEASE, DON'T MAKE ME DO THIS. PLEASE.
IT'S GOING TO BE AWESOME.
I'M SO EXCITED.
ME TOO. I'VE NEVER WITNESSED A REAL LIFE MIRACLE BEFORE.
I'LL SAY A LOAD OF HAIL MARYS AND THAT. PLEASE CAN I JUST GO BACK TO THE HOTEL. I'VE GONE ALL DIZZY.
DO NOT LOSE FAITH, HOLY FATHER.
YOU CANNOT BACK DOWN NOW. TWO BILLION CATHOLICS HAVE TUNED IN TO SEE THE BLINDFOLD TIGHTROPE MIRACLE OF NIAGARA FALLS.
THE CARDINAL IS RIGHT. YOU SIMPLY CAN'T BUY THIS SORT OF PUBLICITY.
ST PETER'S SQUARE.
I'M LOOKING FORWARD TO HIM PERFORMING A LATIN MASS HALFWAY ACROSS.
WOW! HE'S REALLY GOING TO DO IT.
YES.
YOU JOIN US HERE LIVE AT NIAGARA FALLS WHERE POPE FRANCIS IS ABOUT TO MAKE HISTORY BY BECOMING THE FIRST PONTIFF TO WALK ACROSS NIAGARA FALLS ON A TIGHTROPE...
...WHILST BLINDFOLD!
AND YES! WE CAN CONFIRM THAT HE HAS TAKEN HIS FIRST STEP ON THE HIGH WIRE!
FUCK SHIT FUCK SHIT FUCK SHIT FUCK SHIT!
IS THE INFALLIBLE POPE ALSO UN-FALLABLE? WILL FRANCIS MAKE IT ALL THE WAY ACROSS? OR WILL THE DAREDEVIL PONTIFF PLUNGE TO HIS DOOM IN THE FOAMING WATERS OF NIAGARA FALLS?
DON'T MISS THE NEXT THRILLING INSTALLMENT OF POPE ON A ROPE!

RAFFLES Th

A-HEM... LORD RAFFLES TO SEE YOU, SIR... IN THE ORANGERY.
AH, CAPITAL. I HAVEN'T SEEN HIM FOR MONTHS.

WHAT-HO, RAFFLES OLD BOY. FANCY JOINING ME IN THE LIBRARY FOR A SNIFTER?
DO I ANUS, BUNNY. NO, YOU AND I ARE GOING OUT... WITH THESE COPULATING THINGS!
致命的炸弹

I SAY! WHAT ARE THEY..?
FIREWORKS, BUNNY. MISFEASANT ONES FROM THE ORIENT. A VERITABLE PYROTECHNICAL CAVALCADE.

HE WAS ON THE BENCH WHEN I WAS UP FOR AFFRAY IN FEBRUARY.
INDEED. YOU GOT 8 MONTHS, DID YOU NOT? SOMEWHAT HARSH.
INDEED, BUNNY. THE OLD QUAYNTE GAVE ME A PROPER ROCKET...

...SO I THOUGHT I MIGHT CORDIALLY RETURN THE FAVOUR... RIGHT THROUGH HIS FUCKING LETTERBOX.

FIZZ!
QUICK, BUNNY... ABSQUATULATE!

SHORTLY, IN THE PARK...
HERE, PUSS PUSS PUSS PUSS PUSS...!
OH, WHERE CAN HE BE, VARNEY..?
TING! TING!
HE IS USUALLY SO PUNCTILIOUS WITH REGARD TO HIS EVENING REPAST.

AH! I BELIEVE I SAW SOME MOVEMENT IN THAT RHODODENDRON BUSH, M'LADY...
FIZZ!

BANG!
MEEOW!
SCREAM!

RUN LIKE COITUS...! IT'S THE PUTRESCENCE!
PHEEP!

IT'S NO USE, RAFFLES! I FEAR WE ARE CIRCUMSCRIBED ON ALL SIDES!
NO FECULANT, SHERLOCK.

NEXT DAY, AT THE OLD BAILEY...
I FEAR THEY HAVE US BANG TO RIGHTS, RAFFLE
LADY MARCHMAINE PICKED US BOTH OUT OF THE IDENTITY PARADE.

ENTLEMAN THUG

ZZ Top Split Shock

Three former Amigos: Gibbons, Hill and Beard

TEXAN rock legends *ZZ Top* were on the verge of a sensational split last last night following a furious row between two band members. Worried fans now fear that the group's 15th album could well be their last unless drummer *Frank Beard* and beret-wearing bass player *Dusty Hill* can patch up their differences.

The two rhythm and bluesmen locked horns after Beard invited lead guitarist ***Billy Gibbons*** to his birthday party at the pictures but failed to invite Hill.

treat

Beard, 63, told reporters that his mum had said he could go to see *Pirates of the Caribbean 4* at the nearby AMC Cinema for a birthday treat and that he could take a friend. "I told her that Billy and Dusty were both my best friends and I couldn't decide which to take and I asked her if they could both come," he told a press conference in the Houston Hilton. "But she said that my sister was coming along too and there was only room for one of my friends in the car," he added.

Beard told reporters that he eventually decided to invite Billy Gibbons as he had hosted a sleepover at his house for the three band members the week before. And he asked the 63-year-old guitarist not to mention the trip to Hill.

But whilst queueing for a hot dog, the pair bumped into Dusty's elder brother Randy.

"My brother Dusty was real cut up when I told him I'd I'd seen Billy and Frank down at the AMC," Randy told reporters. "He was real mad with them, a cussin' an' a swearin'. An' then he went an sat in his bedroom all afternoon playin' his ole' bass guee-tar. He wouldn't come down for his tea nor nuthin'," he added.

When Beard discovered that Hill was upset, his mum, Ada Beard, called Dusty's mum and promised to take him to the baths with them sometime to make up for his disappointment. But according to Randy Hill, Dusty said that they could 'stuff their trip to the baths', and suggested that he should 'take his bum-chum Billy as he loves him that much'.

revel

Dick Weinerberger, spokesman for RCA Records tried to play down the rift, describing it as a 'storm in a teacup'. "It's something and nothing. Next week, they'll be back in the studio doing what they do best; recording gritty, raunchy rhythm and blues," he said.

Welsh Couple Jailed

Pair 'assisted English tourists'

A MARRIED couple have appeared in court in North Wales charged with assisting tourists. Hywell Gwent and his wife Blethyn were alleged to have given correct directions to two holidaying English families in a people carrier.

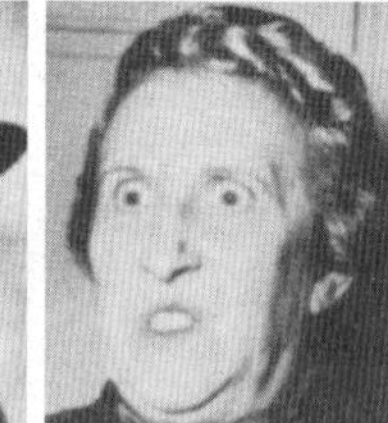

Welsh wrongdoers: Hywell and Blethyn Gwent found guilty of aiding and assisting.

Llanwryddlwtddd Crown Court heard how the tourists became confused by the dual language road signs and asked the Gwents for help. Glaxo Mabinogion, prosecuting, alleged that not only did the defendants give correct and concise directions, but they also asked the tourists further questions about how their holiday was going. They then wished them well for the rest of their visit, he said.

drinking

In mitigation, defence counsel Daffydd Llfflggh claimed that the Gwents had been drinking heavily and were thus not responsible for their actions. "They now deeply regret what they did," he told the court.

guilty

The jury retired for thirty-five seconds before finding the defendants guilty of all charges.

After sentencing Mr and Mrs Gwent to life plus forty years, Judge Goat Inbreed had harsh words for the couple. "As a result of your actions, two English families managed to locate a bed and breakfast for which they had been searching for 36 hours," he said.

inebriation

"Your state of inebriation, which should have led you to direct them to certain death over a cliff in the traditional Welsh manner, instead turned you into normal human beings eager to help people in need. Such behaviour has never been tolerated in this principality and never shall it be," he added.

tourists

And Judge Inbreed had this warning for any other tourists seeking directions: "People seem to keep wanting to come here, but while there's spunk in my balls not one of them will ever receive a friendly ear or food and drink without piss in it."

The tourists were later destroyed in a controlled explosion.

SID the SEXIST

TYNESIDE'S SILVER-TONGUED CAVALIER

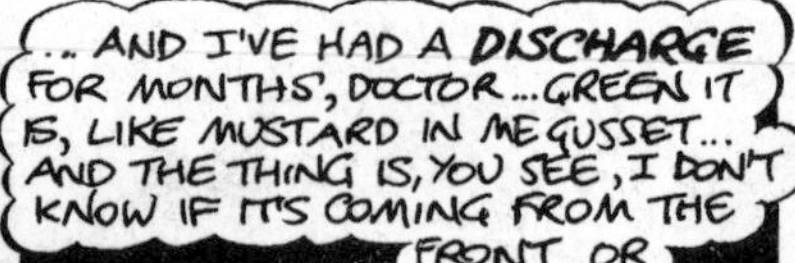

You'll find more of this bollock